WHEN SURVIVORS GIVE BIRTH

Understanding and Healing the Effects of Early Sexual Abuse on Childbearing Women

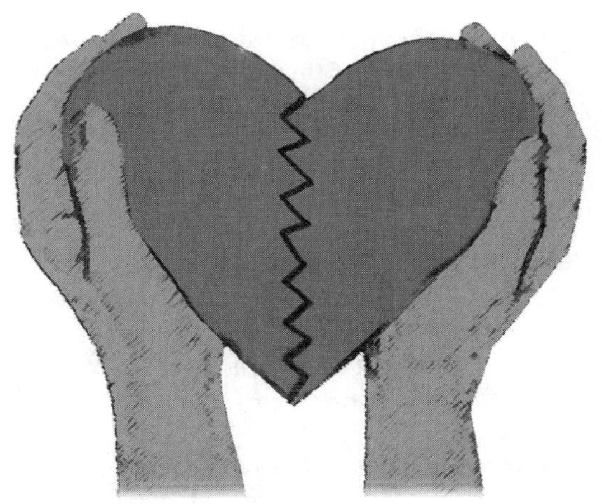

Penny Simkin, PT, and Phyllis Klaus, CSW, MFT

foreword by E. Sue Blume, CSW, DSW, author of *Secret Survivors*

Seattle, Washington
Portland, Oregon
Denver, Colorado
Vancouver, B.C.
Scottsdale, Arizona
Minneapolis, Minnesota

First Printing, March 2004
Second Printing, July 2005

ISBN: 1-59404-022-2
Library of Congress Control Number: 2004102527

Printed in the United States of America

For additional copies or information contact:
Penny Simkin, Inc.
1100 23rd Avenue East
Seattle, Washington 98112
206-325-1419
Fax: 206-325-0472
www.pennysimkin.com
Email: pennyink@aol.com

Design: David Marty Design
Editor: Carole Glickfeld
Cover artwork: Lynn Hughes

Classic Day Publishing
Houseboat #4
2207 Fairview Avenue East
Seattle, Washington 98102
1-877-728-8837

About the Cover

The cover art was inspired by Wandy Hernandez, a doula and trainer of doulas with the Chicago Health Connection. As part of her own training, Wandy was asked to portray the role of the doula, using art materials. Wandy immediately thought of a teen mother whom she had accompanied through labor and birth: "She had been abused sexually and physically throughout her short life and was terrified of going through childbirth. I saw her as a child with a broken heart, about to become a mother. My role was to hold her broken heart together during this frightening time. I held her and told her she was strong and that she was safe." Inspired, we asked Wandy if we could base our cover art on her imagery. She graciously allowed us to do so.

Lynn Hughes, graphic designer, created the art for our cover based on Wandy's concept.

Dedication

We lovingly dedicate this book to our husbands, Peter and Marshall, and our children and grandchildren, who continually remind us of the importance of loving, supportive families.

Above all, we dedicate this book to the children who are being abused today and who will someday become parents with struggles greater than they should have to bear. We hope we can, in some small way, contribute to the cessation of childhood sexual abuse.

Acknowledgments

First and foremost, we thank our clients, from whom we have learned so much.

We also thank: Wandy Hernandez for the inspiration for our cover art. We thank the following contributors: Connie Wescott, for three stories in Chapter 1; Carole Osborne Sheets, for the section on body work in Chapter 8; Yeshi Sherova Neumann, for Chapter 12; Carla Reinke and Ann Keppler, for Chapter 13; Kristine Zelenkov, for Chapter 14; and Nicole Hitchcock Streiff, for the poem, "This Daughter," as well as her expertise and assistance in preparing the references and resources. We are especially grateful to E. Sue Blume for the Foreword and for carefully reading and commenting on the manuscript. We also thank the following for their helpful comments on the manuscript: Marshall Klaus, Dana Blue, and Cinda Weber. We are most grateful to Leslie James, Tracy Sachtjen, Brenda Sutherland Field, Shona Simkin, and Shirley Baek for valuable help with manuscript preparation; Polly Perez for helpful advice on publishing options; Jan Dowers for her ever present helping hands; Sandy Szalay, for her ongoing warm support and those beautiful flowers; and Elliott Wolf of Classic Day Publishing, who provided encouragement and concrete publishing assistance when we really needed it.

Finally, we thank Kathy McGrath for her continuing enthusiastic support, her in-depth reading of the manuscript, her helpful comments, and her occasional nagging for us to finish the book.

The stories in this book are based on real situations, but the names and identifying details of the clients and professionals have been disguised to protect their identities.

Our intention with this book is to suggest practical techniques to aid readers–abuse survivors, health care providers, mental health professionals, and others–in understanding and healing the effects of childhood sexual abuse.

This book is sold with the understanding that the authors or publisher shall have neither liability nor responsibility for any injury caused or alleged to be caused, directly or indirectly, by the information here. We have strived to ensure the accuracy of this book. However, its contents should not be construed as psychological or medical advice.

Because every individual's psychological and physical health needs are unique, readers should consult qualified healthcare professionals for recommendations appropriate to their own situation.

Table of Contents

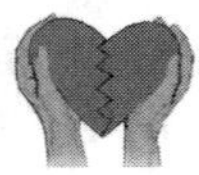

Preface

In the mid-1980s in our work with childbearing women—Phyllis as a psychotherapist and counselor and Penny as a childbirth educator, counselor, and doula—we began to learn that women who had been sexually abused during childhood were often especially anxious during pregnancy, and frequently went through difficult or even traumatic experiences with birth and early parenting. They often could barely tolerate physical examinations and invasive procedures. The unpredictability of labor and birth, the prospect of great pain, and an inability to control their own behavior and the labor process were especially troubling. These women had difficulty trusting their doctors, midwives and nurses. They worried about their ability to be good parents. Many were estranged from their families who had conducted or condoned or failed to prevent the abuse.

At that time there was no information in the medical and social science literature on the impact of childhood sexual abuse on women's childbearing. In fact, it was not until 1992 that the first journal articles on this subject were published in *Birth: Issues in Perinatal Care*. It was even later, in 1994, that the diagnostic criteria for Post-Traumatic Stress Disorder (PTSD) were revised by the American Psychiatric Association (and published in the 4th edition of their *Diagnostic and Statistical Manual*), making it clear that a frightening or life-endangering childbirth often meets the new criteria for a traumatic event, and the negative emotional aftermath of traumatic childbirth often meets the criteria for a diagnosis of PTSD. Since the criteria for PTSD were revised, many papers have been published on PTSD after childbirth. Some of these report that women with prior mental health disturbances or a history of childhood sexual trauma seem particularly vulnerable to PTSD after childbirth.

When we began working with pregnant abuse survivors, however, we realized that our best and really our only source of knowledge was the women themselves. Our sessions with individual women who came to us for counseling or psychotherapy taught us that the trauma of early sexual abuse was sometimes reenacted during prenatal care, labor, birth and/or the postpartum period.

As you will see, many of the same anxieties and self-protective reactions that were caused by early sexual abuse are rekindled during pregnancy, maternity care, and parenthood, perhaps more than during other periods in life. This may be due to uncontrollable factors, such as rapid changes in the woman's body during pregnancy; the uncertainty, vulnerability and pain of labor; the pressure and stretching as the baby descends through the vagina; and, in the end, responsibility for a tiny, dependent human being. The increased attention paid to the woman's genitals by medical professionals who are strangers with authority and power, along with the numerous invasive procedures that constitute a large part of maternity care, also feel overwhelming to many survivors, whose bodies, along with their trust in powerful people and their self-confidence, were violated during childhood. There is great need for education of professionals, who often find themselves baffled, disturbed, or upset by poor relationships with their survivor clients, and who may unintentionally cause harm or even a reenactment of the original trauma.

Our primary goal with this book is to provide every interested group–survivors, their families, their doctors, midwives, nurses, psychotherapists, social workers, and other caring professionals—access to the same information. Other goals are to educate our readers on the long-lasting damage sometimes caused by early abuse; to provide skills to survivors and caregivers to communicate effectively with one another; to develop strategies to help women maintain emotional well-being during childbirth and early parenthood; to help caregivers provide safe and appropriate care to survivors; and to provide mental health workers and other paraprofessionals with birth counseling techniques. We will describe the approaches we have used successfully to enable survivors to have rewarding and empowering childbearing experiences.

This book is a compilation of what we have learned from survivors of childhood sexual abuse, concerned maternity care professionals, and from the enlightened writings of experts on other emotional and health effects of childhood sexual abuse, trauma, and post-traumatic stress disorder. We aim to prevent retraumatization of childbearing women survivors, or better yet, to promote healing of old wounds during the challenging childbearing period.

We are especially grateful to the hundreds of women who have come to us with their stories and their fears. They have been our teachers, and through this book, they can be your teachers as well.

– Penny Simkin and Phyllis Klaus, 2004

Foreword by E. Sue Blume

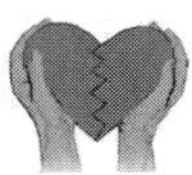

E. Sue Blume is the author of Secret Survivors: Uncovering Incest and Its Aftereffects in Women. *This book is based on E. Sue Blume's internationally recognized* Incest Survivors Aftereffects Checklist. *This groundbreaking work opened society's awareness of the prevalence and often hidden nature of childhood sexual trauma and its consequences, so often overlooked. On "60 Minutes," Morley Safer referred to Secret Survivors as "one of the bibles of the recovery movement."*

Imagine this: You have just found out you're pregnant. You should be filled with joy—after all, this is what you've wanted for so long. But all you can think about is how much you dread every moment of what's to come. You like your birthing professional well enough, but examinations make you feel violated. The thought of so many people seeing you and touching you there is horrifying, as well as things they might do that you don't want them to do, like cutting you. Everything makes you feel powerless. It's as if nothing you want or need matters, as if you have lost all control over what happens to you. They may not even be able to guarantee that the person you have chosen to attend to you is the one who will be there when you give birth. Give birth...to your own helpless, dependent child. The thought makes panic flood through you.

Something about this feels horribly familiar. Maybe you are starting to have flashbacks of the abuse you suffered as a child. Or maybe you don't know why you are having all these reactions. You might not remember that you suffered a childhood trauma at all. But you are having such strong reactions—all negative—and they do seem to tell a story.

Your dream has turned into a nightmare.

If you were that survivor, would you know how and where to find the help you need? If you were her OB, midwife, nurse, or doula, would you have access to resources, training, or professional literature that could help you help her?

And if not, why not?

The tragic answer is that in the area of women's health (including sexual health) and reproduction, no requirement for continuing education about incest, no textbook on incest and childbirth, have existed. These are issues that should have been incorporated into the core knowledge base, with special emphasis on incest.

This denial of incest by professionals does not surprise me. I have already seen it in my own field. As I discussed in *Secret Survivors,* when my own work with survivors of child sexual abuse began in the early 1980's, practitioners of psychotherapy/psychiatry (now generally referred to as psychopharmacology) did not understand how many women in treatment were survivors of incest and often missed even its most obvious implications and consequences. Incest had nowhere been addressed in my graduate program, even in a semester-long course on human sexuality. Common emotional and behavioral consequences of incest were given fancy psychiatric labels, medical diagnoses, and elaborate psychodynamic/ psychoanalytic explanations, but their now obvious connection to childhood sexual trauma was overlooked. No mention of incest could be found in professional considerations of depression and suicide, anxiety and panic disorder, sexual "acting out" (including involvement in pornography or prostitution) and dysfunctions, attachment disorders, adult victimization patterns and pathological passivity, addictions and eating disorders, and self-injury. These "normal" emotional and behavioral responses to the abnormality of incest were minimized, stigmatized, pathologized, drugged and shocked away, but never appreciated as the inventive (albeit often misdirected!) strivings for health that they were.

When incest had been mentioned in the literature, it was dismissed as "rare." Yet newer studies, with improved methodology, were offering estimates of its prevalence among women at 25, 38, even 62 percent. As horrendous as these figures were, they did not take into the account those incest histories that are not remembered because of dissociation, a physiological and psychological response to extreme stress. Thus it is not possible to know exactly how widespread child sexual trauma is, or when a particular woman is a survivor. She may not know. Or she may not tell.

As time went on, mental health professionals did become more aware of the possibility that their clients were survivors, and more survivors began to face their histories. Breaking the secret has not been an easy task, however. A backlash occurred with unsubstantiated claims made that incest disclosures are false memories. These have been sadly effective in exploiting society's desire to deny the reality of childhood sexual trauma.

Yet the truth is astonishingly persistent. Gather together any group of women and raise the issue, and one after another will share that yes, she, too, was victimized. Often, these survivors have never disclosed their history to anyone before.

Pregnancy vindicates the truth of memories of childhood sexual trauma. The survivor may not remember her abuse, but her body tells her story. When aspects of dissociated abuse manifest in the pregnancy and birth experience, attempts to dismiss incest memories as "false memories" can be seen as the empty theories they are. Birthing professionals and the women they care for are the living witnesses of the essential truth of these and all abuses. This especially applies to those who have been the most denigrated and victimized by the organized attacks of the backlash, survivors of organized, multi-perpetrator groups (including what is often referred to as Ritual Abuse survivors).

It is not hard to understand why a history of abuse would intrude upon the birth experience. Incest often teaches life lessons that are the opposite of what its victim needs. She learns not to trust her own perceptions because someone she knew and trusted told her that it was okay to hurt her. She learns to expect emotional and maybe physical pain. She has no sense of her right to empowerment or how to exercise her own power. Since her emotional, and, often, physical boundaries have been violated, she has not learned that she is entitled to establish those boundaries as an adult, or how to do so. She has no sense of ownership of her life.

Nor does she have any sense of her value, because she has been treated as only an extension of someone else's needs. She learned that her emotional and physical survival may depend on her acquiescence. She learned that love equals abuse, trust equals betrayal, and dependence equals pain.

Since her body—especially its sexual parts—are the battlefield on which incest is played out, she may devalue and disown it, and often sees it as dirty or as betraying her. Likewise, she learns that sexuality is not about her needs, let alone her pleasure, and often regards her sexual organs as dirty or evil. She may develop extreme needs for physical privacy. And she is likely to have an aversion to doctors.

She may devalue herself also as a woman, believing that all women are powerless to fight anything that anyone wants to do or take. This message is often supported by a patriarchal culture and its institutions.

She may feel hopeless and helpless, or filled with rage that can turn easily on her caregivers. She is likely to be hypervigilant, highly sensitive to slights or abuses. Her perceptions of what is abuse may be distorted.

Because she has learned that touch is a violation, the incest survivor should never be touched without her permission, or by surprise. Because she was robbed of choice, service providers should be careful to involve her in all decisions that affect her. Because incest is the ultimate disrespect, caregivers should always take the time to treat her with carefully considered respect. She must be handled as tenderly as a newborn, but not babied or patronized. She is not fragile; look what she has withstood. She has paid a high price for the recognition of her right to be in charge of her life.

Not all of these lessons apply to all survivors, and not all of them last a lifetime. With support and treatment, many if not all can be overcome. But not every pregnant survivor completes treatment, and even some who have considerable recovery behind them might be triggered anew by the experience of childbirth.

Finally, it is not only pregnancy and birth that are influenced by the aftereffects of incest, but also what follows. Discussions of postpartum depression, suicidal urges, and psychoses must also include a consideration of childhood sexual trauma. This book discusses the many emotional complications that an incest history will produce after childbirth. But a more practical context exists for these strong emotional reactions. They can also be justified fears, manifestations of an incest survivor's real (although perhaps dissociated) knowledge that those who have so badly abused her will also victimize her child.

Could the murders of some newborns and other children be the products of their mothers' desperate, though twisted attempts to protect their children? Having survived an indescribable reality that they knew no one would believe—tortures for which they saw no other escape—what if these mothers knew, on some level, that their children would be next?

A society can be judged by how it protects its most vulnerable citizens—those who cannot advocate for themselves. Having failed to prevent her childhood victimization, we now have the responsibility of supporting the safety and recovery of the survivor, made even more difficult because sexual abuse is so common, and so often kept secret. As Yeshi Sherover Neumann says so passionately to her colleagues in Chapter 12, "We must assume that every women with whom we do a pelvic exam may have experienced sexual abuse—perhaps a long time ago, perhaps yesterday. If we do not treat the woman with respect, tenderness and patience, we are adding another layer of mistreatment. There is no middle ground."

Birthing professionals have the additional responsibility to identify and develop an awareness of specific issues that affect survivors in their care. It can be quite a challenge to find the delicate balance between what the survivor needs and what she wants.

When Survivors Give Birth will help you.

Authors Penny Simkin and Phyllis Klaus say, "We realized that our best and only source of knowledge was the women themselves." That ability to honor survivors' experience, reflected clearly on these pages, is a model for all practitioners. But they do more than present survivors' wisdom. They bring considerable knowledge and experience too, and there is wealth there. The presentation of communication skills and exercises, which have value for everyone, should be required reading for all health professionals. (We therapists get big bucks for teaching these skills. Take advantage of what you find here and use it in all your relationships.) The many examples of problem situations, and the variety of suggested resolutions, are valuable not only in their own right but also in stimulating readers to find their own solutions.

If you are a pregnant survivor, or work with one, you may well see yourself on these pages. If you find yourself identifying with some of the less than perfect examples, the authors will gently show you how to translate victimization into victory, lack of awareness into sensitive care. This validating educational tool can help childbirth professionals rise above mistakes and omissions of their field, and survivors to become midwives for their newly empowered selves.

In the end, this is a revolutionary book, far more radical than its gentle, nurturing tone would suggest. It offers the profoundly subversive suggestion that incest survivors are entitled to be partners with their caregivers in pregnancy and delivery —partners who are consulted, and whose wishes make a difference.

When allopathic treatment won the political and legal battle to monopolize medicine in the early 20th century, support and assistance for the natural process of childbirth was transformed into the myth that pregnancy is a disorder requiring the routine administration of invasive, dangerous, and often unnecessary medical interventions and technology. This paradigm put women passively on their backs, both literally and figuratively, while their babies were "delivered" by obstetricians.

There have always been caring professionals both within and outside of the practice of Western medicine who objected to aspects of this model. However, their ability to practice woman-centered birthing has met resistance from a system both materially and politically invested in the ways of the past century. That has been an isolating experience. If your goal is to provide appropriate, respectful services, you will find both the support and information you need on these pages.

Incest is a manifestation of the carnage that imbalances of power can create. Justice and morality demand that we correct this imbalance by restoring power to the victim. But current childbirth practices, as often practiced, do not do that. If any population dramatizes the abusiveness of patriarchal medicine, it is incest survivors. If any population demands that caregivers respect their equality, it is incest survivors. Likewise, if any healthcare issue demands that caregivers respect the equality of the recipient, it is pregnancy. After all, who deserves to be honored more than she who creates life?

While working within the framework of standard Western medical practice, along with its "non-traditional," centuries-old sisters, *When Survivors Give Birth* offers its readers the opportunity to examine their attitudes and adjust their interventions to sensitively meet women's needs. Women have been expected to accept the submission required in the patient role and to tolerate it without complaint. And many do, even though it is hurtful to them. In the end, treating us as children puts all of us at risk. Therefore, it is not just pregnant incest survivors who will benefit from what can be found here, but all pregnant women... and not just pregnant women, but all women...and not just women. All of us stand to benefit from a relationship with our medical caregivers that allows us the dignity of self-determinism: one that does not do "to" us, but treats us as partners in our care, as persons entitled to know the whole truth of what is going to happen to us, so that we can make real choices—that treats us not as defective body parts to be fixed, but whole entities with a striving for health who need and deserve support.

Last year, a friend recommended a physician who, she warned, had no "bedside manner". I saw him anyhow. At one point, in a disagreement over something, he said impatiently, "The problem is that you want to be the captain of the ship. But you aren't. I am the captain of the ship!" He was wrong, of course. Because that ship was my body, and I am, indeed, the captain. He was my employee. If you prefer, consultant. Well, ex-consultant.

If anyone deserves to be seen as the captain of her own ship, it is the incest survivor. But while her trauma history may make her particularly sensitive to certain mistreatments, the concerns of the incest survivor are simply exaggerations of what all women struggle with every day. The empowerment and consideration that the incest survivor requires are entitlements that we all share, and on which we should all insist.

– E. Sue Blume, CSW, DCSW

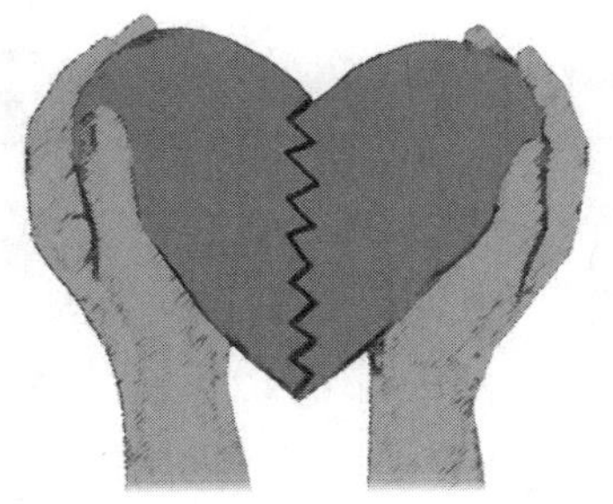

Part I:
The Long-Lasting Impact of Childhood Sexual Abuse

1
Childhood Sexual Abuse and How Society Perceives It

- I tried to tell my mother about my brother messing with me, but she wouldn't believe me. It kept getting worse 'til I couldn't walk sometimes. When my teacher asked me what was wrong, I finally told her. They took him away and my mother never forgave me for breaking up the family.
- On my daughter's fourth birthday I started having panic attacks and flashbacks of being abused by my uncle, when I was four and staying at his house.
- I learned the hard way that you can make a fool of yourself and get hurt when you are not in control. In labor, I had an epidural to avoid the humiliation of losing control.

What Is Childhood Sexual Abuse?

Childhood sexual abuse takes place between a child (anyone under 18 years of age) and someone whom the child perceives as more powerful than the child herself.

It consists of any activity—physical, psychological, or verbal—that causes sexual arousal in the abuser or in someone else. Physical sexual abuse may include intercourse, vaginal or anal penetration by fingers or objects, oral sex, fondling the child, or making the child fondle the abuser. It may be accompanied by physical violence, or by kindness, favoritism, rewards, or flattery.

Psychological sexual abuse may include exposing the genitals, voyeurism, intrusive interest in the child's sexual development, or forcing the child to view pornographic materials or witness inappropriate sexual activities.

Verbal sexual abuse includes erotic talk or innuendo, accusations of "sexy," "loose," or "whore-like" behavior, or other explicit language.

Many of these activities leave the child victim hurt, frightened, or confused. She feels that something is wrong, that maybe she is to blame, and is not sure of how or whether to stop it. These feelings are increased when the abuser is someone she cannot avoid, whom she loves, or on whom she depends for shelter and food. While familiar adults (parents, stepparents, grandparents, or other relatives) are the most likely abusers, others include baby-sitters, mother's boyfriends, respected elders, neighbors, schoolmates, religious leaders, or strangers. Sometimes a sibling or cousin, or someone whom the girl is dating, who is close in age to the victim, is the abuser.

Ritual, or cult abuse involves groups of perpetrators and victims in a closed social group. It is characterized by many extremely damaging forms of sexual, physical and psychological violence, brainwashing, enforced secrecy, and isolation from the outside world.

Incidence of Abuse and Characteristics of Perpetrators

There are no data available on national rates of childhood sexual abuse. The estimated incidence, based on a number of studies and surveys, is between 25 and 40 percent of girls, 20 and 25 percent of boys. These rates are similar to those reported in Canada, Sweden and the United Kingdom. The incidence of ritual abuse is unknown.

Most perpetrators are male, by a ratio of 10 males to 1 female. Perpetrators tend to abuse numerous victims. In more than 80 percent of cases, the perpetrator is known to the child.

The following stories illustrate the three types of sexual abuse and show how early abuse affected the victims later in life.

Brandy

Brandy's sexual abuse was physical.

When she was a child, Brandy's male baby-sitter would stroke her. Brandy was always fully clothed, yet she felt it was somehow wrong. She could tell it was wrong by the way the stroking was done. Nobody else had ever touched her in such a way. And then there was the secrecy—he told her not to tell anyone. Also, Brandy didn't like the strange look on her baby-sitter's face when he rubbed her.

Brandy woke up screaming from the same nightmare two or three times each week. One night, she ran into her parents' room and climbed into their safe and warm bed. It was then that she told her parents about her baby-sitter. Brandy never saw the baby-sitter again. Nobody ever touched her like that again. She felt safe.

When she married, her husband knew about the baby-sitter and he understood that in their lovemaking she did not enjoy being stroked. Even within their marriage, it brought back feelings and memories of the abuse. Later, when they were in a childbirth class preparing for the birth of their first child, they chose not to participate in the long stroking massage that was taught in class. Between the two of them, they knew what would be best, so they chose to use different comfort measures.

Trudy

The story of Trudy provides an example of psychological abuse.

Trudy's father wanted to make sure his daughter lived a "clean life" and didn't become a "loose woman." He meant that she should not be sexually flirtatious or promiscuous. When Trudy entered adolescence, her father became very controlling and strict. Sometimes, if she looked at a boy a certain way, sat a certain way, or even dressed in a way that her father disapproved of, she was punished.

Her punishment was to undress in front of her father. Slowly, she had to take her clothes off at his command. After she was standing nude, her father would walk around her several times, then sit and stare at her. After this discipline, he would tell her not to act like a whore or he would treat her as one.

The humiliation of being stared at deeply affected her; she felt that she had transgressed, but also that somehow her father enjoyed what he was doing. Years after her abuse, there were times when she felt much shame and anxiety when she was seen undressing by a family member or friends.

The situation that finally caused her to seek counseling involved her family doctor, whom she had known for years and was quite comfortable with. She was in his office because she thought she had discovered a lump in one of her breasts. During the breast exam, he asked her to sit up and drop the sheet so he could observe for symmetry in the breasts. She did as asked. As he began to look at her breasts, she began to cry uncontrollably. Her physician tried to console her by giving facts about breast cancer. He had no idea that it was being stared at, not a fear of breast cancer, that caused her breakdown.

Rebecca

Rebecca grew up with verbal sexual abuse.

She remembers her parents telling her as early as age four that she needed to look good when she grew up. They dressed her in provocative clothing and put make-up on her. They told her for years that she should "look sexy" and if she were sexy, men would just "eat her up." She was told that if she looked good she wouldn't be able to keep the men "off you."

By the time she was fourteen, Rebecca was 80 pounds overweight and had no idea why she was having such a hard time with her weight. In college, Rebecca started seeing a counselor who helped her view the correlation between her weight and what she grew up hearing. Rebecca didn't want to look sexy. She didn't want men to eat her up. Rebecca wanted to keep men off her and she hid behind her weight. In counseling, she worked through many issues and lost the extra pounds. However, even after that, she never wanted to look sexy and made it clear to anyone in her life that she was not a sex object.

One year after college, Rebecca married a man whom she loved and trusted. Two years later, while pregnant with her first child, the past verbal sexual abuse came to the surface in a prenatal appointment with her doctor. He told her that she had gained more weight than he would like in one month. That statement was fine, but then the doctor said "Now, you don't want to gain too much weight, because you want to look sexy after the baby comes, don't you?" While such a statement would offend anyone, Rebecca felt the same shame and fear she felt as a child, and was particularly humiliated, rather than angry at the doctor. She left his office that day and never returned.

Rebecca was wounded as a child by verbal sexual abuse. To some, her abuse may seem minute compared to physical atrocities we have seen or heard about. However, Rebecca's abuse is real, leaving a trail of mixed messages and damage.

These stories are not meant to shock, but to illustrate the impact of childhood sexual abuse on one's later life, and particularly on the survivor's experiences with pregnancy, childbirth, and early parenting. Childbearing is certainly one of the most public, physically exposed, and emotionally challenging episodes in a woman's life, and how she experiences it is profoundly affected by previous events and relationships. Yet, with all our knowledge about abuse, it is rarely applied in a manner that benefits childbearing women.

Sexual Abuse of Children: Evolution of Awareness

The high rate of incest and other forms of child sexual abuse has only recently become clear, but one might ask if sexual abuse is a new phenomenon in our culture or if it has always been there, hidden from our awareness.

It is quite clear that abuse of children has always occurred, but much of what in the past was considered acceptable—discipline, play, affection, or inconsequential fondling—has been relabeled as abuse because of its lasting harmful psychological effects on the child.

The modern history of western cultural attitudes toward childhood sexual abuse begins with Sigmund Freud. At the beginning of the twentieth century, attitudes toward abuse were characterized by denial that it existed, even though Freud and others had briefly made a connection between "hysteria" and early incest. *Hysteria* is an ancient term used to describe a cluster of vague and mysterious symptoms suffered primarily by women, including muscle paralyses, amnesia, seizures, and numbness in parts of the body.

Hysteria was not taken seriously until some of the leading neurologists of the late 19th century, including Freud, Charcot, Janet, and Breuer, began to study severely afflicted women. They determined that hysteria was caused by psychological trauma severe enough to produce an altered state of consciousness (now referred to as dissociation) and loss of memory. Treatment to aid the patient in remembering would alleviate the symptoms. Thus "psychological analysis," sometimes called the "talking cure," was developed.

By listening to women, these men of science learned a great deal about mental processes in a time when cultural views of males and females did not support the perception that women possessed valuable knowledge. In 1896, Freud published the first paper that linked hysteria to early childhood sexual experiences. But only one year later he reinterpreted his findings, and in 1897, he denied that the sexual encounters reported by his patients ever happened, and he labeled them as fantasies.

Why the switch? After the publication of his 1896 paper,

Freud found himself ostracized by his colleagues and the families of his patients. He was a lonely and unsupported figure in the midst of a backlash. In her book, *Trauma and Recovery*, Judith Herman states, "Hysteria was so common among women that if his patients' stories were true, and his theories were correct, he would be forced to conclude that what he called 'perverted acts against children' were endemic... among the respectable bourgeois families where he had established his practice. The idea was simply unacceptable."

Because of his enormous influence in the field, Freud's rejection of his own work led to decades of denial of the reality of childhood sexual abuse and its after-effects. From this point on, Freudian psychoanalysis was based on his theory that all women unconsciously recognize and despise their fundamental inferiority. Accordingly, they feel defective compared with males and are ruled by castration complexes and penis envy.

Such a theory was culturally compatible with the status of women in late 19th Century Western society. Women were subordinate to and dependent on men and had few opportunities to participate in meaningful activities outside their homes. Such a view of women prevailed through the 1950s in Western culture. When the role of women in society began to change and the women's movement gained momentum, Freud's perceptions of women and his denial of the existence of child abuse were challenged and revised or discarded by numerous influential experts in the field.

In the 1970's and 1980's, studies of combat veterans, kidnapped children and survivors of other severe traumas (torture, natural disasters, accidents) in which the victims were powerless or helpless, showed that psychological after-effects can be both immediate and delayed, and are long-lasting and profound. Sexual trauma was recognized as being similar in its lasting effects to other trauma and terror. An explosion of interest in sexual abuse ensued, resulting in research, new therapies, media attention, and publications for both lay people and professionals. Only then did the prevalence of the secret terror of sexual abuse begin to become apparent.

Ironically, Freud's original discoveries linking hysteria to child sexual abuse were legitimized 75 years later. The time was right. Public attitudes toward women had softened, and women of all races and ethnic backgrounds from all walks of life—public figures, prisoners, professors, prostitutes, career women, homeless women, the rich, the poor—began revealing their own dark stories of abuse, with its aftermath of pain and terror, and the price they paid for their victimization. At the same time, men began to reveal their own secret painful stories of sexual abuse by trusted figures in schools, churches, gymnasiums, as well as their own homes. Child sexual abuse is now a crime with severe penalties for perpetrators.

Public Awareness

Today, though there is still need for improvement, the public is now more sensitive to and more aware of childhood sexual abuse, and victims are better understood and treated more sympathetically by law enforcement officials, the press, juries, and the courts. Psychotherapists are more skilled, knowledgeable, and effective. Perpetrators are more likely to be punished. Child protection agencies and medical personnel are more aware, more sensitive and more astute in identifying and protecting victims. State governments have updated their laws to protect children and adults from sexual violence and sexual harassment.

Experts in childhood sexual abuse have developed programs that teach children important information to protect themselves against sexual abuse. Through puppet shows, skits, and discussions, children learn to recognize appropriate and inappropriate touch or actions; they learn to trust their own feelings of what feels odd; they learn about their right to protect their own bodies and not to have to touch anyone else's body; they learn how and to whom to report inappropriate actions, even when the perpetrator is a close relative or friend, or someone else who has power over them.

Levels of Remembering

In today's more sympathetic climate, more people than ever, mostly women, are recalling and talking about their early sexual victimization. Many others, however, keep it secret or seem to forget that it ever happened, perhaps out of shame, a threat of horrible consequences if they tell anyone, or a belief that the disclosure would be futile. Or they may believe it is over or not worth mentioning, which may be a way of minimizing or denying the lasting effects. Other victims have not disclosed their abuse because they truly have little or no conscious memory of it. Some forms of abuse such as psychological or verbal abuse are still minimized.

One might wonder how anyone could "forget" such serious events. The explanation is based on a complex, self-protective, psychological mechanism that banishes the reality from awareness. This mechanism of dissociation often occurs in human beings during and after all types of trauma, including sexual trauma.

Some victims block out awareness and memory of both the abuse and the accompanying pain, terror, and helplessness by "dissociating" ("stepping out," "leaving my body," "going on automatic," "going somewhere else," "checking out," "blanking out"). One woman later described how she coped with her abuse during childhood: "I would stare at a spot on the ceiling and pretty soon I was up there where it wasn't happening. I just left my body down on the bed with him." At the time, by thus blocking the experience, she protected herself from it. When she began to recall, years later, her memory was of being up on the ceiling, looking down on herself and the perpetrator.

During severe trauma the victim's ability to remember

can shut down and the experience becomes set apart or dissociated from ordinary consciousness. It may remain hidden from memory for years or exist as fragments of memory at a semi-conscious level. Memory of the actual abuse may thus be inaccessible to the woman for many years, but recall can be triggered later in a variety of ways. Recall seems to occur most commonly when the survivor reaches an age and level of maturity at which she is strong enough to confront and deal with the pain of healing—usually in her thirties or forties. Sometimes, however, recall is triggered before she is really ready to deal with it, for example, during childbearing.

Even though children may have no awareness of their abuse, they often develop self-comforting mechanisms to deal with the trauma, such as thumb-sucking, rocking, repeating nursery rhymes, or meaningless words ("Zam, zam, zing, zing;" "Pop, whoosh, whee"). These behaviors sometimes emerge later during periods of unusual stress, such as labor, when the abuse is retriggered.

Ruth

Ruth had a history of severe childhood sexual abuse. She went for counseling to process the traumatic labor and birth of her first child. She described an exhausting, debilitating backache during labor that lasted for hours and was finally relieved with an epidural.

In reviewing her birth experience, she remembered that the only way she could cope during labor was by holding her teddy bear and repeating a singsong nursery rhyme over and over until she got the epidural.

As she emotionally stepped into the memory of that experience, she remembered that holding and rocking the teddy bear had helped her comfort herself after being abused as a child. During the abuse she would repeat to herself, "Jack and Jill went up the hill to fetch a pail of water...Jack and Jill...up the hill...fetch a pail of water...Jack and Jill..." Her abuse occurred between the ages of three and seven.

She came for counseling when she realized that throughout her life she used these childish methods to handle stressful emotions. She wanted to learn more adult ways to handle fear, stress and tension. (In Chapter 9, these methods are discussed further.)

As dissociated memories of sexual abuse re-emerge, they often manifest as shadowy, vague dreams, daydreams, or feelings of panic, anxiety, snatches of memory, or flashbacks of abuse. This may happen years after the abuse. Victims are unsettled by these events, wondering what, if anything, these vague symptoms mean. Depression and anxiety often accompany such memories, which intensify under periods of stress or when incidents reminiscent of the abuse occur. Many victims find these feelings upsetting enough that they seek professional assistance.

Summary

In summary, the incidence of childhood sexual abuse and its long-term impact continue to trouble and confuse us, but we are unlikely to repeat Freud's mistake of repudiating the truths he discerned. There is too much reliable evidence from too many sources to deny the existence and far-reaching implications of childhood sexual abuse. Today's focus is, with minor exceptions, on learning not whether, but how childhood sexual abuse affects adults, and on finding ways to heal the emotional wounds.

2
Sexual Abuse of the Child and Its Impact on the Adult

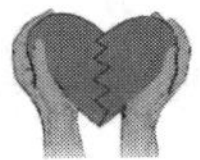

- I'm a very modest person, always have been. I wear baggy sweatshirts to hide my shape and hate wearing bathing suits. I'm mortified that people saw me almost completely naked in labor.
- Whenever I'm in a restaurant or waiting room, I have to sit facing the entrance—I even sleep facing the door of my bedroom—because I have to see who is coming at me. When I was being given an epidural in labor, and I couldn't see the doctor who was working on my back, I freaked out.
- I've suffered all my life with stomachaches, constipation, and migraines. No doctor has ever been able to help me, so it didn't surprise me a bit when I had terrible nausea and bowel problems during pregnancy.

Many children who have been abused in any way—sexually, physically, verbally, and emotionally, or a combination of these—have common manifestations later. As adults, many hold negative feelings about themselves. They may believe they deserved the abuse because of some inner evil in themselves, or they may have been told that they "asked for it" by flirting or behaving seductively. They may unconsciously create extreme defenses, such as "numbing out" (that is, having little emotional response to anything or losing physical sensation in parts of their bodies); hypervigilance or hyper-alertness; and an obsessive need to maintain order and predictability in their lives. They may have inexplicable feelings of panic, fear, or terror. Many worry that as parents they may hurt their own children. They may perceive relationships with other adults to be abusive or unfair; they feel like victims. They may have other physical, psychological, social, or sexual problems.

Fortunately, not all victims of abuse are permanently or deeply hurt. Some children heal without professional help because they have caring adults around them and a generally positive life situation. Others receive the help and protection they need from family or other sensitive adults, the abuse is stopped, and the child lives a normal life.

Patricia

Patricia received appropriate care after her abuse and was spared lasting negative effects.

At age twelve, Patricia was accosted by an older boy and forced under threat of a knife to perform oral sex. She ran home and told her parents, who believed her, completely validated her feelings, called the police immediately, and arranged appropriate counseling for her. Patricia put any feelings of shame, guilt, or blame onto the abuser where they belonged, and was able to work through her fear and distress. In time she recovered from the trauma and placed the experience into perspective without future negative effects.

If Patricia had kept quiet as her assailant warned her to do, if her abuser had been someone whom she loved or trusted, if her parents had not believed her or had blamed her, if the police had minimized or exaggerated the event, Patricia may not have recovered. Later, she may have been beleaguered by nightmares, unusual fears, difficulty in relationships, or other emotional problems.

Let us examine how the dynamics and effects of childhood sexual abuse continue or resurface in adulthood.

In childhood, a girl's feelings about her body are in formation. The child does not fully understand the differences between right and wrong, good and bad. Childhood is the time for learning such things. From a young age, she has learned some rules about her body: for example, about covering some parts of her body when in public; about passing gas; about privacy; about exposing or touching her genitals. Most children are not taught rules of sexual conduct until adolescence, if at all.

At a time when her body image is forming, someone whom she cannot avoid, someone she trusts, loves, or depends on, uses her for sexual stimulation. She submits, sometimes willingly, sometimes unwillingly. She may not even realize that being treated this way is abnormal. Because of the difference in power between her and the abuser, she cannot successfully resist, even if she wants to. It rarely occurs to a little child to resist. More likely she passively submits by pretending to be asleep or by following orders. Sometimes the sexual abuse is accompanied by rewards—promises of special treatment, gifts, extra love, or compliments, favoritism and praise. Sometimes the so-called reward is winning a perceived competition with her mother—taking her mother's place as her father's sexual companion, for example, when the mother is absent, ill, sexually unavailable, or emotionally distant from her father. Sometimes abuse evokes pleasurable but confusing sexual sensations. It is always shrouded in secrecy and accompanied by threats of harm or loss or danger if the child tells anyone about it.

Jane

Jane is the fourth daughter of a highly respected public figure. His family revered him, as did the public. He was champion of the poor, friendly with the press, idealistic, and extremely capable. Her mother, who wished she had given him a son, centered her entire world on him, and Jane and her sisters grew up to be loving, obedient, and respectful of their father whom they idolized almost as a god. He in turn expressed pride in his daughters and loved to show off his family in public.

Several nights a week, however, he would come into Jane's bed, fondle her, make her perform oral sex, or have intercourse with her. He told her that she was his special little girl—the only one who could give him pleasure. But she must not tell a soul. He told her that if she didn't keep the secret, he would die. She felt proud and loved, although she would "freeze" and dissociate during the sexual encounters, sometimes feeling she was suffocating.

Her sisters, who did not know about the abuse, were jealous of Jane, because they thought she was their father's favorite. They even resented her asthma attacks, which gained her a great deal of attention.

Her mother was emotionally distant and her attention consisted mainly of nagging Jane to be clean and pretty and to stop biting her nails, which she did relentlessly: "Your father wants to be proud of all of you; you could have beautiful hands if you'd just stop biting your nails."

Jane had no close friends, only a cat that she adored. She felt "different" from other children and was quiet and shy in school. She repressed her awareness and memory of her father's abuse for years, and did not begin to retrieve memories until she was in her mid-thirties, after the nightmarish birth of her first child. At that time, she and her husband Ron entered marriage counseling for their problematic relationship. In addition, Jane was sleeping poorly, having disturbing dreams and intrusive shadowy memories of past abuse. She wondered what they meant. At first she thought she was suffering from postpartum depression, but eventually in therapy she recognized she was suffering the after-effects of sexual abuse by her father and the significant impact the abuse had on her birth and her relationships. She entered individual therapy, as did Ron, who had been a victim of sexual and physical violence by his stepmother. Now, the two are functioning much better together and individually, and are continuing with therapy.

Jane's first labor was induced, because her midwife believed she was overdue. Jane agreed to it, even though she was reluctant. She had wanted to go into labor spontaneously and was doubtful about the need for an induction. It became nightmarish when her fetus went into distress and she was rushed to the delivery room with no explanation. Her buttocks were exposed and she felt on display during this dramatic journey down the hall. In the delivery room, the fetal distress self-corrected and everyone calmed down. The expected emergency cesarean was suddenly transformed back to a vaginal birth, but Jane had dissociated by then, was unaware during the birth, and in the end was traumatized by the entire event.

As the couple mulled over the events of her labor, which preoccupied them for months, Jane came to blame the midwife who persuaded her to be induced in the first place. She saw the induction as the origin of all the subsequent problems. The midwife, who was supposed to protect her from such horrors, had failed her.

Jane also became more and more distressed about her husband's lack of support during the birth. She saw him as passive and ineffective. Jane recognized that she felt betrayed by Ron who had withdrawn during her most frightening moments. After all the classes that prepared him for a major support role, she felt abandoned.

As for Ron, he stated that he had felt completely inadequate, fearful of losing Jane, and intimidated by the midwife's change in behavior. The midwife had always seemed sensitive and kind, but during the crisis with fetal distress, had become forceful and authoritarian. When he tried to fulfill his role by asking, "What are our options?" she snapped, "There are no options. No more questions!"

In the end, with the obstetrical events resolved, Jane and Ron were left with the emotional trauma—Jane feeling angry at Ron's inadequacy and Ron feeling misunderstood and beset by guilt over his powerlessness.

In therapy Jane realized that the negative feelings toward her midwife were very much like the feelings she harbored toward her mother, who failed to protect her from the horrors of abuse. Ron recognized that what he felt was controlling behavior by the midwife triggered the old helplessness he experienced with his controlling stepmother.

When Jane learned that Ron had tried to be assertive on her behalf, she was able to understand his feelings and forgive him. They also came to see that the midwife's behavior was driven by need for rapid action caused by the baby's worsening condition.

Sexual abuse is often accompanied by violence—physical, verbal and emotional. The child experiences physical pain, force, restraint, and terror. During the abuse she may experience any or all of the following: inability to breathe, gagging or choking; helplessness; pressure on her body, severe pain and bleeding in her genitals. She cannot escape. In order to find a way to survive, she must adapt. Her adaptive survival responses take a great toll on her, both mentally and physically.

All of the above produce confusion in the child and a warped self-image, a confusing sense of place in the family, and negative feelings about her body. Attempts to hide from or avoid the perpetrator or to get help from other adults (by hinting, since she may be afraid or ashamed to directly describe her abuse) usually fail, and the child's helplessness leaves her with few survival mechanisms other than dissociation and loss of memory.

Lack of memory of abuse does not eliminate the pain; rather, the pain finds expression in indirect ways. What symptoms or behaviors might indicate that the child is being or has been sexually abused? There are four broad categories: precocious or abnormal sexual behavior; physical or somatic symptoms; inappropriate psychosocial behavior; and mental health disturbances. No child victim exhibits all the behaviors listed below, but if many are present, they could be indicators of sexual abuse and should be further investigated. Of course, as one reads the list below, one must recognize that sexual abuse is not the only possible underlying cause for many of these symptoms. Some can result from other types of abuse, family dysfunction, and other traumas.

Sexual behaviors: aggressive sex play, extreme masturbation, premature sexual interest and activities that are more typical of older people.

Physical or "somatic" manifestations: frequent stomachaches, stress-induced asthma, migraines, bed-wetting, constipation, vaginal/anal infections, and sexually transmitted diseases.

Psychosocial disturbances: regression (thumb-sucking, bedwetting, extreme dependence on comfort items, such as teddy bear or blanket); running away from home; poor school performance or very high (but never high enough) achievement; raging or destructive behavior against other people, animals, things, or oneself; feelings of shame and guilt ("I am bad"); loneliness, isolation, lack of friends; adult-like care-taking behavior; substance abuse; and, re-enactment of abuse through play.

Mental health disturbances: self-abusive behavior (head-banging, cutting, nail-biting), eating disorders, nightmares/sleep disorders, phobias, obsessive-compulsive disorders, depression, dissociation, memory loss, hyper-vigilance, anxiety, rebelliousness or overcompliant, submissive behavior.

As the child grows up, if the symptoms are unresolved, they may continue to manifest themselves in more adult forms. These include bodily complaints and medical problems; changes in personality; self-destructive behavior, such as substance abuse, self-mutilation (scratching, burning, cutting); thoughts of suicide; phobias; fears of invasive medical or dental procedures; a tendency toward re-victimization and domestic abuse; psychological disturbances (obsessive-compulsive disorders, anxiety, depression; and dissociative disorders such as dissociative identity disorder, formerly called multiple personality disorder); sexual dysfunction, ranging from repulsion by sex to sexual addictions, prostitution, teen pregnancy, and violent sexual activities; and difficulties in relationships, such as an inability to maintain friendships, and friction with co-workers and employers. Adults sometimes exhibit diminished pleasure and an inability to recognize or express feelings.

As we become more enlightened about connections between the psyche (mind) and soma (the body), we recognize that many illnesses have emotional and physical components. In a recent review of research on the effects of trauma, Teicher revealed that chronic severe childhood abuse results in alterations in brain development, as well as behavioral functions. The various types of abuse (physical, sexual, emotional) affect boys and girls differently, with sexual abuse having the greatest effect on brain development of girls. Neglect, on the other hand, had a greater effect on boys.

Emotional distress aggravates physical illness just as physical illness takes an emotional toll. The process of somatization is the physical manifestation of deep and repressed emotional or psychic pain. Such pain cannot be totally repressed; it tends to find a way out. It may show up metaphorically as one or more of many physical symptoms. A woman's chronic severe asthma may be a metaphor for the suffocation felt during forced oral sex, and her tense painful vagina (vaginismus), a metaphor for self-protection against penetration or intercourse. Characteristically, these problems are vague, confusing, and frustratingly difficult to cure.

For most survivors, such pain or illness represents a cry for help. The real problem may be so unspeakable that she repressed it, but her need for care cannot be repressed.

In fact, some chronic complaints have long been considered to have a strong psychosomatic component. The following conditions are well understood to result from or become worsened by unresolved childhood sexual, physical or emotional abuse, or other unusual distress: migraine headaches; a variety of chronic pain syndromes; digestion-related illnesses (ulcers, spastic colon, irritable bowel syndrome); urinary difficulties; severe chronic constipation; eating disorders (morbid obesity, anorexia, and bulimia); some allergies and asthma; fibromyalgia; TMJ (tempero-mandibular joint syndrome); chronic fatigue syndrome; and others. Such conditions are often debilitating and do not respond to treatment.

People with such complaints sometimes go from one doctor to another, accumulating a thick medical chart, a record of their frustrating and fruitless search for a medical cure. Many people also seek care from alternative practitioners (naturopathic and homeopathic physicians, chiropractors, acupuncturists, herbalists, spiritual healers, and others). They are rarely asked about, nor do they usually report their early abuse, because neither doctor or patient realizes that it could be a vital piece of information.

It is important to recognize that no individual exhibits all these signs and symptoms, nor is every person who exhibits one or a few of these problems necessarily a survivor of childhood sexual abuse. It is, however, beneficial for both women and their caregivers to consider the possibility of childhood sexual abuse when several of these symptoms or conditions are present with no obvious cause.

Maria

Maria's story illustrates the process of somatization.

Ever since childhood, Maria, 34, had migraine headaches, nightmares, abdominal pain, and chronic constipation. Until the age of ten, she wet the bed, for which her mother beat and shamed her regularly.

Her father, a construction worker, drank heavily after work and almost every night would enter her room and perform oral and anal sex on her and her younger sister. Under the pretense of religion, he was strict about his daughters' social lives when they were teenagers and wanted to make sure they remained virgins, which to him meant not having vaginal intercourse.

As an adult, Maria sought strong medication and many types of treatment for her migraines—for example, biofeedback, massage, and visualizations, all to little avail. She missed several days of work with each migraine.

Maria had difficulty with relationships, especially when they became intimate. She reported "numbing out" when having sex with her husband, and found herself flying into a rage at the least provocation. Her rages increased after she became pregnant.

During pregnancy with her first child, Maria heard a guest on a TV talk show describing her own experiences of childhood sexual abuse and subsequent violent outbursts of rage. Maria felt nauseated and began to tremble. She experienced a flashback to an incident of her father in her bed and her own feeling of helpless rage.

She sought therapy because she was frightened about this flashback and also worried that she might hurt her baby in one of her rages.

Until therapy, Maria had never connected her outbursts of temper and her migraines with anger at her father and mother. She could not express her feelings toward her parents because the strong religious and cultural values of the family required that children always honor and never defy their parents. This internal conflict of self-blame and guilt over negative thoughts toward her parents led to severe headaches. In processing this conflict, her headaches diminished.

She also realized that her mother's beatings were based on jealousy of Maria for "seducing" her father. In her therapy she could now express her rage, hurt, and shame, and then Maria began to feel compassion for her sister and herself for the trauma they had endured. The frequency and intensity of her rages decreased, and she was able to learn more appropriate ways to express negative feelings. She was relieved to discover that she now could avoid transferring old feelings of rage toward her parents onto her child.

As we can see from Maria's case and many others, if childhood traumas are disregarded or unnoticed, they do not go away as the child grows older. Rather, they persist, giving rise in adulthood to further, more complex symptoms.

The Process of Recall

While some women never forget their abuse, others suppress the memory. Women survivors ponder with anguish why it took them so long to remember the abuse. As one woman said, "I hate it that I didn't even begin to figure out what he did to me until after he died! And he still has power over me. He has ruined my sex life. I'm afraid to be alone. I can't trust my husband with our little girls. Will this ever stop? Will I ever be normal?" Sometimes abuse memories start coming as body sensations, flashbacks, or through remembered fragments of events.

Particular developmental stages, major life transitions, or meaningful events may activate or intensify these memories, such as:

- Commitment to a serious love relationship, which may trigger a belief that people whom you love hurt you;
- Marriage and forming a family (reminding her of her own family);
- Pregnancy and childbirth (which bring some identification with her own infancy or childhood), including changes in body image, greater dependence on others, anxieties about invasive medical interventions, pain, or helplessness;
- Becoming a parent and breastfeeding;
- Her child (especially her daughter) or grandchild reaching the age at which she herself was abused;
- Death of the perpetrator;
- Major stresses in her life, such as quitting smoking, having surgery, divorce, death of a loved one, moving, and others;
- Disclosure by others who were abused by the same offender;
- Media coverage of child abuse.

Elaine

Elaine, 35, married her college sweetheart, had 2 boys and then a girl, and was a stay-at-home mother. When her daughter Lori was 7 years old, Elaine was ready to take up some activities to pursue her own interests. Having been athletic in her college years, she looked forward to continuing her tennis playing in an adult amateur league.

She enrolled Lori in an after-school recreation program at their church. Father Donald was a favorite with all the children, and the program sounded perfect for Lori. Although Lori seemed to be thoroughly enjoying the after-school program, Elaine started to be plagued with debilitating pain, very poor sleep patterns, became quite depressed, and was eventually diagnosed with fibromyalgia.

Fibromyalgia is a confusing disease. Doctors as well as patients are often frustrated in their attempts to reduce symptoms and find a cure. Although taking appropriate medication, Elaine presented for therapy to help her with the depression, sleeplessness, recurrent nightmares, and to strengthen her resolve to recondition her body.

Elaine noticed her anxiety increasing when she thought of Lori at the church. Elaine also experienced panic attacks with increasing severity and frequency.

In her own self-exploration in therapy, Elaine recalled many episodes of sexual abuse at the hands of a priest whom she loved, during after-school programs at the Rectory. She had participated in this program from ages 7 to 10. During this time, the priest made her his special helper, inviting her to assist with preparing activities for the other children and staying later to clean up. He would supply cookies and milk and praise for her help

She remembered that the priest made her perform oral sex and raped her anally, and afterward he would tell her to get down on her knees and pray to God for forgiveness because she was bad and had sinned. She was left with excruciating guilt, shame, and certainty that God would punish her. She dissociated during these episodes of abuse, but the priest continued to be her favorite.

With painful and persistent work in therapy,

Elaine came to recognize that someone she loved and trusted had abused her, and it was not her fault.

Elaine's self-recrimination was so deep that it was only by helping her see the innocence of her own daughter (if such an event were to happen to Lori), that she could begin to recognize her own innocence as a child. She could then understand that the priest was wrong. He was the adult in a power position, and was using her for his own stimulation in a way that made her believe she was condemned forever in the eyes of God.

Over time she could release her anguish; her panic and fibromyalgia subsided, and self-forgiveness and healing prevailed.

For other women, news coverage of an incident of childhood sexual abuse may trigger flashbacks or memories. Some women seek therapy after hearing someone's abuse story on television or reading a newspaper account about the abduction of a child. These women will often find themselves overcome with distress, panic, or a sick feeling, and begin having flashbacks. For some women who have been in and out of treatment for various ailments for years, seeing a story of someone else's abuse helps them to finally realize the connection between their symptoms and having been abused.

Childhood Sexual Abuse as Trauma

Childhood sexual abuse is listed as one of the possible causes of post-traumatic stress disorder (PTSD) by the American Psychological Association in the fourth edition of its *Diagnostic and Statistics Manual* (DSM IV-TR), which is considered the authority on mental health disorders. Traumatic events are defined there as life threatening, out of the ordinary, catastrophic, terrifying, and/or accompanied by a sense of helplessness. Childhood sexual abuse meets the criteria for trauma.

People who have been abused may experience many post-trauma symptoms, such as nightmares, sleeplessness, flashbacks to the event, intrusive thoughts, feelings of panic (difficulty breathing, sweats, and fast heartbeat), avoidance of anything associated with the trauma, and dissociation. These symptoms may occur immediately after the trauma, causing acute anxiety, and if not resolved, may persist over time. Or, they may surface later, having been repressed at the time, but precipitated by a triggering event. The DSM-IV-TR denotes these levels of trauma symptoms as Acute, Chronic, or Delayed.

Bonnie

Bonnie's story illustrates delayed trauma symptoms triggered by childbirth events.

Throughout much of Bonnie's childhood, her father "played" with her by tickling her. He would chase her, catch her, and then hold her down, tickle her, kiss her, and fondle her breasts, buttocks and genitals. She knew when he was going to do this and would try desperately to get away, but was never successful. She felt helpless, but couldn't help laughing as he tickled her. He'd say, "You little flirt, pretending you don't want me to do this." She could not get away from him because he was too strong. Her laughter would give way to tears and then to crying, and eventually to screaming. Finally, he would stop.

When she grew up she did not look back on her father's actions as abusive, because it was supposed to be play, and she remembered laughing during it. Years afterwards, when she was in labor with her first child, she was in bed with fetal monitor belts, an intravenous line, and a blood pressure cuff attached to the wall. She had a panic attack over these restrictions on her movements. Her reaction seemed disproportionate until later, when Bonnie connected the childbirth events with being restrained while her father abused her.

Others, like Bonnie, are also surprised by their degree of distress over routine aspects of maternity care. For abuse survivors, subsequent distressing or traumatic events can bring up the same feelings of helplessness and fear that they felt with the abuse. If the trauma of the original abuse was never resolved, they are more at risk than others for retraumatization, and may suffer from chronic post traumatic stress disorder.

Much of this distress can be reduced for pregnant abuse survivors if, before labor, they have an opportunity to explore some of the features (events, procedures, and care policies) of childbirth that might bear similarities to their abuse, and to plan strategies for avoiding or coping with them. (Chapter 10 guides the reader through such a process.)

Women often dread the prospect of deeply exploring the origin of abuse-related symptoms. Nevertheless, once they do take that step, they usually feel relieved and unburdened of guilt and responsibility. Their discovery of an explanation for often debilitating and worrisome symptoms provides perspective and insight. We have witnessed that the capacity for healing is enormous, though it requires hard work, perseverance and courage.

One woman summed up her journey in this way: "I'm not just a survivor. I'm an overcomer!"

3
Impact of Childhood Sexual Abuse on Pregnancy

- From the moment of Joseph's conception I felt victimized—my body overtaken yet again, and when I learned the baby was a boy, just the thought of it was frightening—I didn't like the idea of a penis growing inside me.
- Becoming pregnant was the highlight of my life. My body felt normal for the first time.
- As my pregnancy continued, I was surprised by the intensity of my feelings. I knew I would fiercely protect my baby.

Pregnancy is a time of monumental change for women — a time when the past, present and future all come together, a time of openness, a time of vulnerability. Being pregnant causes memories of one's own childhood to surface. Past events are stirred up. The present evokes the paradox of excitement over the baby on the one hand, and fears and anxiety on the other. Thoughts of the future bring hopes of dreams fulfilled and eager anticipation of joy and love, along with apprehension over the demands of parenting and the effort it will take to keep the child safe and happy.

For many survivors of childhood sexual abuse, pregnancy represents a confirmation of normalcy. One survivor spoke of feeling safe and valued as her pregnancy evolved, having more confidence in her body, in the baby growing inside her, and in her ability to parent. Another enjoyed being nurtured and taken care of by her partner without having to be sexual.

For others, however, pregnancy and birth may unexpectedly bring up issues and feelings related to the abuse whether or not they have resolved the abuse. It is most upsetting for a woman to discover or relive past trauma at a time when she would like to prepare to welcome a new baby.

Therefore, pregnancy and childbirth may represent a challenge to every survivor. How she is treated by her loved ones and professional caregivers can make the difference between confirmation of her self-worth and retraumatization.

Let us examine the variety of ways this early trauma may resurface in pregnancy. We want to reiterate that no single person exhibits all of the manifestations of abuse described here, but survivors often show several or many of them.

Becoming Pregnant

The decision to become pregnant or continue a pregnancy may bring up anxieties about keeping her child safe from the kinds of danger she herself encountered as a child. A woman may be haunted by the thought that she is bringing a child into a life of abuse and hurt.

For the woman who becomes pregnant unintentionally and who does not envision herself as a caring, loving parent, pregnancy and the prospect of parenthood may represent one more abuse, or a kind of punishment inflicted on her by the baby's father, society, or God. She feels victimized, helpless, and unable to control her own destiny.

Many survivors believe they are abnormal, dirty, or damaged inside. Such feelings may be linked with reluctance to become pregnant. To become pregnant may be seen as a way to prove to themselves and others that they have overcome the damage and fear caused by the abuse. If these women and their partners have difficulty conceiving, it may be devastating, because physical injury or infection resulting from early abuse sometimes contributes to infertility. Invasive fertility procedures may be especially humiliating to the survivor, and reproductive "failure" can add to feelings of inadequacy and shame, which may continue even after she becomes pregnant.

For some survivors, pregnancy is one of the most positive experiences of their lives. As one woman said, "All my life I had felt there was something wrong with me, that my body didn't work right. I'd always thought that my uncle broke something in there. I wasn't at all surprised that I couldn't get pregnant for all those years. When I finally did get pregnant, I was so relieved! I felt great, even with morning sickness. My body was doing something right! Pregnancy made me feel normal and helped me feel better about myself."

As the pregnancy continues, common discomforts, often taken in stride by others, may cause great anxiety and become severe, sometimes to the point of being debilitating. Those include fatigue, nausea, joint pains, backache, Braxton-Hicks contractions, sleeplessness, heartburn, constipation, and more. Perhaps because their bodies have been a source of pain and worry, survivors perceive these symptoms as further evidence of abnormality, that pregnancy is a drain, or that they are somehow different from other women.

Some survivors deny or reject the pregnancy. The very thought of being pregnant may be horrifying. Some even feel compelled to abort. Some women try to hide their unwanted pregnancy with loose clothing and by eating poorly to avoid gaining weight. They describe shame and resentment over the weight gain, growing abdomen, and breast enlargement that represent proof of their sexual activity. Others may go through months of pregnancy without awareness and suddenly deliver their babies without warning. This is especially true of teens who have become numb to bodily sensations, including pain, fetal movements, and contractions. Many of these young women have completely dissociated from any awareness of their pregnancies, which is a direct result of sexual abuse. We all have read of cases where a baby is born in a public restroom to a young mother who thought she had a digestive upset.

Some abuse survivors choose to become single mothers or to have lesbian relationships and do not want a man involved with their child. Even if married, they may prefer alternative means of conception over intercourse, or they may choose to adopt a child to avoid the issues related to pregnancy.

Challenges in Pregnancy

As their bodies undergo the inevitable physical changes of pregnancy, survivors sometimes express disturbing reactions. They may struggle with their new identity ("I don't know the real me"); loss of sensation ("numbing out") from a large part of their bodies ("I have no feelings from the waist down," or "I have never felt my baby move"); or chronic tension and pain in the pelvis.

The stress of unresolved childhood sexual abuse may be a significant component of some pregnancy complications, such as hyperemesis gravidarum (severe, constant vomiting), pregnancy-induced hypertension, unexplained bleeding, prematurity or post-maturity. Along with medical treatment of these conditions, practitioners can help pregnant women by acknowledging and discussing the psychosocial aspects of their physical problems, and, if necessary, recommending counseling, psychotherapy, stress-reduction techniques, and emotional and social support. (See Part II for a description of these techniques.)

When an abuse survivor is feeling especially stressed,

her caregiver or any other maternity service provider may suggest that she ask herself, "What does this bring to mind? What is going on in my life right now that may be causing this distress?"

Rosa

When Rosa reported to her therapist that she was feeling especially distressed, her therapist asked her to think about recent events that might be causing the distress. Rosa suddenly understood. Her uncle, who had abused her off and on for years, recently called out of the blue, and ever since, she had felt anxious and had many strong uterine contractions. Upon reflection with her therapist, she recognized the connection between her anxiety and the phone call. Her contractions diminished.

Betty's more severe case illustrates the physical effects of unresolved abuse during pregnancy.

Betty

Expecting her first baby, Betty became severely ill and dehydrated with hyperemesis gravidarum (almost constant vomiting) and required hospitalization. After appropriate but unsuccessful medical treatment, her doctor recognized the possibility of an emotional link, and referred Betty for psychotherapy. Betty soon discovered she harbored a hidden fear that if her baby were a girl, the baby would not be safe. She realized that she was projecting some of her own prior lack of safety during childhood onto her unborn baby. This seemed to be causing the nausea and vomiting—which evoked memories of the nausea and vomiting she experienced after oral sexual abuse by her grandfather. Once this connection was made she could "separate" the baby she was carrying from herself as a child in the past and the vomiting ceased. She learned to imagine a safe place where her baby would be protected from harm. (Her safe place was the arms of a guardian angel.) She also learned a method of mentally "containing" her abuse experiences to keep them from surfacing.

Fears, Phobias, and Anxieties during Pregnancy

During pregnancy, the effects of abuse may resurge not only as physical manifestations but as emotional or psychological distress as well. They may appear during the prenatal period as unusual fears, anxieties, or phobias about the pregnancy, the fetus, tests and exams, or the upcoming labor. It is likely that the woman herself has little or no idea that her reactions are connected to her abuse. In fact, it comes as a relief to many, and helps them make sense of these unusual fears or anxieties, once they make the connection.

Survivors may have overly negative, positive, or unrealistic beliefs about the fetus. They may describe their bodies as being invaded or "taken over" by the fetus or "out of control" from the changes occurring. Or they may perceive the fetus as a "parasite" that drains their energy.

Emma

Emma was surprised to hear other pregnant women talk with excitement about their unborn babies. She found the fetal movements annoying and even painful. She often had negative images and disturbing thoughts about the fetus. The thought of breastfeeding was abhorrent to her. She couldn't picture herself sharing her breasts. She worried that if the baby were a boy these feelings would be even worse. Emma needed help to bond prenatally with her baby. In exploring these disturbing thoughts with her therapist, she began to understand that she associated her negative feelings about the fetus with past abuse by her father, which began when she was a baby. Her feelings of being taken over as a baby were recreated when she felt taken over by her fetus. It was important for her to learn to visualize her fetus as a separate little being, independent from her abuse memories. This helped her feel closer to her baby.

In contrast with Emma, Holly idealized her baby.

Holly

Holly saw her unborn baby as the saving hope of her unhappy life. She felt trapped in a loveless marriage, unable to turn to her husband for nurturing. She had enormous difficulty being intimate, tried to avoid sexual relations, and had numerous physical complaints. She had been sexually abused by a stepbrother throughout her teenage years and saw herself as having no power and little worth. She expected this baby to be her friend, someone to love her and to give her life meaning.

She was unconsciously displacing onto the baby her need to be taken care of and to be given what she had not received as a child. Being able to talk about some of these expectations in therapy helped her understand that they were unrealistic. She began to distinguish her own needs from what her baby would need, to recognize that she had the ability to assume the caretaking role with the infant.

A strong gender preference may lead to anxiety over being able to love a baby of the "wrong gender." For example, although a gender preference is common among expectant parents, the reasons behind a survivor's gender preference may be very different. One abuse survivor felt that a girl baby would not be safe, just as she herself had not been safe. Another could not tolerate the idea of a male fetus inside her, associating his maleness with her perpetrator.

Others fear having a defective child, "a monster" who might reflect their own negative self-image.

Marsha

Between 6 and 8 years old, Marsha suffered sexual abuse from her stepfather. She always believed she was dirty and dark inside, and the pain of the incest caused her to think her body was damaged. She experienced other abusive relationships as a teenager, not knowing how to protect herself. When she became pregnant at 36, she identified her own sense of abnormality with the fetus. Believing that the childhood damage she suffered could cause a defect in her infant, she worried about whether she could have a normal baby. Facing prenatal tests was scary for her. She dreaded learning that she had an abnormal fetus.

On the other hand, she wanted desperately to know if her baby and her body were normal. She shared some of her anxiety with her caregiver without giving any details of her history of abuse. She said she'd had some abdominal problems as a child and wondered if everything was normal. During her first physical exam, the obstetrician sensed her anxieties without knowing the reason, and explained each aspect of the exam, what he was looking for, and what he found, emphasizing the normal aspects of her body, uterus, and fetus. Since she was over 35, genetic tests were recommended, but it was important for Marsha to know that most women over 35 are advised to have these tests, that there was nothing unusual about her, and that the tests were a way of ruling out many conditions of concern. Her obstetrician then referred her to a careful and sensitive ultrasonographer who explained what he observed, denoting how every aspect of the fetus and her body looked completely normal. She now began to trust that her insides were healthy and underwent other tests as a matter of course, without further incident.

For survivors, invasive procedures such as vaginal exams and blood draws may remind them of violations from their childhood. For example, a routine vaginal exam may evoke flashbacks of rape or feelings of being used. Many women need help to distinguish health-promoting tests from past abusive invasion and disrespect for their body boundaries. (For examples of ways such procedures can be conducted sensitively, please see Chapters 12 and 13.)

Jill

Jill was sexually abused for many years by a brother, 14 years older, who often took care of her. When pregnant with her first baby at 29, she did not understand why the thought of prenatal tests terrified her. Her caregiver did not take the time to explain the reasons for the tests, assuming that she knew, and Jill was too shy to ask questions.

At the time of the first blood draw, she panicked and felt faint. The nurse thought that she was simply afraid of needles and suggested that she rest a moment. They tried again, were not successful, and Jill realized that her reactions were extreme and abnormal. She had to find a way to steel herself for these tests. She also needed to understand the purpose of them.

She sought counseling. Through role-play, she practiced talking to her caregiver, which helped her overcome her shyness in asking for information. Jill eventually received the information she needed and also learned some relaxation exercises, enough to get through the tests. In counseling, she came to realize that she associated the blood draws with her brother's invasive abuse.

Many pregnant survivors have learned to be strong, independent and "in control" as a way to protect themselves from the circumstances under which their abuse occurred, when they felt weak, dependent, helpless, and out of control. Inherent in pregnancy, however, are greater dependency, diminished physical capabilities, and a sense of being out of control of one's body.

Ben and Loretta

In a counseling session to learn relaxation and visualizations for labor, Ben and Loretta revealed some current difficulties in their relationship. Ben said of Loretta, "She has always been the strong one in our relationship and I have depended on her to keep calm when I would get stressed out. Now, she snaps at me for no reason and demands a lot more of me than she used to. Sometimes, I don't feel like coming home after work." As Ben distanced himself, Loretta found herself in a double bind—on the one hand needing him and on the other hand resenting that she felt so dependent. As a youngster she had learned not to show the helplessness she felt during abuse by becoming strong and self-sufficient. Now, this outer shell of protection was eroding, and neither Ben nor Loretta could adjust to this shift in their relationship.

Their counselor helped them realize that pregnancy brings changes in emotions and shifts in roles in all couples, even when abuse is not a factor. The abuse, however, may have created more distress than usual. Loretta made the connection between her early abuse and a fear of being needy. By using good communication skills, they were able to openly discuss their feelings. Consequently, they became more comfortable in their shifting roles, and Ben became more involved and dependable.

Dreams may be expressions of the survivor's anxiety and can provide keys to the underlying causes. In many cases, childhood abuse appears symbolically in dreams. It has been shown that repetitive nightmares and disturbing thoughts can cause a physiological stress response and may contribute to some complications of pregnancy, such as elevated blood pressure, premature labor, and others. (Chapters 10 and 11 offer techniques for understanding the meaning of dreams.)

Efforts to take better care of themselves during pregnancy, such as giving up smoking, alcohol, and drugs, may also cause unexpected stress. Those activities have served to protect survivors from intrusive feelings and to allay the internal tension that often accompanies a history of abuse. In stopping these habits, resurfacing memories and feelings may cause unexpected anxiety.

Choice of Caregiver

Unless she already has a relationship with a family doctor who provides maternity care, a pregnant woman must choose an obstetrician or midwife and a location for birth. Many survivors find it difficult to take these steps because they know that prenatal care involves disclosure and investigation of personal matters, such as background information, medical and psychosocial history, unhealthy habits, and sexual history. Along with such sensitive discussions come requirements that she expose her body and allow various invasive procedures. These components of care, which are often distressing to the survivor client, are considered by the caregiver as essential. If the caregiver does not understand the woman's hesitation, or is annoyed by it, it can seem like another instance of abuse to her.

In order to avoid revealing personal matters, many survivors avoid medical care, except for emergencies. However, becoming pregnant leads many to overcome this reluctance because they do not want to take chances with their baby's well being. Others delay or avoid prenatal care completely. Sometimes, if they have one doctor with whom they finally feel comfortable, they dread having to find a different caregiver who specializes in maternity care. Obviously, this is one advantage of having a trusted family doctor who provides maternity care. This model of family practice maternity care is uncommon in the United States and central Canada, except in some rural areas, but is widely available in the eastern and western parts of Canada.

Some survivors seek alternative types of care (midwifery, out-of-hospital birth) because they have had unpleasant experiences with conventional medicine, or are drawn to the type of care offered by midwives. Compared to most obstetricians, midwives spend more time with their clients, use fewer invasive procedures, pay more attention to the psychosocial aspects of childbearing, and personalize their care to the individual. Furthermore, midwives are almost always women, and most survivors prefer female caregivers. There are exceptions, however, among survivors who were victimized by women or who felt unprotected by the adult women in their lives.

It is not only the gender but also the style and philosophy of the caregiver that determines whether the survivor will in the end feel comfortable or more secure. Sometimes survivor clients feel very let down or even mistreated by female caregivers who did not live up to their expectations. One survivor said, "I went to this one doctor because she was a young woman and I thought she'd be more understanding than an older man doctor. But she wasn't. She didn't spend any time with me. All she cared about were my blood pressure and test results. I was glad she was not on call when I went into labor."

Pregnant survivors sometimes want more from their caregivers than they provide. Though some midwives, family doctors, and obstetricians are exceptions, most caregivers focus heavily on following the clinical aspects of the pregnancy and devote little attention to psychosocial aspects. They oversee tests of the health and well-being of the mother and fetus, and see the mother regularly for brief conversations, some advice, and a few hands-on assessments. The office nurse does other testing and some teaching, but there is little time scheduled for client and caregiver to get to know each other or to discuss important personal concerns. As for group practices, a client may hardly know the doctor or midwife who cares for her in labor.

Out-of-hospital birth center and home-birth midwives place the greatest emphasis on exploring personal matters, developing rapport, and individualizing care. Hospital-based midwives and family physicians fall between the busy obstetrician and the out-of-hospital midwife in time spent on psychosocial matters.

Some survivors shop carefully for a caregiver and ask questions about the services offered. This gives them the best chance of finding the care that seems safest (physically and emotionally) and most appropriate among those available in the community and through their health care coverage. See below for suggestions for questions to ask in selecting a caregiver.

Even more important than knowing their options and making the best choice is for women to have realistic expectations. Every caregiver has many clients and little time (with the exception of some midwives with small practices). A client can be hurt if she wants or expects too much. Survivors who seem most satisfied are those who recognize that no single caregiver can adequately meet all their needs, even when the caregiver is respectful, kind and interested. The most helpful caregivers also realize that they are limited in what they can do, and are careful not to promise too much. They identify good services in the community for their clients, such as childbirth education classes, prenatal yoga classes, La Leche League, support groups, doulas, massage therapists, counselors, therapists, and social workers. Many women find books and the Internet to be valuable sources of information and support. They create their own "village" of support, information, shared experience and friendship.

That is not to say, however, that a survivor and her doctor or midwife cannot have a satisfying partnership. Good communication skills and clear expectations make for a rewarding relationship. (Chapters 6 and 7 discuss ways that survivor clients and their caregivers can work well together, despite time constraints.)

Questions to Ask When Selecting a Caregiver

The woman's search for an obstetrician, family doctor, or midwife begins by consulting her insurance plan to find which caregivers are covered, checking for convenient office locations and learning the hospital(s)or birth centers where they attend births, or if they attend home births. Then she should seek information on potential caregivers from such sources as their other clients, childbirth educators and others who work with pregnant women.

Before the initial appointment, the woman can learn the credentials (education, certifications, experience, etc.), hospital affiliations, back-up arrangements, number of caregivers in the group, and logistical matters, in a phone conversation with the caregiver or the office receptionist.

During her first appointment, the woman should ask questions that will help her determine whether the caregiver is right for her, and she is right for the caregiver. Following are possible questions:

- What do you see as my role and responsibilities during pregnancy and birth? How do you prefer to work with your clients?
- How do you feel about my partner, other family or friends, or a doula attending my birth (whether vaginal or cesarean)?
- What are your feelings about childbirth preparation classes? Do you have any recommendations for good classes? (If the woman is interested in a particular method or a particular childbirth educator, she might ask the caregiver for an opinion.)
- What are the chances that you will be present when I give birth? Who covers when you are not available? Will I have a chance to meet that person?
- How do you feel about birth plans? If I prepare one, will

you check it for safety and compatibility with your practices and hospital policies?

- Do you have the flexibility to accommodate individual preferences or needs of your clients?

Other questions might pertain to any specific health concerns or emotional issues, or the caregiver's usual practices. If she is comfortable doing so, she might also ask about the caregiver's experience working with survivors of childhood sexual abuse and other abuse.

Dissatisfaction with Her Present Caregiver

Sometimes, after a woman has seen a caregiver for some time, she begins to discover that she disagrees with the caregiver's approach or feels uncomfortable or vulnerable. She should pay attention to those feelings and try to act on them in one of the following ways:

- Express her discomfort, using "I messages" (see chapter 7), and describe what would help her feel more at ease. A sensitive caregiver is likely to respond considerately. Together they can clarify misunderstandings and improve the relationship.

- If the above does not succeed, the woman might consider changing caregivers. This is not always easy, especially if her health insurance plan limits choices, or or if there are few choices in her area, or if another caregiver is unwilling to accept a patient of a colleague or one who is in advanced pregnancy. Before deciding to leave a caregiver, she should check on the availability of other caregivers.

- If neither of the above options works, she will have to find a way to minimize the negative aspects of the relationship. She might discuss her concerns tactfully with the office nurse, her childbirth educator, counselor, or doula. Once in labor, the woman might share her concerns with the nurse, if she or he seems compassionate.

It is always unfortunate when a woman is unhappy with her caregiver, on whom she must depend for her clinical well-being and that of her baby. It is worth the effort to minimize any discomfort, and to establish a better relationship.

Disclosure of Abuse

Women have to ask themselves whether to disclose past or current abuse to their caregiver. Below is a discussion of possible risks and benefits, as well as concerns of many survivor clients. (In chapter 6, we further discuss the issue of disclosure of abuse and how the caregiver should respond when a client reports such a history.)

Potential Risks

A woman might fear that she will be labeled as "bad" or will be blamed for letting the abuse happen, thus intensifying her feelings of shame. Having not been believed as a child, she may wonder if a caregiver will believe her now. She may not want to shock or upset the caregiver with the true story. She may worry about being judged as "defective" or needy. It is also possible that her story of emotional pain will be minimized, ignored or misunderstood. She may be concerned that information placed in her chart will be seen by many caregivers and reveal her secret. If she has not shared this trauma or some details with her partner, she may worry that her caregiver could inadvertently reveal these things. Finally, she may be afraid of bringing it up again, not wanting to re-experience the painful memories.

Potential Benefits

In today's more knowledgeable climate about abuse and its effects, there are caregivers who want to provide empathic and sensitive care and avoid adding to a survivor's distress. By disclosing her abuse to such a person, the survivor gains a greater sense of safety, control and choice. The caregiver may also direct her to some helpful resources. For women who have come to terms with their abuse issues, who are comfortable discussing their history and needs, disclosing their abuse may seem very natural, and they may be able to work well with sensitive caregivers in an equal relationship.

Forms of Disclosure

A woman may be asked about an abuse history on printed forms and with direct questioning.

Family history form

In beginning prenatal care, most women are given a few pages of printed forms to fill out. They contain yes-no questions about medical history, family history, and personal, social, and developmental history. There may be questions about recreational drug use, sexuality, past or present domestic violence and child abuse—physical, sexual, or emotional. With some questions, it is obvious that the answers are relevant to the woman's present and future healthcare. But the purpose of others, especially those relating to abuse, may not seem as clear. It may seem risky to the survivor to check the "yes" boxes. The truth is, some caregivers follow up appropriately on affirmative answers and open the door to further discussion of the abuse and how it affects the woman's life. But others are uncomfortable with "yes" answers on abuse or have no idea how to respond appropriately. They do not follow up, which is hurtful to the woman who has taken the risk of disclosure.

Some women leave questions unanswered until they have the chance to ask the caregiver: "I'm curious about what you do if a woman answers 'yes' to the questions on drug use, domestic violence, and childhood abuse. Will you explain?" The caregiver's response to this question indicates whether he or she will be knowledgeable and sensitive. Others answer "no" on the form, but may disclose their abuse history later if they develop a sense of trust.

In many hospitals, in an effort to provide better care, the nurse is required to ask many of these questions when a woman is admitted in labor, and to record the answers electronically, even when the woman has been asked before and the information is available in the chart. Unfortunately, such questions may create anxiety, especially if the woman is accompanied by someone from whom she prefers to withhold this information. In fact, many nurses are uncomfortable asking such questions while the woman is trying to cope with labor, and know no appropriate response to make should the woman answer "yes."

Questioning by the caregiver

As part of a face-to-face interview, some caregivers routinely ask about childhood and current abuse. The woman may feel anxious about answering, especially if she has never told anyone, or if previous attempts to share that information elicited thoughtless, inappropriate responses such as blaming the woman, minimizing her abuse, disbelieving her, or exhibiting extreme anger at the abuser or curiosity about what actually happened. Some fear that even if they decide not to talk about it, their genitals may be scarred or different in some way and that the caregiver will be able to see it. Some wonder how much to disclose, or if they will become upset when telling their story. Some wonder how the caregiver will react. Will the caregiver be nosy, uncomfortable, disgusted, or disbelieving? What will the caregiver do with the information—write it in the chart for everyone to see, keep it confidential, talk about it to others? Will disclosing her abuse improve the chances of a positive birth experience?

If the question is asked sensitively, the woman may feel safer in disclosing and discussing her abuse. For example, Barbara Wijma, a Norwegian midwife who specializes in the care of abuse survivors, suggests the following wording, "Many adult women were abused as children, that is, hit or beaten, shouted at, or forced to do sexual things. Did anything like that ever happen to you or is it happening today?"

The caregiver might also raise this question if the woman has a cluster of symptoms often exhibited by abuse survivors (discussed in this chapter and Chapters 2, 4, and 5). If she has been abused, some concerns and symptoms will likely make more sense, be more understandable, and be easier to treat. In fact, sometimes a woman with typical symptoms of past abuse will deny any such history. She may truly have no memory of it. In such a case, without discussing it further, the caregiver can provide the same sensitive and empathic treatment as he or she would give a survivor. Then, no harm will be done.

Self-disclosure by the woman

If the woman's trust in her caregiver grows or she begins having distressing thoughts, and feels a need to confide in someone, she may bring up the abuse herself: "I've been having some nightmares and scary thoughts and I need some help. I think it's related to being abused by my cousin when I was a girl." Or she might decide to explain some of her lack of ease with the caregiver: "There is something important that I want to discuss with you. It has to do with how I react in new or strange situations, and how I deal with stressful things like vaginal exams, blood draws, and pain. I was sexually abused as a child and it had some long-lasting effects that will probably show up at times in my appointments or in labor." Using "I" messages will help keep the discussion safe and non-threatening. (See Chapter 7.)

Unfortunately, caregivers are not always knowledgeable or empathic. It is a gamble for a woman to disclose her abusive past to a near-stranger, albeit an experienced professional. If she wants her caregiver to know and the caregiver seems wise and understanding, or asks sensitively about abuse, then she may want to take the gamble and tell of the abuse. Otherwise, she may feel safer keeping the information to herself.

Issues of Control

Some pregnant survivors are intimidated by medical personnel and the medical system. The caregiver may represent authority, power, and control similar to authority figures of her childhood, some of whom abused her. The caregiver may do things to her body that are painful or humiliating, as her abuser did. Many survivors cope by avoiding medical care or presenting for prenatal care very late in pregnancy. Others are extremely passive—they do not ask for information and do not inform the physician about pre-existing conditions or their concerns, for fear of bothering him or her. They feel unseen or unimportant, just as they felt when they were being victimized. Some feel very needy and dependent on a caregiver and feel rejected or abandoned when the caregiver seems unavailable to them.

Still others feel distrustful of "authority figures," and manifest this as anger and a need to remain in control. Loss of control is associated with being hurt, while remaining in control means being safe. In her great need to gain or maintain control over treatment, a survivor may pose numerous questions to her caregiver, express strong opinions, or present a lengthy, detailed birth plan, which to the caregiver may seem impossible or unreasonable. One doctor said, "You're tying my hands. I can't guarantee that labor will proceed in any single way." More likely, the doctor simply becomes upset with the woman. Caregivers have been known to say that the lengthier the birth plan, the greater the chance of a cesarean. They may not realize that the birth plan indicates the survivor's need to feel in control of what is done to her by powerful people during a stressful and unpredictable process. This need drives them to make numerous demands on the staff. Unfortunately, such behavior may cause negative treatment in return, and lead to a type of unintended re-victimization. We will discuss more appropriate ways for a caregiver to respond to a client's need for control in later chapters.

June

June sought counseling because she dreaded her prenatal appointments. In her role as department manager responsible for seven employees, June saw herself as competent, self-sufficient, and decisive, but her confidence left her once she arrived in the caregiver's office, where she felt rushed and unable to ask questions. Her caregiver assumed she knew more than she actually did, and seemed pressured to complete the appointment quickly, allowing little or no time to check on June's feelings or her understanding of various procedures and pregnancy-related events.

In June's case, the obstetrician's lack of communication made her feel stupid, unable to make decisions, or even ask good questions. Her feelings of inferiority were greater when her appointments were with the only male in the practice, who seemed nice enough, but June could not trust him. She felt suspicious that he was being manipulative, but could not be sure.

As a child, June was coerced into sex by her uncle, and during her teen years, by an older boyfriend. She had worked hard in therapy for years to overcome those old feelings of inadequacy, shame and intimidation. It was depressing to have those feelings rekindled at this time. June recognized the association between her uncle, boyfriend, and her male doctor, when her counselor asked her, "What is it about the doctor that makes you dread seeing him?" Her counselor guided June to follow feelings that emerged from that self-searching question. She soon realized that when in the doctor's presence she felt like a powerless girl again. That insight was the beginning of a realization that she was attributing abusive tendencies to her doctor that were really a remnant from her earlier feelings during her childhood abuse.

In her counseling sessions, with role play and containment exercises, she practiced separating the old feelings and abuse memories from the present time, and soon was able to reclaim her adult self while in the caregiver's presence. As she gained the confidence to ask questions, the doctor responded appropriately. (See Chapter 9.)

Delayed Recognition of Abuse-Related Events in Childbearing

Many women who have had complications in pregnancy or birth do not realize until years later, while in therapy, that their problems are related to early abuse.

Gerri

Gerri had always looked back on her childbirth as normal, except that she could not push the baby out. She absolutely could not push. She had felt herself holding back. In therapy in her 50s, she recognized that she had been frightened of losing control of her body and by the strong feelings in her vagina. "Something about pushing was sexual. I didn't like feeling the genital power of my muscles and the urge and thrust of my body."

Anne

Anne described dissociating during labor. She had two children and remembered being "on the ceiling" during both labors. She birthed normally, but she remembered she had "numbed out" and gone "to the ceiling" in a similar way when her father came into her room at night.

For others, however, childbearing proceeds without any apparent effects of past abuse.

Jean

Jean had three completely normal and satisfying childbirth experiences in which she took a great deal of pride. At age 50, however, she started having flashbacks of severe childhood sexual abuse (triggered by the incapacitating clinical depression of her husband—similar to the depression of her father who abused her). As she confronted the horrors of the abuse that occurred from age 2 to 10, and as she dealt with terrible feelings of shame, self-disgust, and blame, seeing herself as "evil, wrong, bad," she held onto these births as the only evidence of her self-worth.

"Having a child made me feel that my body was normal, that I wasn't defective, that I could produce something out of myself that was beautiful." In every other aspect of her life she continued to negate herself. Eventually, with intensive psychotherapy, she was able to release the trauma and reclaim for herself a more positive image.

Some abuse survivors who have been in therapy seek counseling when they become pregnant. They know that the effects of the abuse may not have been completely erased, and they want to master helpful techniques to use with stresses as they arise.

In conclusion, pregnancy may bring a variety of abuse issues to the surface. If recognized and handled appropriately, there is great potential for healing. For some survivors, pregnancy proceeds normally without negative repercussions. Respectful individualized treatment by a woman's caregiver is sought and expected by everyone, but for abuse survivors, it is one of the most effective ways to avoid retraumatization and to promote healing.

4
Childbirth for the Childhood Sexual Abuse Survivor

- With my first birth I can't remember anything from the time they put in the forceps until I saw this little hand on my chest. Then it dawned on me that I'd had a baby.
- I'm haunted that I made a spectacle of myself in labor. I'll never forget the way the doctor looked at me when I was kneeling on the floor. I saw this "Aren't we being a little dramatic here?" look on his face.
- I've never felt so powerful in my life! It was such a great feeling! Even though it hurt like hell, the pain never took me over. And everyone kept telling me how well I was doing.

Thus far, we have explored many aspects of pregnancy and maternity care, but it is labor and birth that represent the climax of the entire process. The woman's body undergoes the most basic and profound of all bodily processes, and within hours, she is transformed into a mother.

Women remember their childbirth experiences clearly

and vividly. In long-term studies of women's satisfaction with childbirth, Penny Simkin and Jo Green, Celia Kitzinger, and others found that positive, satisfying memories are less likely to result from such factors as length of labor, complications, or even type of delivery than with feeling in control, feeling a sense of accomplishment, and feeling well cared for by nurses, doctors, or midwives. Negative or unsatisfying memories are associated with feelings of being out of control, and receiving disrespectful care from nurses and doctors.

In another part of her study, Simkin compared women's immediate written descriptions of their first childbirths with their descriptions many years later, and found that the memories—both positive and negative—are accurate, vivid, and still laden with emotions, including pride in themselves, enhanced self-esteem, joy, love, or anger, sadness, and remorse. The study made it quite apparent that the way a woman is cared for affects how she remembers and feels about her childbirth for a very long time, if not for the rest of her life. In addition, Phyllis and Marshall Klaus and John Kennell report that the nurturing a woman receives during this vulnerable time can influence how she nurtures and feels about her infant.

Challenges in Labor and Birth

Many events of labor and birth can be challenging for most women but may be especially difficult for the abuse survivor. Some challenges are intrinsic to the labor and birth process, and are not within the control of the mother. These carry an element of unpredictability, and include:

- Uncertainty over when labor will start
- How long it will last
- How much it will hurt
- How and how well she will handle the pain and lack of rest

- The possibility of injury to her pelvic floor
- Possibility of problems for the baby

Added to these intrinsic challenges are extrinsic challenges, that is, the frequently used procedures and routines of maternity care in modern hospitals. Their purpose is to improve safety, efficiency, pain relief, and predictability. Because they are outside the usual experience of most people, they require great adjustments on the part of the woman and her partner. These include:

- The high-tech clinical environment—beeping machines and equipment, medications for numerous purposes
- Uniformed nurses and doctors who are usually strangers and who wear masks at times
- Items attached to the woman via wires and tubes—blood pressure cuff, intravenous line, electronic fetal monitor, bladder catheter, oxygen mask, epidural catheter, and others
- Invasive procedures—breaking the bag of waters, inserting the IV, blood draw, vaginal exams, inserting catheters
- Instruments such as forceps or vacuum extractor, or surgery—episiotomy or cesarean—to assist delivery

Most hospitals, in an effort to put women more at ease, provide amenities such as bathtubs, rocking chairs, birth balls, hot or cold packs, warm blankets, television, radio, a chair-bed for the partner, and other comfort items.

Other crucial influences are the personal characteristics that each laboring woman brings into labor—her self-image, fears, beliefs, worries, personality, and her usual way of responding to pain and stress. These affect how she copes with the intrinsic and extrinsic challenges, how she communicates with staff (and how they respond to her), and ultimately, how she feels about her birth experience later.

All these challenging elements are part of mainstream

birth in North America, and even though medical, technological and surgical interventions contribute to improved safety, efficiency, or pain relief for mother or baby, they require great adjustments. Because most women believe that a safe birth depends on being in the hospital and cooperating with staff, they find ways to make the unpleasant parts tolerable. They go to classes to learn what to expect, what choices they have, and how they can help themselves. They tour the hospital to take the surprise out of the hospital experience. They bring husbands or loved ones and some bring doulas into the hospital. They try to adjust and adapt to the ways of their hospital. A kind nurse, midwife, or doctor can make a big difference by recognizing and helping to alleviate the stress inherent in the situation.

The small percentage of women who want to avoid the high-tech atmosphere of most hospitals seek safe low-tech alternatives, such as care by midwives or family doctors, in free-standing birth centers, or home birth. If the woman needs medical intervention, she goes to the hospital. The rate of transfer to the hospital from such settings for medical assistance is approximately 25 to 30 percent for first time mothers, and lower for second or third time mothers. The safety of planned out-of-hospital birth for healthy women, attended by competent midwives, with hospital backup available, is very high. Unfortunately, such care is not available everywhere in North America.

The challenges for women in out-of-hospital settings are intrinsic to the birth process—pain, unpredictable onset and length, and the requirement for stamina and hard work. The woman must rely more on herself to deal with these challenges than the woman in the hospital. For women who are transferred, the challenges include the disappointment over having to go to the hospital, the logistics of moving to a new location in the midst of labor, adjustments to the hospital setting and necessary interventions, and distress over whatever problem made the transfer necessary.

How Survivors Can Reduce the Risk of Traumatic Birth

Many abuse survivors, for very good reasons, have issues with control, helplessness, exposure, restraints, trust in their bodies, trust of strangers and authority figures, pain, especially genital pain, penetration of their bodies, and discomfort with new situations. Those who choose hospital birth try to lessen the distress by prior planning and preparation and communicating their needs to the staff. Those who choose out-of-hospital birth do so in hopes of avoiding those issues, but must also prepare for the possibility of transfer, which will bring about the circumstances they had hoped to avoid.

From published studies and our experiences in counseling sexual abuse survivors, we have learned that survivors with unresolved abuse issues are more likely to feel misunderstood or poorly treated by caregivers and to experience complications in labor than are women without an abuse history. We have found that these risks can be reduced if the abuse survivor can identify and express her needs, or even resolve some troubling emotional issues before the birth. Before further discussing examples of traumatic births experienced by child sexual abuse survivors, we want to reiterate that a history of abuse is not inevitably linked with a traumatic childbirth. Many survivors give birth without any apparent effects from abuse.

Rowena

Consider the case of Rowena, a survivor of emotional and sexual abuse.

Rowena was the only daughter in a family of four children. Her abuse occurred at age twelve after her parents had separated. All the children remained with their father. She recalled that during her parents' separation, her father emotionally and sexually abused her. Her brothers, influenced by their father, followed his lead. They teased her and called her names, and molested her. Rowena became aggressive and suicidal; she skipped school, and became sexually reckless as a means of gaining acceptance. She longed for her mother's love and guidance, but her mother was unavailable to her. When Rowena married a number of years later, she had no idea that her abuse history could affect her childbirth experience.

Before their first pregnancy, she and her husband John had carefully prepared for conception; she ate well, took vitamins, and both discontinued the use of alcohol. They were overjoyed when their pregnancy test was positive. The pregnancy went well except for some bleeding after intercourse at 5 months, possibly due, their midwife said, to a slight, but not dangerous, separation of the placenta. Rowena reacted with self-blame and extreme anxiety over the possibility of prematurity. They had no intercourse for the rest of the pregnancy.

They prepared for the birth by reading, attending natural childbirth classes, and practicing labor comfort measures together. They selected a motherly nurse-midwife, an experienced middle-aged doula in hopes of satisfying Rowena's deep need for maternal nurturing, and a family–centered hospital. They did everything they could to ensure a safe and rewarding birth.

Unfortunately for Rowena, she had a difficult and prolonged labor, which required numerous invasive interventions. Although these interventions were necessary for the safe passage of her baby, they were terrifying and caused flashbacks to her abuse.

Labor began with ruptured membranes at 8 a.m. on a Sunday morning. After 24 hours of mild contractions and no sleep, she and her husband went to the hospital. By Monday afternoon her cervix was dilating at a rate of about one centimeter per hour, and by 7 p.m., her cervix was 7 centimeters dilated, where it remained until 10 p.m. She walked and climbed stairs for an hour to speed her labor, but made no further progress. The monitor indicated that her contractions were ineffective. At 11 p.m., thinking her body had failed her, she felt she had no choice but to agree to Oxytocin augmentation. For the first time during her labor, Rowena felt frightened of the pain. She received a light epidural block, which was inadequate. She still felt areas of pain in the anesthetized areas. Later she described her feelings at this time: "I was confined to bed with a zillion tubes in me."

At 2 a.m. on Tuesday, Rowena's cervix had closed to 3 cm, but the midwife didn't tell her until later. [Authors' note: Closing of the cervix by as much as 4 cm is a highly unlikely event; one wonders if this exam or the previous exams were incorrect.] The midwife increased the Oxytocin, had the anesthesiologist modify the epidural, and Rowena slept for 3 hours. She awoke in "incredible pain, and hysterical. It was the first time I lost it emotionally." The epidural catheter must have migrated and no longer provided pain relief. The doula was there "in my face, insisting that I follow her with the breathing to give me some sense of control." By 8 a.m., she was almost completely dilated, with a "lip of cervix", remaining and her midwife manually opened the cervix the last little bit, which was very painful for Rowena.

She pushed for one and a half hours, with little apparent progress, and the fetal heart rate began dropping during contractions. Rowena was not aware of how serious this was until a physician appeared to try to deliver the baby. After an episiotomy, two failed attempts with a vacuum extractor ("I remember the vacuum cup as huge...") and one failed attempt with forceps, the baby was finally delivered.

In Rowena's words, "I had incredible pain with the forceps. I was being ripped apart. I was screaming. I thought I was dying. I wanted to pray, but couldn't find the words.

"When the baby came out, I didn't even know he was out, and I didn't know it when they put him on my chest. My husband cut the cord, but I never knew it. Later I gradually became aware of some small hands on my chest and that was my first clue that my baby was there."

Rowena was not able to sit at all for 2 weeks because of pain in her perineum. Shortly after the birth she began having nightmares of betrayal and confusion—trusted friends chasing her and "marching horrible things like bugs and knives into my vagina. My vagina became my whole person. I was petrified of sex for months."

After all the careful preparation—pre-conception self-care, reading, classes, careful choices of caregiver, doula, and hospital—Rowena felt betrayed, let down, and abandoned by the entire system. She suffered from post-traumatic stress disorder (PTSD) related to the birth and made worse by her earlier unresolved trauma.

It is particularly distressing for all involved when

a woman does everything advised for a good outcome and yet ends up disappointed and traumatized. Perhaps if her abuse and her anxiety had been recognized during her pregnancy and if Rowena had received counseling that explored and dealt with her deep fears, the birth may have been different, at least in its psychological after-effects.

During her second pregnancy, Rowena sought therapy for her abuse issues. With all these unresolved issues and the due date approaching, she began to dread her upcoming labor. Her therapist referred Rowena to a birth counselor, and in two sessions, they reviewed her previous birth, explored her fears for the upcoming labor, and planned strategies, including limits on the use of forceps. (See Chapter 10 for a description of the methods used.) She learned effective ways to discuss her fears and limits with her caregiver, her partner and her doula.

During her second labor, because she had prepared the birth plan, the staff was more enlightened about her fears and how she needed to deal with them. This labor and birth proceeded normally, even though Rowena experienced some challenging circumstances, such as having the same midwife as the first time (with whom she had been very angry), the same birthing room, and extreme fear when she had to start pushing. This time, however, she was able to tell people what she felt, as these triggering events came up, and she could get their help.

There was no repeat of the first traumatic experience. Rowena gave birth to a healthy daughter.

Joanna

Joanna, a 34-year-old first-time mother, had for years been sexually and emotionally abused by both her uncle and her father. Her childhood experiences led her into a long period of substance abuse, depression, chronic fatigue syndrome and great difficulties in her marriage. She had devoted much effort to healing, and had overcome many after-effects of her abuse. But since becoming pregnant, she had no confidence in her ability to cope with pregnancy, birth, or the demands of parenting. She had quit work in order to spend more time and energy on self-nurturing.

In childbirth class, the intimacy, touching and comfort between the other couples in the group was hard to witness, and it was impossible for her and Paul, her husband, to participate. In fact, she did not share most of her classmates' enthusiasm for their husbands' presence at the birth. She was not sure that she wanted hers to see her in a "state of helplessness," but she did want him to see their child being born. He wanted very much to play a supportive role in labor, and to share in the birth of their baby.

Joanna also did not feel completely confident in her doctor, whom she found gentle, understanding and kind, but whose technical competence she doubted.

Joanna's greatest fear was that something in labor would trigger "body memories" or feelings of victimization that would have to be processed right then. She wanted a doula with the background and skills to help with that. Even though she was no longer using drugs, she also had a fear of using narcotics, due to her addiction and sensitivity.

She met with a skilled birth counselor who helped her identify specific triggers and devise appropriate strategies. Joanna discussed these with her doctor and prepared a Birth Plan, using "I-messages," to explain her needs to the hospital staff and to request their support (see Chapter 7).

After extensive preparation—childbirth classes, birth counseling, interviewing and selecting her doulas, and informing her doctor of her abuse issues—she awaited the birth of her baby. Here is her birth story:

Joanna's contractions began at 11 p.m. on a Wednesday night, to her great excitement. She and Paul eagerly began using their special aromas and their breathing techniques, along with music. They did not sleep all night and by morning were tired and discouraged that the contractions were irregular and not intensifying, yet strong enough to keep her from sleeping. In a phone call in the morning, her doula suggested that since they could not sleep, they should get up, greet the day and keep life as normal as possible.

The doula joined them in the late morning, and helped Joanna relax. Eventually, Joanna's contractions, still uncomfortable, slowed to 8 to 12 minutes apart, and she decided to try a nap. Paul left to do some errands and the doula stayed in the other room, at Joanna's request. As she lay there trying to relax during the painful contractions, Joanna had flashbacks to her abuse, remembering how she would also try to relax during the pain. Her fear of losing control (which she always tried to prevent in all aspects of her life) was heightened as she realized that this labor was out of her control.

She began to cry and tremble and called the doula. Her doula held her in her arms and let her sob and wail for a half hour, without trying to stop her. After some time, Joanna said that she felt mixed-up, that one part of her was very afraid of having this baby, but that another part wanted it. Acknowledging and voicing her fear and releasing some of her intense emotions helped her relax, and finally she was able to sleep for a few hours.

Contractions resumed some hours later and they went to the hospital at 1 a.m. on Friday. Joanna's clear and assertive birth plan helped the staff understand her special needs. (See Appendix 5 for her birth plan.) The labor progressed slowly. Joanna used the bath, breathing patterns and a focal point (a book of photographs of beautiful places in Canada, and later her doula's eyes.)

Labor progress stalled at 5 cm. for several hours, despite intense contractions. Joanna recognized that Paul's presence was making her "hold in" her pain because she did not want to show him how weak she was. She asked Paul to leave, and he did, though he felt hurt. The doula tried to help him understand that it was not his behavior or lack of support that was behind Joanna's request, but rather her own need to be perceived by him as a strong person. He was not invited back for 6 hours.

Joanna stated several times that her entire pelvis, vagina, and low abdomen were "gripping" throughout each contraction and she could not release them. She decided to take narcotics, despite earlier concerns that they could cause a relapse into drug abuse. She had written repeated warnings in her birth plan that she was chemically sensitive, and her doula tried to remind her that she had wanted to avoid narcotics. Her need for pain relief, however, overrode those concerns. Unfortunately, she had terrifying hallucinations as a result of the medication (panda bears hurtling at her through many windows), "like a bad LSD trip," and had to be given a narcotic antagonist to stop them. Then she asked for an epidural, which worked very well. When she became comfortable, Paul was asked to return.

In two hours, Joanna's cervix dilated completely, perhaps because the epidural allowed relief of the tension in her pelvis, and it was time to push. The doula showed Paul how to take an active coaching role, telling Joanna when she was having a contraction, and urging her to push hard enough to reach an intensity of "100" on the electronic contraction monitor: "That's the way! A little more! 85, 90, a little more, YOU DID IT! Yes, that's great!" Joanna loved pushing and Paul was glad to participate in a meaningful way. She made good progress, partly because the epidural had removed all the pain that was so frightening to her. As she said, "I had the time of my life pushing him out. It was a true celebration—a victory—over everything I had gone through."

Later, Joanna said, "The most empowering thing about my birth was my newfound ability to stay in my body, stay aware of my emotions, and move through it moment to moment."

As can be seen from Joanna's story, even with her thorough preparation, some unexpected abuse-related events occurred—the flashbacks to the abuse, the fear of being out of control, the narcotic's side effects, and her extreme pelvic tension. She had, however, set up a support system that could deal with those unexpected problems fairly well. Joanna was still helped to work through each of these potentially upsetting events as they arose, because the staff was informed of her needs and because she had a knowledgeable doula.

The early labor visit from her doula, and the doula's presence helped bring Joanna back from her flashback and face her fear. The quick recognition by the nurse of the hallucinations as a side effect of the narcotic, and her actions to counteract them helped to keep that unpleasant event from ruining Joanna's whole experience. By validating Joanna's decision to use the epidural and finding ways to involve Paul during the pushing (after his long absence from the birthing room), the doula and staff helped minimize the negative impact of unexpected events.

Joanna's advance preparations helped her identify triggers and develop strategies to deal with them. She was also able to set up a protective environment for herself with her doula, an informed staff and her understanding husband, to ensure that unanticipated negative events would not turn the birth experience into a re-traumatization. In fact, her birth was empowering and triumphant.

Triggers That Threaten a Woman's Psychological Well-Being

As we have seen in Rowena and Joanna's stories, the birth process is deeply influenced by the woman's ability to trust and respond to the power of her body to open and release the baby. Without this ability, the likelihood of a safe, spontaneous and fulfilling birth is jeopardized. Understanding and preparing for the events of birth helps any woman to feel more in control and less fearful. For the childhood sexual abuse survivor, however, seemingly normal events and interventions commonly used during labor may have a double or hidden meaning, and be especially troubling. We refer to such words or actions as "triggers." Although not always recognized as such by the survivor, these triggers bear some similarity to her abuse. Her reactions, which may seem exaggerated or inappropriate, are intensified by such associations. Once this is understood by the woman and her care providers, her reactions suddenly make a great deal of sense. Indeed, she has very good reason for the way she reacts.

Just as "intrinsic" and "extrinsic" describe the challenges that come with childbirth, we are now using the same words to describe triggers. Some triggers are intrinsic; that is, they come with the spontaneous, uncontrollable process of labor, and are evoked by previous negative experiences involving the same parts of the body. Painful, escalating contractions, nausea and vomiting, bloody excretions, instinctual reactions like moaning, trembling, grunting, or crying out, and the feeling of the baby in her vagina can evoke conscious or unconscious trauma memories. Her own changed appearance (lack of makeup, sweating, uncombed hair) may make her feel ashamed or unattractive.

Something as seemingly innocuous as unexpected touch can elicit bodily tension, fear, memories of the abuse, reenactment of pain, and make the woman feel helpless, invaded or unsafe. Survivors may withdraw from any type of touch (even touch meant to soothe) and may even feel discomfort initially with the baby's body against or at the breast. Some positions used by laboring women, such as on hands and knees, squatting, lithotomy, or pulling their legs apart, may trigger abuse memories or feelings of helplessness or degradation.

We refer to triggers that are not caused by the labor and birth process itself as extrinsic triggers. Extrinsic triggers are evoked by clinical procedures, the sights, smells and sounds of the hospital environment, clinical staff or family members, and that may bring up feelings of uneasiness, helplessness, distrust, isolation, fear, loss of identity, and danger. Environmental triggers include the hospital atmosphere, beeping equipment, smells, and institutional appearance. Interpersonal triggers include lack of privacy and quiet, lack of respect for the woman's modesty, conflict with loved ones or caregivers, and being left alone when frightened. Care-related triggers include vaginal exams, injections, attachment to machines and containers, being questioned and watched by uniformed strangers.

Especially during times of stress, words or actions by the nurse or caregiver can be interpreted negatively or evoke an unintended reaction in the childhood abuse survivor, for example, "Open your legs," "Relax your bottom," "This will hurt only a little," "Relax and it won't hurt so much." These comments, meant to help, may be the same words her abuser used. A nurse on the phone to a laboring woman: "If you're still walking around, talking and eating, you don't need to be here" (received by the survivor as rejection). "Trust your body," "Do what your body tells you to do," may be meaningless or frightening to a woman who experiences her body as a source of anguish, shame, damage, or poor health. For the woman who has spent a lifetime working to disconnect from her body or has felt betrayed by her body, these words are inappropriate.

Vaginal exams, catheters, IV's, sutures, needles, can raise anxiety, and feelings of mutilation and invasion as well as trigger horrible memories in victims of ritual abuse. The grogginess, numbness, or side effects of narcotics and anesthesia may also add to feeling out of control, even though they bring pain relief.

Even if the woman does not remember having been abused, her body may. We refer to physical reactions like those described here as body memories. (See Chapter 2.)

Control in Labor

Control is the antithesis of victimization. The concept of control has three aspects: 1) control over what is done to the woman by the staff and her own support people; 2) control over what her own body does; 3) control over her behavioral reactions or responses to contractions and procedures.

Having some control over what is done is a high priority for many survivors, for whom being abused is equated with helplessness and a loss of control. Being an equal partner in decision-making and being able to state her needs and concerns will help ensure that she is not unwittingly victimized by the staff or her loved ones.

Some women have so much fear of being taken advantage of or becoming powerless that they behave in a defensive, demanding, hostile, or self-protective way. It helps if the caregiver interprets these reactions as a fear of losing control, rather than as symptoms of a hostile personality. If the caregiver recognizes that there are very good reasons for such "extreme" behavior, he or she is more likely to respond sensitively and patiently, and many of these barriers in the client-caregiver relationship can be overcome. Informed choice is a highly desirable principle of maternity care, and when practiced, neither the woman nor her caregiver loses control, and neither has to behave defensively.

The bodily process of labor is outside one's conscious control. Yet a crisis often comes when a woman in labor realizes that she is truly helpless to control this inevitable process. Ideally, the woman recognizes that she does not need to try to control the process, and finds it possible to let go and place her trust in the process. Yet the survivor may feel this as a flashback to her helplessness during the abuse or to the aftereffects. Some women fight hard against this feeling, struggling against its relentless power and pain. They may tense, thrash, resist help, or cry. Or they may beg for relief, for a way out. Other survivors withdraw, become submissive and may even dissociate as a way to cope with the overwhelming distress. Medications can bring great relief of both the pain and the fear.

Still others, like Rowena and Joanna, whose stories were

told earlier in this chapter, may unconsciously keep the labor from going out of their control, at least for a while. There is ample evidence that stress, anxiety, and fear cause the release of labor-stalling hormones, such as epinephrine (also called adrenaline), norepinephrine, cortisol, and others.

Unconscious mechanisms and deep-seated fears sometimes prevent progress in labor. As a result, unwanted procedures or interventions must be utilized to ensure the delivery of the baby. Unfortunately, such circumstances sometimes result in emotional or physical trauma. Such trauma may be reduced by prior preparation on the part of the mother (as illustrated by Joanna's story), and by considerate and respectful care during labor.

The third aspect of control during labor—self-control—concerns all women, not only abuse survivors. Self-control refers to one's behavioral responses to painful contractions or procedures, and to the actions and words of others. Many women, having heard horror stories about birth, dread the prospect of panicking, screaming, passing out, or whimpering. They worry that the pain will make them behave in a shameful way, making fools of themselves, or embarrassing their partners, when they really want to give birth with dignity.

It helps to explore what a woman believes constitutes acceptable and unacceptable behavior. An empathic friend who has given birth, a doula, childbirth educator, birth counselor, midwife, or sensitive doctor may help allay some fears, and reframe the woman's perceptions of the sounds and behaviors so that they seem helpful and acceptable, even empowering. Rhythmic moaning (sometimes quite loud), swaying, stroking, and tapping are frequent behaviors of women who are coping well. Before the birth, "rehearsing" these rhythmic sounds and movements desensitizes women and makes such behavior less embarrassing or even quite empowering. If, however, the woman is unable to release her discomfort over the prospect of such behavior, then it will be wiser to help her master more "acceptable" coping techniques (for example, relaxation breathing, mental control, and passive relaxation). An epidural often gives women with these concerns a greater sense of control over behavior and appearance. On the other hand, to women for whom control means being able to escape or protect themselves physically, the epidural means a loss of control, because she cannot use her legs very well and she has several restrictive lines connecting her arms and trunk to various devices. As one survivor said when an epidural was being offered, "I have to feel that I can run away," even though she knew this was not a rational concern.

Control in labor has different meanings for different people, yet holds a high priority for most women. After all, the opposite of being in control is being out of control, and most women fear that alternative. By learning the realities of labor and exploring her own personal meaning of control, each woman will better anticipate her own needs and be more able to set up a plan for helping her remain in control.

Clinical Challenges in Labor and Possible Solutions

Throughout this book we describe and give examples of ways in which the clinical course of labor may be influenced by childhood sexual abuse. The table (on several pages at the end of this chapter), "Clinical Challenges in Labor and Possible Solutions," lists some of these clinical problems, possible abuse-related causes, and suggests possible solutions for the caregiver and staff. These may or may not solve the problems, but at the very least, they will help ensure that the woman is better understood and her concerns treated respectfully and considerately. Such care minimizes the likelihood of re-traumatization.

A truly positive birth experience includes both a good clinical and a good emotional outcome for both mother and baby. A healthy newborn with a depressed or traumatized mother is not a good outcome. While more of a challenge for abuse survivors, a good outcome is very possible if both the woman and her caregivers possess a true understanding of her needs. Unfortunately, the usual preparation—books, classes, and brief appointments with her caregiver are not enough to meet the needs of a woman with excessive anxiety or inner turmoil. Self-help work, short-term counseling, and communication with her caregiver are advantageous to both the woman and her caregiver in planning for the birth. Once in labor, of course, all women benefit from considerate, kind care.

When client and caregiver work together successfully, with help as needed from other key persons as described in this book, the chances are markedly improved for a good physical and emotional outcome for both mother and baby, a substantial degree of healing for the mother, and the beginning of a healthy lifelong mother-child relationship.

Clinical Challenges in Labor and Possible Solutions

Clinical Challenge or Complication	Possible Psychological Causes	Possible Solutions
1. Prolonged prodromal labor (non-progressing contractions).	• Reluctance to enter the process that results in parenthood. • Recognition that she is out of control over her body. • Self-fulfilling prophecy: Her body won't do this correctly because it is damaged, defective.	• Talk it over. "Why do you think it is taking so long to get into labor?" • Help her shift control from her body to her conscious responses to her contractions, which she *can* control. • Reassurance that prelabor often takes a long time, while the cervix ripens, effaces, and moves forward. • Patience, nourishment, help with sleep (bath, massage, sleeping medications).
2. Resistance to or inability to tolerate vaginal exams, blood draws, IV's, catheters, etc. (physical struggle, tension, panic, fainting).	• Association with rape or genital pain, especially if done by same gender as her perpetrator. • Phobia over blood. • "Invasion" of body boundaries may represent a metaphor for rape, defenselessness, etc. • Fear of having genitals exposed, visible to strangers.	• Do as few of these procedures as possible and tell her that. • Should have been discovered before labor and noted prominently in the chart. • Get the woman's permission. • Proceed slowly, step by step, regulated by the woman. • Have a trusted, kind, familiar person with her. • Respect her modesty as much as possible.

Clinical Challenge or Complication	Possible Psychological Causes	Possible Solutions
3. Strong preference for one careprovider or gender of careprovider ("wrong" gender is on call). This may apply to doctor, midwife, nurse, anesthesiologist, pediatrician.	• Distrust of authority figures of that gender (associated with gender of perpetrator). • Client may believe other women are, like her or like her mother, weak, incompetent, untrustworthy or evil.	• Validate her need and try very hard to honor this need (and, if impossible, tell her that you tried). • Should have been discovered ahead of time. • If possible, arrange for person of client's desired gender to do vaginal exams and other invasive procedures. • Use active listening; try not to take it personally.
4. Labor progress stalls in active phase.	• Labor pain is reaching a point where she can no longer remain "in control." Deep fear of pain behaviors (screaming, thrashing, panicking) associated with being helpless and out-of-control during abuse. She keeps the labor at a level where she can remain in control. • Deep fear of vaginal birth, preference for a cesarean for "failure to progress." • Fear leads to increased production of stress hormones (catecholamines), known to slow labor.	• Talk it over: "Why do you think your progress has stalled?" • Pain medications or an epidural may diminish the output of catecholamines, and enable further interventions, such as oxytocin or second stage interventions.

Clinical Challenge or Complication	**Possible Psychological Causes**	**Possible Solutions**
5. Struggling during administration of epidural, even though she requested it.	• Anesthesia placed by unseen person at her back may remind her of abuse from behind at night. • Reminders to "lie still and it will be over sooner," may be what she heard before. • If partner is asked to leave for the procedures, it magnifies her helplessness.	• Speak to her face-to-face before beginning procedure. • Describe every step. • Ask her for feedback. • Have her partner or doula at her face and the nurse offering encouragement and praise. • If necessary, speak firmly and confidently. No coaxing or sweet-talking.
6. Woman appears "out-of-touch," in a trance. Difficult or impossible to speak with her (dissociation, blanking out). "Coming back" may be either a shattering, upsetting process, or merely like gradually waking up.	• This may be a survival technique, used since childhood to "leave" during pain or terror. • Dissociation blocks not only the experience, but any memory of it as well.	• If possible, find out ahead of time if she sometimes dissociates, and how she feels about if for labor. • If she doesn't want to dissociate, partner, doula, nurse, or caregiver should maintain eye contact, keep talking to her and asking her to respond by words, actions. Keep her in the present.

Clinical Challenge or Complication	Possible Psychological Causes	Possible Solutions
7. Delay or failure in descent in second stage.	• Fear of vaginal birth: the pain, stretching, possible tearing, episiotomy. • Perception of baby as "perpetrator," hurting and damaging her. • Reluctance to become a parent. • "Holding back" – tension in perineum. • Fear of exposure or expelling feces.	• Reassurance. • Hot compresses. • Associate birth more with bowel movement than rape. Ask her to sit on the toilet for a few contractions. It often helps a woman relax her perineum and bear down effectively. • Remind her that the pain is coming out of her body; the baby is her ally in getting rid of the pain. Tell her, "This is not rape. Push the pain out, along with your baby." • Cover her vaginal outlet with a hot compress. The cover feels safer, the heat helps her relax, the pressure gives her feedback on where to push, and hides feces. • Ask her why she thinks the baby is not coming. If she answers that she doesn't want it to come out or that the baby doesn't want to come out, try to help her see that holding the baby in will not take care of the problem. Let the baby out and we'll figure out what to do. • Episiotomy, vacuum extractor, forceps (will not solve underlying emotional etiology).

Clinical Challenge or Complication	Possible Psychological Causes	Possible Solutions
8. Lack of interest in the newborn; wants father or others to hold baby; resists attempts by staff to give baby mother.	• Baby as perpetrator. • Dissociation during birth may delay bonding. • Traumatic birth may override thoughts for baby. • Abuse in childhood may have left woman with little instinct of mothering.	• Allow expressions of anger, lack of confidence, dislike toward baby. Encourage a more positive family member to be with baby. • Don't rush contact between mother and baby. Give mother time to recognize that labor is over, to "come back." Most abuse survivors do "take in" the baby. • Model ways to hold child; encourage positive gestures by mother; point out how baby responds to her; show her infant cues. • Make sure mother has resources and follow-up after leaving hospital.
9. Reluctance or inability to breastfeed (extreme pain, disgust, lack of milk supply).	• Flashbacks to abuse brought on by baby having access to breasts, sucking and hurting them. • Baby as perpetrator, manipulative, willful, hurtful, selfish. • Modesty issues around exposure of breasts.	• Recognize that sometimes abuse survivors cannot breastfeed. Follow their lead. • If a woman wants to breastfeed but cannot, pumping and feeding by bottle may be okay. • Help mother recognize that a young baby cannot manipulate or deliberately hurt her. Help her reframe her perceptions. • Refrain from touching woman's breast.

5
Post Partum

- "I can't sleep even when I have the chance. Every time I start to drift off I feel I'm back in labor with them chanting at me to ' push, push.' It hurt so much."
- "How can I trust my husband with the baby? What does he do when he changes her diaper?"
- "What are the rules? If I touch my baby's penis, am I molesting him? If I pat my daughter's cute little bum, am I abusing her? I just don't know."
- "Letting the baby suck on my breast any time he wanted was more than I could stand, though I believe in breastfeeding."
- "My father keeps asking why I won't bring the baby over—as if he's forgotten all about the way he abused me!"

The period after birth is a highly sensitive time for every new mother. She is recovering from the enormous changes in her body, her emotions, and her relationships. These "normal" adjustments occur abruptly, are not easily prepared for, and can feel overwhelming, and may even be experienced as some type of loss.

Normal postpartum adjustment includes hormonal and physical changes, breast-feeding challenges, and learning about infant care. Furthermore, the developmental shift from woman or couple to first-time parenthood or an expanding family entails complete responsibility for the physical and emotional well-being of a tiny helpless human being.

Until they actually experience it, women cannot fully imagine the immense changes in daily routines of eating, sleeping, and intimate relationships. Along with fatigue and sleep deprivation, the emotional lability, teariness, anxiety, and confusion that make up the "baby blues " in the first few weeks can be distressing.

The new relationship with the baby, the changes in her relationships with her partner, family, friends, and colleagues, changes in her own identity, and loss of control over her life test the self-confidence of the most capable woman. Where formerly she may have had a fairly predictable and well-organized life of work, social activities, and outside interests, she now gives it all up to devote herself to the continuous needs of the baby. Even though she had looked forward to parenthood, she may find herself sometimes grieving the loss of her former life.

In today's culture, new mothers often find themselves alone at home with the baby a few weeks after birth, lacking emotional, social, and even practical help. It is understandable that periods of sadness, loneliness, and distress can occur at times in all women. In addition, most assume that they will handle everything as well as before, and are shocked that it is so difficult. The discrepancy between the expectation and the reality of motherhood creates self-doubt and feelings of inadequacy.

Survivors' Issues in the Postpartum Period

For survivors of childhood sexual abuse, the postpartum period may present other challenges in adjustment. No woman would experience all of them, but most survivors will experience several or more.

For the woman whose negative self-image has put her at risk for perfectionist behavior and for setting unusually high standards for herself, the overload of expectations may be impossible to meet, and cause great distress or a profound sense of failure. Conversely, for the woman who finds daily living a difficult challenge, these added stresses might become debilitating. Survivors are also at greater risk for problems with their physical health and recuperation, relationships with loved ones and others, their sexuality and their mental and emotional health. Many lack confidence and satisfaction with parenting, breastfeeding, and bonding. The strain of this period sometimes leads to postpartum mood disorders, such as depression, anxiety, and posttraumatic stress responses.

Becoming a parent sometimes evokes fears and reminders of her own childhood with its hurts and betrayal, thus causing difficulties in caring for the baby and problems in the marital relationship. When these fears come up, some survivors, not recognizing that these are triggers from the past, may unwittingly project their distress onto the infant and see the baby as vulnerable and unsafe. This leads to overconcern for the baby, and an inability to allow anyone else, even the father, to hold or care for the baby.

When the baby has breastfeeding and sleep problems, or seems to be demanding, colicky, or hard to soothe, some mothers feel like failures, or become angry with the baby. They may believe the baby is rejecting them and likewise feel rejecting of the baby. They may characterize the baby as difficult or fussy. Bonding may take longer; they may feel ambivalent toward their babies and fearful of being alone with the infant. Because the woman has a deep wish to love her baby, she becomes distressed over these negative feelings when such anxieties arise. If the only love she ever knew was accompanied by pain, violation, shame, and fear, it is not surprising that she feels ambivalent. Her own needs as a child to be lovingly held, reassured, and safe were not met. She has no model of loving parenting in her own background and may question her ability to parent. "Can I love my baby?"

The survivor may worry that she is like her parents or the abuser. She may worry about molesting or otherwise harming her baby, or even want to do it at times. On the other hand, she may in some way identify with the baby's helplessness and become overly protective, anxious, and distrusting of others with the baby. Some survivors start to worry early on about potential dangers to their child in the future.

Survivors often have feelings of depression, anxiety, low energy, and low self-esteem. They worry that these feelings will affect their child, or that the child later will see them as helpless or ineffective, perhaps the way they perceived their own mothers. This negative self-perception is reinforced if everyone focuses on the new baby without recognizing her as a good mother, or by using comments that appear to criticize her. "Don't hold the baby that way. Let me show you how."

Judy

Judy felt inadequate and worried about whether she could be a loving and confident parent. She was afraid that she would resent or hurt her baby or be unable to protect him.

Judy's mother was single and alcoholic. She left Judy on her own much of the time. An elderly male neighbor invited her to his house several times a week. He always had a treat for her but would want her to sit on his lap and watch TV with him. He would fondle her, breathe hard, and rub against her. She was aware of his erections but did not know what they were. She didn't like sitting on his lap but being with him was better than being at home alone. As she grew up, her teen years were turbulent, even though her mother was in a recovery program. Eventually, she and her mother developed a closer relationship, but when she became pregnant, her feelings of abandonment by her mother surfaced in the form of grief over the mothering she did not receive and tremendous anxiety and self-doubt over her own abilities to parent. Her husband, Ken, a gentle nurturing man, had faith in Judy as a mother, but to help her feel more confident, found some good books about parenting, breastfeeding, and baby care, and also checked into parent-infant classes in their community.

Their baby was easy-going and Judy received good help with breastfeeding from the hospital nurses. They also had a postpartum doula during the first two weeks, who made it possible for Judy to get some much-needed rest, but also taught her some basic infant care skills, and also how to read her baby's cues for hunger, overstimulation, bowel movements, and loneliness. With this good start, along with her reading and parenting classes and Ken's support, Judy gained confidence and competence in her mothering. She also realized that the poor mothering she had received would continue to affect her unless she made up for it by getting counseling and support, learning about child development, and communicating openly with Ken and her child. She began to feel that she could break the cycle of neglect and abuse that had plagued her family.

Relationship with Partner and Family

Sometimes problems with one's partner arise in the postpartum period. The survivor may not be able to trust her partner as a parent, even if there is absolutely no indication that he or she would ever be abusive. She may ask herself, "Will he abuse my child?" "How do I know he won't turn out to be like my father or my stepfather?"

Some women, who have no recall of their abuse, may be unaware that their own abuser still poses a danger, now to her child. The cycle of abuse continues.

Sexual difficulties may arise. For many women it is important to separate breastfeeding from any aspect of love-making related to their breasts. This association is uncomfortable and confusing, and can trigger abuse memories. Sharing her breasts with her baby may feel like incest to her. She may also resent her partner's continued sexual interest in her breasts. Sexual intercourse, often uncomfortable or painful the first several times after birth, may make her feel discounted, devalued and used.

Fathers or partners also feel stressed or overwhelmed, especially if the new mother does not trust him or her, and feels depressed or incompetent herself. Partners need a great deal of help and support for themselves, along with assistance in finding appropriate professional resources for the mother.

Furthermore, many partners have their own history of sexual abuse, and the helplessness they felt then may return during this sensitive time of birth and afterwards. This is particularly likely if the birth was traumatic, and left them feeling useless, impotent, or removed emotionally. Sometimes partners develop PTSD reactions, such as flashbacks and nightmares. Early abuse leaves many survivor partners anxious about their ability to protect their babies. They may mistrust anyone's (including the mother's) ability to take care of the baby safely and correctly. They become overbearing and watchful, trying to control how the baby is cared for.

George

George tearfully shared the memories of his abuse history. His grandfather, whom he loved, was his caretaker for the first four years of his life while his single mother worked. His grandfather molested him continuously during that time especially while holding him on his lap. Memories of the abuse, repressed for years, came up and led to deep concern for George when he held his own baby on his lap. He also worried about the safety of the baby with a sitter when his wife had to return to work after 6 weeks. His fears began to affect his relationship with his wife, whom he believed to be too lax about the baby's care. Through therapy he eventually could heal the grief, betrayal, and anger of those early experiences and see their baby and the baby's situation as very different from his own babyhood. George was then more able to trust his wife's judgment and his own in making decisions about the care of the baby.

Problems may come up with the baby's grandparents, if either or both were abusers. Many survivors never allow their children to spend time alone with the grandparents, and even have difficulty letting their parents hold or take care of the child in their presence. This is problematic for the new parents, because on the one hand, survivors feel badly that their children will not know their grandparents, and yet, they have a great deal of anxiety and distrust of the people who abused them. Each time the grandparents ask to see the grandchild, the old fears and bad feelings come up for one or both parents.

Impact of a Negative Birth

What is a "traumatic birth"? In the language of obstetricians, "traumatic birth" refers to births that incur serious physical damage to mother or baby. For example, a sudden emergency cesarean perhaps with inadequate anesthesia; shoulder dystocia; severe perineal damage; fetal asphyxia; vacuum extractor or forceps injuries; severe hemorrhage; newborn disabilities or death. These are acknowledged as traumatic, either because the mother or baby is injured or because painful, frightening or extreme action was necessary to prevent even more serious harm. Women who undergo such trauma also suffer psychological trauma, and most caregivers recognize their need for explanations and debriefing on what actually happened.

Sometimes, even without physical trauma, events in childbirth cause psychological distress. If a woman has previously suffered trauma that was never resolved, she is more likely than a woman with no unresolved trauma to experience post-traumatic stress symptoms. These events fall into the following categories:

- Invasive interventions that the woman perceives as physically damaging to her body;
- A fear she or her baby is dying;
- Unexpected or unremitting pain:
- Feelings of betrayal or lack of support by her partner, support people and/or caregivers;
- Lack of control or feelings of powerlessness and helplessness without the ability to make decisions;
- Humiliation, embarrassment, feelings of inadequacy or shame;
- Lack of privacy, nakedness, exposure;
- Unexpected situations, deviations from planned care and sudden emergency;
- Lack of knowledge of what's occurring;
- Losses around infant, stillbirth, miscarriage, prematurity, and separation;

- Feeling forced to accept unwanted interventions or feeling that desired interventions were withheld.

The psychological trauma is frequently unacknowledged by the woman's caregivers and sometimes by her loved ones.

Aftermath of Traumatic Birth

Women carry their negative memories and disappointments into the postpartum period. They may be angry at their caregivers or their partner, believing they were not protected or cared for as they needed to be. They blame the staff for the outcome. The new mother may be angry at herself for her inability to give birth as she had hoped, or to ask for help or to communicate her needs. Sometimes physical symptoms persist. She may continue to have excessive pelvic pain or debilitating afterbirth pains long after the birth. She may also suffer from posttraumatic stress disorder (PTSD).

The aftereffects of a traumatic birth may include a curious mix of vivid flashbacks to the events of childbirth combined with significant gaps of understanding or losses of memory. These may occur because she was not informed at the time by her caregivers, or she may have been given pain-relieving drugs that interfered with her memory, or because she was unable to stay focused while under such stress. She may also have dissociated or experienced an amnesic response. Such "missing pieces" or memory loss may cause great anxiety for the abuse survivor because it replicates the distress of the dissociation or numbing response she had as a child. She may become obsessed with remembering the birth and need to talk about it over and over again, persisting in finding answers. Conversely, survivors may attempt to protect themselves from being flooded by panicky feelings or memories by avoiding anything that reminds them of the birth. For example, a woman may drive blocks out of her way to avoid going near the hospital, or may not return to her caregiver for her 6-week postpartum check up. Survivors may also feel depressed, distanced from the baby or their partner, angry, and distressed that they feel so bad at a time when they are supposed to feel good, (having just had a baby).

Ingrid

Ingrid's story illustrates how childhood abuse and other predisposing factors place one at greater risk of traumatic birth and PTSD than women whose lives have been relatively free from serious stresses:

Ingrid's alcoholic father victimized her sexually, physically and verbally from the age of 7 until the age of 14. Ingrid's dysfunctional mother had left the family when Ingrid was 6; leaving Ingrid the major caretaker of her younger sister. Ingrid left home at age 16, became heavily involved with drugs and alcohol and remained in an abusive relationship with a boyfriend for two years. When she met her husband, a "special" man who does not drink, she gave up her destructive habits.

During Ingrid's first pregnancy, her husband, a career military man, was away a lot, and she had the added stresses of moving, illnesses (a Bell's palsy and bronchitis), and high blood pressure, for which labor was induced. Within a short time the oxytocin-induced contractions became close and strong, and at 5 centimeters she requested an epidural. Ingrid found the administration of the epidural to be scary and "traumatic." She had a fear of needles being put in where she "couldn't watch them." She screamed and was told by her nurse, "You don't need to scream," and when she said, "It's something I need to do", she was told, "It's something we don't need to hear." She cried. Labor progress stopped and after 17 1/2 hours of labor including 5 hours at 5 cm, Ingrid's baby was delivered by cesarean section for failure to progress.

Ingrid felt confused and nauseated, was "forced to be still" and felt as if she were "exploding" as she waited for the cesarean. She found the restraints and oxygen mask to be scary and made the nausea worse. She had flashes of fear during the surgery and remembers thinking, "This is what it's like to go to hell."

She had no desire to see her baby and closed her eyes until her husband took the baby away.

Immediately after the birth, Ingrid's husband had to leave for military maneuvers. Ingrid developed an infection from the surgery, her baby was colicky and she clearly needed help. She could not ask her long-absent mother for help and her mother-in-law lived too far away. Ingrid felt not only lonely but also inadequate and helpless, and wondered what was the matter with her that she could not manage on her own, even though she had raised her younger sister, and had always felt quite competent in this regard.

Although this birth would have been distressing and disappointing for anyone, it is likely that Ingrid's unresolved abuse issues made it reach traumatic proportions. Much of the trauma lay in the fears she brought to the birth (fears of needles, of helplessness, of restraints) and may have contributed to her need to scream, to her feeling that she was going to hell. All this may have elicited insensitive treatment by her nurse. The association of her early abuse with the birth trauma intensified her confusion and distress, leaving her feeling helpless and overwhelmed. Eventually she fell in love with her baby and began to feel more confident as a mother, her traumatic birth memories faded, and it appeared that she had recovered.

More than two years later, when she became pregnant again, she found herself terrified as she contemplated another birth and was preoccupied with memories. This is an example of Delayed Posttraumatic Stress Disorder. She contacted a birth counselor to try to understand her first birth and find ways to ensure the same thing would not happen again.

PTSD Compared with Other Postpartum Mood Disorders

The distinguishing feature of posttraumatic stress disorder in the postpartum period is that panic attacks, intrusive thoughts, flashbacks and nightmares seem to be triggered by the memories of the birth itself rather than for no apparent reason, as is seen in a general anxiety or panic disorder or in the persistent depressive symptoms of postpartum depression. It has been confusing to caregivers and women themselves when their symptoms have been labeled postpartum depression when in fact they are really a posttraumatic stress reaction to the traumatic, life threatening, or frightening events at birth. However, many studies have reported that people with past trauma are more likely to be re-traumatized than people who never suffered trauma or who were able to resolve earlier trauma.

For the survivor, the association of the birth trauma with memories or events of childhood sexual abuse can seem especially confusing and overwhelming emotionally, leaving them with a sense of helplessness and trapped terror.

Sometimes these symptoms do not appear immediately; the symptoms of PTSD are countered by positive feelings toward the baby or diminished by the all-consuming demands of early parenthood.

Furthermore, abuse survivors have had much practice

with dissociation and repression to protect themselves psychologically during their childhood abuse. They may in the same way repress the distressing feelings and flashbacks to the birth. Later, however, a situation or event that is somehow reminiscent of the events of the birth can trigger some of the above symptoms. This is called "delayed PTSD". For, example, as was the case for Ingrid, a subsequent pregnancy or later hospitalization triggers the disturbing reactions. Sometimes the symptoms arise when the woman has some time to reflect on the birth, or when she is asked to describe it. However, whether these distressing symptoms occur immediately after birth or as a delayed reaction, it is important to get help whenever they arise, in order to understand and process them.

Women and their partners need the opportunity to express distressing feelings related to a negative birth experience. They need permission to feel the pain and anger, and take the time to grieve the experience and eventually move forward. As we have seen, trauma that is not acknowledged will manifest in a variety of destructive and negative behaviors. The postpartum counseling section in Chapter 10 suggests ways to help resolve some of the hurtful birth experiences to prevent the distress from going underground.

Breastfeeding Concerns

Many women look forward to breastfeeding their infant and giving their baby a healthy and loving start in life. Nursing one's baby enhances the special closeness that develops between mother and infant during this period. Once feeding is established many mothers take great pleasure from the experience. Likewise, mothers feel reassured that they are giving their baby the best possible nourishment and protection from disease. They also enjoy the convenience that breastfeeding affords. They tolerate the initial challenges and get through by accepting that it takes time to establish a mutual rhythm between their needs for rest and nourishment and the baby's needs for food and cuddling. It is not uncommon for new mothers to worry whether the baby is getting enough milk, but with support, some instruction and determination, they don't give up, and find every little indication of growth and satisfaction in the baby as evidence of their success as a nursing mother.

For many survivors, however, some of the greatest challenges in the postpartum period occur with breastfeeding. Let us consider how breastfeeding can trigger distress for a survivor of sexual abuse.

The elements of breastfeeding include exposure and nakedness, secretions and dripping from the breast, strong sensations from the baby's suckling, fondling and stroking, as well as continuous demands by the baby. First feedings in the hospital may include a nurse holding the woman's breast and pushing the baby toward it to get the baby to latch on. The woman's breasts increase in size, sometimes painfully, due to engorgement. Sometimes there may be unspoken jealousy in the partner, and comments, criticism, or pressure from others about the way she is breastfeeding. Women feel strong sensations while breastfeeding, which may be painful or pleasurable. Survivors may wonder if these sensations are normal and appropriate or somehow related to their abuse, for example, strong afterbirth pains as the uterus contracts during feedings; cracked nipples; or tingling or aching with the letdown reflex. If the woman is unusually fatigued or distressed from the birth, this may decrease her milk supply and add to her feelings of inadequacy. A crying baby may raise doubts in the new mother about her ability to satisfy her infant or lead her to label him or her as "difficult," and she may feel manipulated and angry with him or her. Nighttime feedings, the baby's touch and natural reaching for the breast, or the older baby's obvious pleasure while suckling her breast may create too strong an association with abuse, and the discomfort she experiences may make her want to discontinue nursing.

On the other hand, many survivors, who expected difficulties in breastfeeding, have been happily surprised to discover that they can breastfeed successfully. They perceive being able to nourish their babies with breast milk as a sign of their competence as mothers and proof that their bodies can do something right. But if breastfeeding creates associations with abuse memories, and the survivor is not able to resolve them, even with the advice and guidance of a breastfeeding consultant, then other feeding choices may need to be considered. Breastfeeding may not be the best choice for some survivors, and, if not, they need to be respected and helped to find more suitable feeding methods.

Maureen

Having a baby became the most important goal in the world to Maureen. After many years of trying to conceive, Maureen achieved her goal of a healthy baby. She was committed to breastfeeding but she found it uncomfortable the first time the baby latched onto her breast. She continued to breastfeed, but her anxiety grew day by day as her breasts became very tender and began to bleed. Sleep deprivation and exhaustion made her more vulnerable, more prone to sadness, anxiety, and insomnia. Maureen described that the more tired she became the more fearful and inadequate she felt as a person and as a mother. She felt more needy of her husband. This was especially disappointing to her since she had held the hope that having this baby would fill her own aching need to be held and nurtured, a longing for mothering she had never received.

One morning while nursing, her baby placed his free hand on her other breast and held it. Maureen felt herself recoil, became nauseous and pushed the baby away. Her discomfort with breastfeeding increased, but Maureen did not understand why. A lactation consultant was called and listened thoughtfully to Maureen's concerns. She then asked Maureen to describe what was especially upsetting when she was nursing. Maureen responded that somehow the latching on was okay, but when the baby's hand touched the other breast, it felt uncomfortable and intrusive in some way. She stated that she felt slightly aroused and she didn't like that feeling. She felt a little scared.

For Maureen, simply being able to think about and express her feelings somehow helped release and relieve some of her tension. The lactation counselor also helped Maureen with strategies which avoided this behavior on the baby's part: for example, wearing clothing, holding the baby's hand, and wearing a string of large bright beads. Two months later Maureen had a flashback in which she saw a little girl's breast being fondled. She was most distressed and could not stop thinking about it. She was referred for therapy and began working on abuse memories, coming to grips with her father's fondling of her nipples when she was a toddler. With support and counseling she was able to continue nursing her baby, and remain emotionally grounded in the present, in her role as a mother, and save her abuse memories for therapy.

Natalie

Natalie, on the other hand, found breastfeeding extremely painful and was unable to produce enough milk to cause a weight gain in her baby. She decided to stop breastfeeding. Here is her story.

Natalie and her sister lived with their father, a "gadfly" who could not hold a job, and mother, a "drone" who worked long hours to support the family. Natalie was "her father's daughter." He regularly slept in her single bed, took her with him on trips, and chose the clothes she wore. Natalie thinks there may have been sexual abuse, but has only unclear memories and is not certain. Her sister was "her mother's daughter" and received little attention from her father. The family moved often; there were no family friends. Natalie and her sister were each other's best friends.

Natalie's breasts developed at an early age, and she had "the largest breasts in my class," for which she was teased and even grabbed sometimes. She felt shame and disgust with her breasts, and at age 18, had breast reduction surgery, "one of the most empowering things I have ever done for myself."

Natalie excelled in school, even though she "hung out with the loser crowd," and began to drink heavily on weekends. She was the first person in her family to be accepted into college, which was met by her father's accusations of being too good for the family, and his refusal to allow her mother to help her financially. She worked her way through the first two years, after which she dropped out, exhausted and burdened by a sense of failure.

She severed all ties with her family, moved miles away, and eventually met and married Robert, a hard-working and ambitious young man. He entered a very demanding post-graduate degree program while Natalie supported him. She said she became the "drone," supporting her unemployed husband.

She became pregnant soon after he entered graduate school. After being treated and placed on bed rest for three weeks for presumed preterm labor, Natalie reached 36 weeks gestation, and returned to work until she went into labor. During her long exhausting labor, she dissociated several times and was helped to return to the present by Robert, who was familiar with her tendency to dissociate during extreme stress.

After giving birth with the help of a vacuum extractor, to a 10-pound vigorously sucking "barracuda," Natalie attempted to breastfeed. Knowing that the breast reduction surgery might reduce her chances for successful breastfeeding, she took a pro-active approach, pumping her breasts after each feeding to increase her milk supply. Her breasts became extremely sore, her perineum was also very sore, and she was getting very little sleep. She cried, "I feel as if I have been assaulted!"

Before long, she had to supplement with formula because the baby was losing weight. She came to dread the feedings and the pumping, which seemed so futile in building up her milk supply. She became depressed. She began to feel her baby was deliberately hurting her, although she was reluctant to express these feelings, even to Robert. With the help of her midwife and her therapist, she re-evaluated her desire to breastfeed. They helped her reframe the meaning of formula feeding for her baby. She eventually decided that formula feeding would probably be best for her and the baby, since the breastfeeding was so painful, was not adequately nourishing her baby, nor was it enhancing the bond between them. She vowed to hold her baby close during feedings, have him sleep next to their bed, and try to retain as many of the side benefits of breastfeeding as she could.

For Natalie, the decision to formula feed was not made lightly, but it enabled her to mother her baby without suffering or resenting him.

In considering Natalie's situation, several factors contributed to her inability to breastfeed. First, breast reduction surgery severely reduces the chances of successful breastfeeding. Second, Natalie's shame over her breasts and the abusive teasing and grabbing to which she had been subjected may have led to an abhorrence of her breasts. Third, the feelings that her baby was deliberately hurting her breasts triggered feelings of being abused by her own baby.

Natalie's case is a reminder that some women who very much want to breastfeed are not able to do so. They deserve support and respect for their mode of feeding.

Postpartum Mood Disorders

The postpartum period is a period of adjustment—physically, emotionally, sexually, and developmentally. All women and their families benefit from support, companionship, information and help. Emotional adjustments after childbirth vary, with some women remaining quite steady emotionally, and others riding an emotional roller coaster that may go on for weeks or months. Survivors of childhood sexual abuse are at greater risk for mood disorders during this stressful time, especially if childbirth was traumatic or if they have flashbacks to the abuse.

The mood disorders of the postpartum period were, until recently, grouped under the umbrella diagnosis, "postpartum depression." Research into the variety of symptoms and reactions women experience in this period has lead to more differentiation of diagnoses, the most common of which are postpartum depression, anxiety and panic disorders, obsessive–compulsive disorder, posttraumatic stress disorder, and postpartum psychosis.

Unrecognized or untreated postpartum mood disorders

can cause severe suffering for the woman and disruption in the family. They can even affect the infant's development. However, if recognized, they can be treated successfully. The most important thing a woman can do when she is unhappy or disturbed after childbirth is to recognize this and seek help. All too often, women and their partners assume that the woman's symptoms are a common though unpleasant aspect of the normal postpartum period. With the numerous adjustments the survivor has to make in this sensitive and vulnerable period, it is wise to have a plan to address concerns or symptoms as soon as possible. However, it is not always clear when the normal transitional issues of the postpartum period become problematic. The questionnaire, "Unhappiness After Childbirth: A Self-Assessment" (Appendix 1), will help the woman recognize whether she is sufficiently unhappy to seek professional help. The woman herself can do the assessment, or her partner, a family member, her caregiver, lactation consultant, or doula can go over it with her. As she ponders how she would complete each statement, it will help clarify how different she is from her usual self, and whether she needs help.

Understanding the more common problematic psychological reactions after childbirth can help the survivor and her family know what to look for and how to handle it in a timely fashion. Refer to Appendix 2 for a brief description of risk factors and each type of mood disorder. In describing the various symptoms of mood disorders, it is our purpose to give general information, not definitive diagnostic criteria for each disorder. Women should know they are not alone when they have these symptoms, there is nothing to be ashamed of, and help is available.

Help in the Postpartum Period

It helps if survivors and their partners know what to expect in the transition to parenthood, how to plan for this sensitive time, and how to recognize postpartum adjustment reactions and disorders. Early intervention is important. If anxiety or concerns arise during pregnancy, talking these over with a caregiver or counselor, and processing some of these feelings and issues can begin to relieve tension. Developing strategies for labor and birth and examining potential triggers of distress in the postpartum period can give the survivor a head start on being prepared. With her partner and other supportive people, the survivor can create a plan for self-care and support in the immediate postpartum period as well as the first few months afterward. Later chapters deal more specifically with identifying and managing distressing aspects of pregnancy and the postpartum period.

Women with mood disorders can be helped with a combination of information, validation, acknowledgement of their experiences, and appropriate psychological and medical support. It is important to have access to skilled and knowledgeable resource people to provide guidance, because with such help, survivors are able to resolve the underlying anxieties or issues that have contributed to their mood disorders. They can also be helped to organize their lives in a way that makes motherhood much more rewarding and successful for them.

The most important point is that postpartum mood disorders can be worked through and resolved.

This Daughter

A double helix daisy chain
Deflowered and disinherited this daughter;
Her bloom sullied by multi-generational shames and privacies.
Psychiatric diagnoses and governmental stipends
canonized the dirt.
She hurts purely and plainly
With full knowledge of what causes the pain.

Seizured revelation uprooted the 33-year inculcation
Of this daughter's self-definition.
The acrid anger of naming manufactured history
Venerates the deconstruction of its heroine survivor.
Self-loathing hi-jacks hygiene, laughter, leaving the house.
Faith is borrowed where spiritual seeking is voted down
In favor of Calvinistic, measurable productivities.
Tangibles make her day.
She is only as free as polypharmacy's ability
To broaden her diminutive destiny.

Unlovingly, unyieldingly excluded.
Her whose madness of just one defiles their consensus,
Bomb-threats the whitewashed House of Family.
Summer pots of sunshine flowers
Left out to battle winter white on white.
The frigid politics of righteous self-propagating estrangement.
Deflowered, disinherited,
Dissipation is her keenest fear.
She is only as powerful as faith's capacity
To overflow her diminutive destiny.

A double helix daisy chain
Disavowed its gene-patterned basis by this daughter.
This daughter of Eve, of Madonna, of all mothers,
all monolithic matriarchs.
Her birthmother chose against instinct
As Nana had done, as Nana's mother had done,
As centuries of patriarchal rule and religion had undone.

Her birthmother, an emotional skeleton
Skinned only by the worth of partnership, the pleasures of
her mate, succumbed
To the passivity of self-preservation:
abdication of her firstborn
To her wifely terror of husbandly abandonment.

This daisied daughter of mothering age and right
Sees through the Propaganda Family with unshuttered eyes.
Recognizes motherhood free of biology's realm, defined by
maternal compassion and tenacity.
She is daughtered by the mothers of others
Who cradle her in gene-free loving as only a Mother can.
She hurts purely and plainly,
This daughter,
With full knowledge of what causes the pain.

– Nicole Hitchcock Streiff, 2003

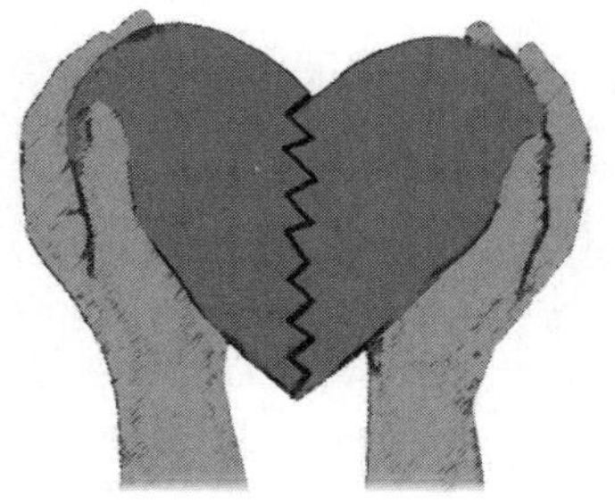

Part II: Communication, Help and Healing

6
The Relationship Between the Woman and Her Doctor or Midwife

- I feel like I am picking a fight every time I mention things that I don't like about the hospital.
- There's one person in the practice who really listens. I hope I get her in labor.
- Survivors need so much time – the one thing that I, as a doctor, can't give them.

Next to the relationship with her partner and other supportive family members, the woman's relationship with her doctor or midwife is the most important one she will have during pregnancy and immediately afterward. The caregiver has responsibility for the health and well-being of mother and baby. The woman must trust and depend on this person to ensure safe passage. When the relationship between the woman and her caregiver is strong and positive, physical outcomes improve from the resulting increase in openness, respect and compliance. Further, for the abuse survivor, there is enormous potential for healing.

Most survivors are unaware of how early sexual abuse

can affect them physically and emotionally during childbearing. Certainly their partners and caregivers are equally ignorant. Even though mental health practitioners have made great strides in helping people work through the trauma of abuse, they are just beginning to explore the application of this knowledge to maternity care. Why? Some reasons have to do with women's difficulty in disclosing their abuse and their caregivers' reluctance to ask about possible abuse. Women may not disclose an abuse history for many reasons: They may have no memory of it; they may believe it would be futile and embarrassing; they may believe it has no relevance; they may believe they have healed and it no longer affects them. Caregivers may avoid the subject for many reasons: They do not know that early abuse can affect the clinical course of childbearing; they may believe that the emotional consequences are more than they can handle; they may feel that psychological issues should be managed by a mental health professional. There are still people, including medical professionals, who cannot accept the reality of abuse, and there still are societal taboos against talking about this subject.

A lack of disclosure of their abuse history sometimes creates a gulf in communication between what the women are trying to say and what their caregivers are actually hearing. Much of what people perceive as communication is actually an illusion. Following are three examples of interactions between women and their caregivers that illustrate how what appears to be open communication frequently misses the woman's significant concerns or needs. The actual words exchanged represent only the tip of an iceberg; most of the significant concerns remain unexpressed, below the surface.

The actual conversation appears in regular type, and the unspoken issues are indicated in shaded type.

Mary

1. Mary is a 34-year-old teacher expecting her first baby;

this is a planned pregnancy that has gone quite well. She is happily married to a successful accountant. Let's examine the spoken communication and unspoken internal reactions of both the doctor and Mary at the 30-week visit.

Doctor: Good afternoon, Mary. How are you feeling today?

> I'm already behind. My last patient took so much longer than she was scheduled for.

Mary: I'm OK, thanks. I had my first childbirth class. I was told to start thinking about my Birth Plan.

> I hope he's not one of those doctors who doesn't like Birth Plans.

Doctor: All the classes promote Birth Plans and we try to follow them, but you have to understand we can't promise you exactly what your birth will be like.

> Oh, no, not today...

Mary: I know, but I have some questions about your routine care in labor. I know a lot of doctors do episiotomies and I don't want one.

> I've got to be sure he doesn't do that to me.

Doctor: I don't do them unless they're really necessary.

Gosh, she's controlling. Does she think I don't know what I'm doing?

Mary: Well, I've been told there are many things I can do to get the baby out without being cut, like massage, oils, not pushing too hard, and different positions. I really want to try these things.

I don't want to be cut down there. Can I trust him?

Doctor: You have to understand that an episiotomy might shorten your labor and could even help your baby. Birth could be hard on the baby, you know.

What's the big deal about an episiotomy? She'd probably tear anyway.

Cammie

2. Cammie, a 17-year-old single woman having her first baby, is 15 weeks pregnant. She comes with her mother for her first prenatal visit to the midwife. She lives with her parents and is in her third year of high school. She has not disclosed the name of the baby's father.

Midwife: Now that we've had a chance to talk a bit, I think it's time to examine you. Have you ever had a pelvic exam before?

She's awfully quiet. It's like pulling teeth to get answers from her.

Cammie: No.

> Why does she have to do that?

Midwife: It's a way for me to learn quite a lot about your pelvis and cervix. If you'll take off your underpants and lie down and spread your legs apart, I'll be able to check your cervix and your pelvis. Now, can you lie down?

> She's awfully tense. This might be difficult.

Cammie: Do I have to? I mean, I already said I'm pregnant. [Holds legs together and starts to cry.]

> I can't do this. I'm not doing this.

Midwife: Let's ask your mom to come in and hold your hand. Good. If you can get your legs apart, I'll do this very quickly. Now, Cammie, it won't hurt nearly so much if you'll just relax.

> I have to hold her legs apart. I've got to get on with it. I'll have to hold her still.

Cammie: No, Mom! Don't do this to me. He's hurting me! Make him stop! You're hurting me! Stop! [She gags.]

> Get away! Stop! Leave me alone! Don't touch me there!

Midwife: It's OK. I'm not trying to hurt you.

He? Why did she say "he"? I've got to check her. We'll have to do this fast.

Vera

3. Vera is a 29-year-old secretary at 34 weeks' gestation with her second pregnancy. Her husband is a self-employed contractor. Her first child was born by cesarean 3 years earlier after a long and difficult labor, episiotomy and attempted forceps. She still has nightmares about the first labor and birth. She prefers not to labor this time but she wants a cesarean and to be put to sleep with a general anesthetic. Her doctor suggests a vaginal birth after a cesarean (VBAC). This physician is one with long experience with VBACs. He sincerely believes that, unless there is a medical reason for a cesarean, second labors have good prospects for a vaginal birth.

[*Authors' note:* Vera's story took place in 1997, when VBAC was the standard of care and cesareans-on-request were frowned upon by medical professionals. Today, professional standards have shifted. Today, Vera would have no difficulty having the cesarean she requested.]

Doctor: Well, Vera, I'm glad we've had a chance to discuss the benefits of a VBAC and, in my opinion, you're an excellent candidate.

Why is she so resistant? Doesn't she believe me?

Vera: But I don't want to go through all that again. It was awful and I get the shakes every time I think about it.

Why is he so resistant? Doesn't he get it? I can't go through another labor.

Doctor: Well, it probably won't be like that this time. The second labor almost always goes better.

I'd almost like to just go along with her. We could plan a cesarean and be all done in an hour.

Vera: You don't know how bad it was. Once is enough.

They treat you like a thing, like you're not even suffering. They won't listen.

Doctor: This hospital does not allow a cesarean without a medical reason. I'd be criticized by the peer review committee. You'll have to go to another doctor at another hospital.

There's no reason to give her a cesarean. I'll never get this by the review board. She is one of the stubborn ones. How can I get through to her?

Vera reluctantly agreed to attempt a VBAC and is now in the second stage of labor, having pushed unproductively for the last one and a half hours.

Doctor: Vera, this has gone on long enough. Now you need to let go and push the baby out.

Unless she gets to work, I may have to do another cesarean.

Vera: I am pushing and it hurts. It's so big.

I can't. I can't. I can't let it come.

Doctor: There's plenty of room. You've just got to relax and don't hold back. Let it come.

It's her own fault. She won't try!

Vera: Don't make me do this!

I'll die if I have to keep on with this. This is torture!

Doctor: Look, if you don't do this, I'm either going to have to do another cesarean or get out the forceps.

Vera: Do the cesarean now. Please. Just knock me out and take the baby. I just want it to be over.

In all these cases, there is dissonance between the woman and the caregiver. To the women, the caregivers appear unresponsive, domineering or controlling. To the caregivers, these women seem difficult, uncooperative or distrustful.

The common theme running through all these cases is the unrecognized and unstated history of previous sexual abuse of the women. If either party had been aware of the potential negative impact of abuse, or if the women had been able or had been helped to express their true needs, the scenarios would have turned out differently.

Examples of Good Communication

Let us replay the scenarios of the first two cases, but this time the caregiver is able to listen to the meaning behind the words, and the woman has learned to be clearer in her communication.

1. Doctor: Good afternoon, Mary. How are you feeling today?

Mary: I'm OK, thanks. I had my first childbirth class. I was told to start thinking about my Birth Plan. I wonder if we could talk about it.

Doctor: I'm glad to hear you are working on that. Birth Plans are helpful and we try to follow them. But I am running a little late today. Could we schedule a longer appointment for next time to go over the whole thing? [Once she agrees...] But if there is a particularly important area you'd like to discuss today, we'd have time.

Mary: One of my big concerns is about the episiotomy. I really don't want one. I've been told there are many things I can do to get the baby out without being cut, like massage, oils, not pushing too hard, and different positions. I really want to try these things.

Doctor: I don't do episiotomies unless they are really necessary. I'm hearing how important it is for you to avoid an episiotomy. Can you tell me what it is about an episiotomy that is disturbing?

Mary: To me it seems like mutilation. I don't want to be cut down there. Many women get them, and I've heard they are almost always unnecessary. I want to try those other things, and I hope you'll help.

Doctor: I'm impressed with all the ideas you have to avoid an episiotomy, and I'll be glad to work with you, but I hope you'll accept my clinical judgment if there's a problem with the baby coming out. For example, if your baby's heart rate is showing that she's distressed.

Although the caregiver never learns specifically about Mary's abuse, he may suspect it when he hears the word "mutilation." However, the doctor validates her concerns, and thus, their relationship is strengthened by addressing them.

2. For the second scenario, consider how improved communication benefits both Cammie and her midwife.

Midwife: Now that we've had a chance to talk a bit, I think it's time to examine you. Have you ever had a pelvic exam before?

Cammie: No. Do you have to? I mean, I already said I'm pregnant. [Holds legs together and starts to cry.]

Midwife: [Instead of going ahead] This seems very upsetting to you, let me take a moment and tell you what's involved. Let me describe it to you. [Describes procedure.] Do you have any questions about this?

Cammie: Please, I don't want to do this!

Midwife: You're really concerned, aren't you? I want to assure you that I won't force you to have the exam. I'm wondering...in my experience, many young women who have had unpleasant sexual experiences, like being forced to have sex, have trouble with vaginal exams. Has anything like that ever happened to you?

Cammie: Yes, but I don't want to talk about it.

Midwife: That may help explain why you're feeling upset. I wish I didn't have to do an exam, and I won't if you truly do not want me to. There are some things I need to learn which I really can't know without checking you. [She explains these to Cammie.] Would it help to have your mother in here and then we'll go very slowly and carefully? We'll work as a team. I want you to direct me in each step as you feel ready.

Cammie: I'll try. I'd like Mom to be in here.

For the survivor, a vaginal exam can feel like a re-enactment of rape. When she discovers that Cammie has been abused, the midwife is willing to go more slowly at the pace Cammie sets. Thus, the survivor has some sense of control as opposed to the helpless feeling she had during the rape. (See Chapter 12 for ways to reduce the stress of a vaginal exam and other medical interventions.)

3. In Vera's situation, if the doctor had understood her reasons for wanting a cesarean, and her fears that the problems of her first labor would recur, he would have discovered how frightened she was of a VBAC. They might have planned some strategies together to avoid the trauma of her first labor.

Differences in Power between the Woman and Her Doctor or Midwife

The probability of a comfortable and equal relationship between the woman and her caregiver is further challenged by the intrinsic differences in power between them.

We all know of births that end well in terms of physical outcomes, but that are marred by conflict, misunderstanding or poor communication between the caregiving staff and the client and her family. In such cases, someone has to "give in," and this person is usually the client. The unequal nature of the client-caregiver relationship works against the client, especially if she is a survivor who has suffered at the hands of more powerful people. See the table on the next page for a comparison of the difference in power between women and their caregivers in several key aspects of the maternity experience.

The Difference in Power Between Caregiver and Woman

	Caregiver:	**Pregnant or laboring woman:**
Physically	is upright	is lying down
	is clothed in a prestigious uniform (scrubs or white coat)	is wearing a hospital issued gown that is open in back
	is strong	is weak
	is free to come and go	is restricted to her room or in bed with intravenous line, monitor cords, and other attachments
	does painful or stressful things to her (vaginal exams, blood draws)	submits
Mentally	has knowledge	has less or no knowledge
	is the expert	is not an expert
	uses medical jargon	does not understand medical jargon
	discusses impersonal risks, benefits, odds, "science"	responds with unscientific, personal feelings and worries
	has machines, tests and tools (blood pressure cuffs, I-V's, syringes, oxygen masks, monitors)	depends on caregiver's use of the machines and interpretation of tests
Emotionally	is not in pain	is in pain
	is not in physical danger	feels she is in danger
	is in control	is stressed, frightened
	remains composed	is in a position where her public person (makeup, clothing, hair style) is stripped away
	is independent	is dependent, vulnerable
	may be a total stranger	Finds trusting an unknown authority figure difficult

If there is trust between a woman and her caregiver, and the woman believes the caregiver is acting in her best interests, she is not threatened by the difference in power. In fact, she appreciates an authoritative caregiver. For the woman who has been abused, however, these power differences may be particularly upsetting because they evoke the power differential that existed at the time of her abuse. They may trigger memories of situations in which she was vulnerable and helpless, had actual physical pain, and suffered sexual victimization and emotional trauma.

Women receiving medical, surgical or obstetrical care should be perceived and treated as people in crisis (that is, in pain, illness, fear, or danger). When in crisis, it is well known that people tend to rely more on a "survival" instinct than on reason to get them through the crisis. The tendency for someone in crisis (whether or not she is a survivor) is to interpret the caregiver's words (or lack of words) and actions negatively or as threatening.

For example, when an anesthesiologist, intending to be reassuring, told a woman about to have surgery, "I'm going to put you to sleep now," he wanted her to think she was about to have a pleasant nap. The woman, however, quite anxious over her surgery and over the prospect of being out of control, recalled her cat or dog who was "put to sleep," or her grandma who, the woman was told as a child, "just went to sleep" when she died. For an abuse survivor, who was drugged by her date before he raped her, the thought of being "put to sleep" reactivated memories of the rape.

Another example is illustrated by Janet's experience. The doctor examined Janet in labor, said, "Mmm, okay. I'll be right back," and left the room without giving a progress report. Janet looked at the nurse and asked, "What's wrong? Is something wrong? Why wouldn't he tell me?" In fact, Janet was making good progress but interpreted the lack of communication as indicating danger. The doctor had merely been preoccupied; when he had reassured himself that Janet's labor progress was adequate, his mind took him to another patient about whom he was worried.

Such a tendency toward pessimism when one is in crisis is rooted in the "fight or flight" response, those primitive responses caused by the release of stress hormones (epinephrine, norepinephrine, cortisol, dopamine, and others) that have ensured the survival of animals when in danger. The same tendency holds for us humans. When our safety is threatened, we assume the worst. The survivor of prolonged sexual, physical or verbal abuse, whose safety was always in question, has a greater tendency than others to interpret situations as potentially dangerous. Without much reassurance, she is likely to go into "survival mode," experiencing feelings of fear and remaining hyper-vigilant or on alert and unable to relax and trust that all is well.

For the pregnant or laboring abuse survivor, the intrinsic vulnerability and lack of power may provoke negativity, suspicion, defensiveness, lack of trust, passivity, or other reactions toward the caregiver. Many survivors have learned over time not to trust authority figures, or allow themselves to be dependent, or to lose control, because they have been hurt by doing so.

Many survivors are further burdened by a tendency to perceive themselves as "bad," "wrong," "damaged," or "inferior," which predisposes them to interpret words or actions as criticism about themselves, even when such words or actions are intended to be innocuous or neutral.

For the victim of childhood sexual trauma, the childbirth experience can take one of three directions in the healing process:

- a negative direction—re-enactment of the trauma (reraumatization)
- a neutral direction—no harm (or healing) done

- a positive direction—a degree of healing (sometimes substantial)

If the caregiver is unaware of the woman's history of abuse, or discounts it, he or she may interpret the woman's fears or concerns as trivial, unreasonable or annoying. In such a case, the caregiver may use his or her power against the woman, and do great psychological harm; for example, forcing a vaginal exam on a terrified pregnant woman; dismissing her questions as trivial or misguided; or performing an unwanted episiotomy when the woman is in no position to know it is happening. Acts such as these are perceived by victims as reenactments of previous violations. Victims see little difference between rape or invasive stroking and a forced vaginal exam. These women are traumatized once again.

Most important for the caregiver is to try to use his or her power and authority to create a comfortable relationship with the woman. This not only prevents a re-enactment of previous trauma; it enhances the woman's feelings of self-esteem and control and improves the psychological outcome.

Claire

When communication is not open and clear, women and their caregivers may find their relationship spiraling downward, as illustrated by the case of Claire.

> Claire was 30 years old, married, and pregnant for the first time. She belonged to a health maintenance organization (HMO). She requested a female doctor, and was assigned Dr. "Smith," a woman, one of the 21 obstetricians who practice there. Claire survived childhood sexual abuse by her stepfather. She asked for a female physician because of a deep discomfort with male caregivers examining or touching her genitals.

Dr. Smith was always reassuring ("Everything is fine...Baby's fine"), but was so rushed that Claire never revealed her history of abuse. The initial pelvic exam was extremely stressful and painful, but Claire did not complain. Dr. Smith did say, "If you'll just relax, it won't hurt so much and I can get this over with more quickly." Claire told Dr. Smith the date of her last menstrual period and the date of conception, which was three and a half weeks later. She was sure of the date of conception because (she did not tell this to Dr. Smith) she had sex infrequently and she had only one sexual encounter that entire menstrual cycle. The doctor disregarded Claire's date of conception and instead, using her dating wheel, calculated Claire's due date based on the last menstrual period. The two dates were almost two weeks apart. Claire was mildly upset over this, but had no idea that it could be important later. The matter did not come up again for months.

Claire had hoped for and prepared for a vaginal birth and desired an epidural in active labor. She wanted to use the techniques she learned in childbirth class until she would get the epidural. There never was a chance to state these wishes to Dr. Smith. Claire assumed she would at some point be asked her desires regarding pain medications, so she did not bring it up.

At 41 weeks (by the dating wheel) and 39 weeks by Claire's calculation, Claire's cervix had begun to change in preparation for labor. It was 1 cm dilated, 50% effaced, and anterior. Dr. Smith informed Claire that it was time "to have a baby." She would be on duty this weekend and suggested inducing labor, since Claire was a bit overdue, the baby seemed a bit large, Claire had an "inducible cervix," and it would be convenient for everyone. Claire protested meekly, trying to remind Dr. Smith of her known date of conception, but the doctor said, "Well, it's clear that you are at term, so we can go ahead on Saturday." She left the examining room saying cheerily, "I'll set it up and my nurse will give you a call. I'll see you on Saturday."

Claire was shocked and dismayed. She felt ignored. She was not even due yet by her calculations. She was afraid she would not be able to handle an induced labor without early use of pain medication. She left the doctor's office upset and confused.

Her husband reacted favorably to the idea of induction ("We'll finally get to see our baby!") and Claire agreed, partly excited, mostly disappointed and fearful. She received no support for her wishes and gave in to the doctor's plan.

The induction was clinically successful, but as the contractions became painful, Claire could only focus on the Oxytocin (the drug, also known as Pitocin, used to cause contractions) as the source of her pain and wanted it turned down. She was unable to use the comfort measures she had learned in childbirth class. She asked for pain medications within a few hours and received narcotics. Although Dr. Smith was on duty, the male resident physician unexpectedly provided much of Claire's care and performed most of the vaginal exams. Claire hated the vaginal exams and even screamed when the doctor was checking her. He spoke to her loudly and firmly, holding one leg while the nurse held the other. Claire, experiencing a flashback to her early abuse by her stepfather, submitted, weeping silently.

She received an epidural at 3 centimeters' dilation;

her labor proceeded rapidly with increasing doses of Oxytocin, but at 10 cm Claire was not pushing forcefully enough, although she was being urged to do so by the nurse, her husband and Dr. Smith, who had now arrived. Dr. Smith told her it was up to her. "You can either get to work and push that baby out or I'll do an episiotomy and go in and get it out with a vacuum extractor." Claire was passive and non-participatory. Her baby girl was delivered by vacuum extractor after an episiotomy.

Claire was exhausted, but held the baby briefly during the stitching. She was glad when her husband took the baby. In the weeks following the birth, the episiotomy healed slowly and Claire was quiet and depressed. She had nightmares and spent a great deal of time reliving the birth experience. She felt guilty for not trying hard enough, for not pushing when told to and for not sparing her baby the vacuum delivery. She also felt angry, believing her doctor should have asked her what she wanted. She felt her doctor had let her down by not being there when she said she would. She felt Dr. Smith had not listened to her regarding her due date. She told her husband he shouldn't have talked her into the induction; she said the induction was the beginning of the end. She kept remembering the awful vaginal exams.

At her postpartum appointment, Claire was subdued and uncommunicative, which made for a quick appointment. She was given a clean bill of health.

Three months after the birth, Claire inquired about seeing her labor and birth records. She wanted to know why she was induced, how long she pushed, and what the staff had written about her. The nurse in Dr. Smith's office told her that her records were all on microfiche and it would be difficult to retrieve them. Claire did not pursue the matter.

Claire vowed never to go to Dr. Smith again. She thought often of writing a letter of complaint, but gave up when she couldn't figure out what to complain about. Unbeknownst to her doctor, their relationship ended negatively.

Dr. Smith's clinical discussions and management decisions were similar to those of many obstetricians today. She made no mistakes and mother and baby were in good health. What was lacking was an appreciation for Claire's perceptions. In fact, Dr. Smith dismissed Claire's information on her date of conception, favoring the standard data obtained from the dating wheel.

A sensitive, empathic caregiver may be unaware of the woman's history of sexual abuse, but nevertheless, by taking the client's concerns seriously, validates and addresses them. The woman is treated with respect and dignity, though she may gain no further insight into her abuse. The Hippocratic oath's tenet, Primum non nocere (Above all do no harm), is particularly meaningful with sexual abuse survivors and can be followed even by caregivers who know little or nothing about sexual abuse. Empathy, kindness, flexibility, listening skills, and respect are the qualities that help ensure that no harm will be done.

The following anecdote illustrates this point. Women sometimes make unorthodox requests, like the woman who requested that no men perform vaginal exams in labor. Her doctor, who was male, was at first taken aback by her request, but rather than trying to persuade her how unreasonable and inconvenient or even insulting her request was, he thought, "Why not?" and arranged to have the female nurse perform the exams. He did explain to his patient that problems might arise in labor where he would prefer to do the exam himself (questions of position or station of the fetus). She agreed, feeling validated and respected.

The Potential for Healing when the Caregiver Understands

A look at Claire's subsequent pregnancy shows how an understanding, empathic caregiver can make an enormous positive difference.

Claire's Second Birth

Three years after her first birth, Claire, now 33 years old, and pregnant again, still belonged to the HMO where her first child was born under "humiliating and traumatic" circumstances. Claire had tried to switch insurance plans, but her husband's employer offered only this health care coverage. Claire felt trapped, but after thinking about the first birth a great deal, became determined not to go through such an experience again.

She sought care from a different hospital in the HMO (so there would be no chance of running into her first doctor) and decided to interview doctors before choosing. She chose the third doctor she interviewed, mostly because he told her she was wise in shopping for the "right doctor."

At her first prenatal appointment, Dr. "Thomas" asked her about her first childbirth. She told him about the induction, the epidural, episiotomy, and vacuum delivery. She wept as she told him. Using active listening, he acknowledged and validated her distress and reflected, "It seems that last time you didn't feel heard by your doctor. We'll do our best to make sure that does not happen again."

Her relief was palpable and she then shared her distress during vaginal exams, without revealing her abuse history. He suggested postponing the exam until the next visit and told her he would make it as comfortable as possible. He asked if she would like him to explain exactly what he was about to do and give her time to prepare herself, then proceed step by step as she gave the okay. Claire thought it might be better that way. "This won't be something I do to you. We'll do it together." Dr. Thomas made sure to flag Claire's chart and write a note so that he would not forget their discussion and their plans.

The vaginal exam went quite well and, for the first time, Claire felt like an adult participating in the exam. (See Chapter 12 for guidance in doing vaginal exams.)

Claire also later felt safe enough to reveal her abuse history to Dr. Thomas, who received the information sensitively and respectfully, adding, "That helps explain some of the problems with your care during your first childbirth and with vaginal exams. Thank you. Will you let me know when my words or actions bring up those memories? I'll try to be more aware. We both want this pregnancy and birth to be positive and fulfilling for you."

He invited her to prepare a birth plan and scheduled a longer visit to discuss it. Claire worked hard on it, and many of her requests were based on what happened during her previous childbirth and what she wanted to avoid. It had an angry, distrustful, hostile tone, including, among others, the following: "No induction; no resident doctors; only Dr. Thomas to do vaginal exams; no epidural; no episiotomy; no vacuum extractor."

When Dr. Thomas saw the plan, he was reminded of other angry birth plans he had received from patients he did not know as well as he knew Claire. It occurred to him that those patients also may have had some early traumatic experiences that led them to distrust their caregivers and to seem unreasonable.

Although he understood why Claire's plan was inflexible, he felt it was unacceptable to him as a clinician. "I can see this plan is largely the opposite of what happened to you last time and I think it's very likely that we can do it this way. There are some things, however, that trouble me as your doctor. May we discuss those?" Because of the trust built between them so far, Claire was as eager as Dr. Thomas to find ways both could feel comfortable with the plan.

Dr. Thomas explained circumstances under which the procedures might be medically indicated and promised those would be the only circumstances under which he would recommend them. He said it was not necessary for a resident to take full responsibility against Claire's wishes and suggested that when she met the resident she could decide whether and how much the resident would participate. He pointed out that with the call schedule, he could not promise to be there, although he would very much like to be. To minimize the impact of having a stranger for her doctor, Dr. Thomas suggested that her final birth plan should include a statement about her previous childbirth and (if she felt comfortable) disclosure of her history of childhood sexual abuse and how it had influenced her. The birth plan, along with a letter from Dr. Thomas would be placed in the chart. Claire would have a copy as well.

Dr. Thomas would also brief the head nurse as to the care plan he and Claire agreed to. He suggested that when they arrived at the hospital in labor, Claire or her husband should check with each person involved in her care to ask them to read the note and birth plan.

Claire recognized that the HMO was a teaching hospital and that residents were a part of the caregiving staff. She also realized that in this system, it was too much to expect that Dr. Thomas would be available night and day. She also felt his suggested changes in her plan respected her needs without compromising quality of care. She rewrote her birth plan, incorporating Dr. Thomas's suggestions, now more optimistic that her concerns had been heard and would be respected.

As it happened, her labor began spontaneously and proceeded normally. Claire felt fine about the resident on duty, who had read her birth plan and Dr. Thomas's note. At shift change, her husband had to ask the new nurse to read and heed the note and birth plan, after she entered the room without knocking or introducing herself. She said, "I hadn't realized..." and apologized. After that, they all worked well together. Dr. Thomas arrived at the end of labor, as Claire was pushing. Claire said the pain was too great, she couldn't do it. Dr. Thomas reassured her, told her to take her time and told her he had good reason to think she could do this. "Look at all you have done, helping me understand, taking all this responsibility, getting so far in this labor. This tells me you can do this last step and be a wonderful mother." Then addressing the unborn baby, "Come on out, sweetheart, and meet your loving parents."

The reminder of the baby, in addition to Dr. Thomas' encouraging words, got through to Claire. She changed her focus from "I can't," to "I can," and the baby was born soon.

Claire felt much better after this birth—empowered, capable, and worthy of respect. She was able to describe the impact to Dr. Thomas at her postpartum visit and, at that time, Dr. Thomas suggested that she was a good candidate for therapy to explore and resolve the abuse and its impact on her life. He sincerely complimented her courage, honesty and fairness in bringing up her concerns and following through on them.

Unhelpful Reactions by Doctors or Midwives to a Woman's Disclosure of Abuse.

It is a sad truth that when caregivers first learn about the abuse that their clients have suffered, they frequently react inappropriately—with discomfort, disbelief, or exaggerated concern. If they have heard or read about some of the devastating effects of abuse, caregivers sometimes feel very sorry for the victim or extend themselves beyond reasonable professional boundaries to "rescue" the victim or make everything right for her. Other caregivers may ask for details, prying for descriptions of what happened. They may inadvertently blame her, asking why she didn't report the abuse or run away. Or they may minimize it: "It was a long time ago. It's over." In the end, none of these approaches helps; in fact, both parties are hurt, and communication comes to a halt. Chapter 10 contains specific examples of inappropriate and appropriate ways of responding when a woman discloses her abuse history.

Because of the inherent differences in power between the

woman and her caregiver, along with her associations of sexuality with pregnancy, birth, and breastfeeding, the survivor may be reminded of her abuser—another authority figure from the past whom she trusted or on whom she was dependent. Sometimes the client unwittingly projects feelings about her abuser onto her caregiver and has difficulty separating the two.

Caregivers sometimes state, "She was angry with me before we even talked," or "I don't deserve this." Recognizing that the survivor of sexual abuse has very good reasons to be angry and to withhold trust, the caregiver must not take the client's strong feelings personally. Though a client may direct some of her hostility toward her caregiver, the caregiver is not her real target. The caregiver who appreciates this truth is less likely to become defensive or hostile and is in an excellent position to assist the survivor. When it appears that an impasse is reached in the relationship, the use of good communication skills can assist both parties to avoid defensiveness and anger and thus to maintain a satisfactory relationship.

A helpful reminder to the caregiver who is the target of a survivor's anger, mistrust or fear is the statement, "She has a very good reason for feeling or behaving this way, but I am not the reason." This helps the caregiver avoid becoming defensive or being drawn into an interpersonal conflict. It also allows development of better communication and a degree of trust between the two.

Some caregivers remain skeptical about the prevalence of childhood sexual abuse and its impact. They may believe the woman is seeking attention, and may be unwilling to accommodate her requests. They may also resist their colleagues' efforts to sensitize them to the situation. Or, they may dismiss her disclosures as "false memories."

From the survivor's perspective, facing a caregiver who does not believe her or who ignores her fears may trigger reminders of the betrayal she experienced when other adults, perhaps her mother, learned of the abuse and did nothing or acted with disbelief or denial. The woman who feels she is being treated this way and is unable to give feedback to the caregiver should seek some supportive person in the system to advocate for her. Or she may have to change caregivers.

Once they learn about sexual abuse and its aftereffects, some caregivers find it so upsetting that they avoid talking about it. They have not been trained in ways to deal with disclosures of this kind. Others avoid a discussion of childhood sexual abuse because they worry that bringing it up will be time-consuming. In a busy practice, keeping on schedule is of paramount importance and often no time is allotted for supportive discussion. The kind of care that would probably benefit the woman most would include continuity of care with one provider, enough time during her appointments to speak about her concerns, and a caregiver who knows not only his or her specialty, but also how childhood sexual abuse may influence the survivor's childbearing experience.

The most helpful caregivers also know that their relationship with their survivor client may be strained at times as she tests her caregiver's trustworthiness. They try to be open-minded and flexible, according to the stated needs and wishes of the woman. They are willing to vary their practice, if asked, in order to accommodate the woman within the limits of safety and reason. They are honest, empathic, and respectful in their dealings with the woman. And lastly, they recognize that the woman has good reasons for not automatically trusting them. They try not to take it personally when the woman seems suspicious or appears to attribute to them (and other authority figures) some of the most disturbing qualities of her abuser(s). Caregivers may have to earn the woman's trust, but by doing so, they ensure a secure relationship from which she may move toward healing.

How far should a caregiver go in accommodating the

woman's unconventional requests or needs? This question often plagues the sensitive caregiver because some requests require quite a lot of adjustment in staffing and changes in routines. Sometimes, special team meetings of nurses and caregivers and others must be called in order to provide for the special needs of the woman. On the surface, all these efforts may appear to indicate cooperative and mutually respectful care, but this is sometimes deceptive, especially if both parties are uneasy with the accommodations. The caregiver is sometimes uncomfortable over some of the woman's demands, and may feel he or she has to relinquish the caregiver's usual role in maintaining safety during labor. For the survivor, what seems like taking control or empowerment may in reality leave her feeling insecure over a lack of clear boundaries. Her specific demands may actually be covering up her fear and anxiety. It may feel at some level that her caregiver is abdicating responsibility, because he or she does not truly care about her. Both caregiver and client are mistaking a shift in power or control from caregiver to client as true cooperation.

We suggest that the caregiver use reflective listening to help the client understand her real issues, so that they can resolve them together. The following story illustrates the pitfalls of going to uncomfortable lengths in accommodating women's wishes. It is followed by suggestions for how to handle such a situation better than it was handled.

Cora

Cora had been terribly traumatized by two previous cesarean sections. This time she really wanted a vaginal birth (VBAC). She chose a doctor who was known for being caring and flexible. Cora was convinced that her cesareans had been unnecessary and were due to inappropriate treatment. She wanted to give herself the best chance for a VBAC.

Much of her birth plan centered on avoiding the pitfalls and problems she had had before. This time she wanted to avoid an epidural, and she wanted a nurse who would support her in this effort. She wanted to be in water for pain relief as an alternative to an epidural; she did not want continuous monitoring or an IV. Cora planned to be accompanied by her partner, a doula, her mother, two sisters, and a friend. She had several other requests in her birth plan, which was five pages long.

The doctor and the staff did everything they could to accommodate Cora. They agreed to use telemetry for monitoring in the bath. The doctor conferred with the nursing supervisor and arranged for hand-picked, experienced and open-minded nurses to be available for every shift from two weeks before until two weeks after her due date. The doctor was eager for Cora to have a better birth than her last ones, but when Cora requested to give birth in the water, he began to feel very uneasy, and so did the staff. He had had no experience with water birth and was not sure it was safe, but, practicing in an area where home water births were not unusual, he agreed. Even though the doctor felt pressured to practice outside his comfort zone, he went to some lengths to learn about water births.

On the surface Cora appeared to be quite sure of herself, but unbeknownst to her doctor, she was not really sure water birth was a good idea. She had heard about water birth from friends in the alternative birth community, and decided to ask about it. Since the doctor agreed, she assumed he was comfortable with it.

Despite these extensive plans, and all the special accommodations, Cora had a cesarean. She dilated completely while in the water, but the baby never descended, even after several hours of pushing both in the water and out, and trying many positions and even Oxytocin to bring the baby down.

In this situation a lack of clear communication between respectful and well-meaning people led to a lost opportunity to explore Cora's desires to control many clinical aspects of her care. The emphasis on controlling the external aspects of her birth (the behaviors of others, the use of water) masked her real anxiety related to a fundamental distrust in her body, and a deep fear of a vaginal birth, which could not have been solved by all the plans in the world. Thus, although Cora's spoken needs were met, no one recognized the needs and fears beneath the surface.

The doctor felt frustrated. In hopes of a better birth experience for Cora, he had agreed to many practices that made him uncomfortable. He had not followed his own instincts. He even felt somewhat guilty for not following what he thought was right, and was left wondering whether Cora might have had a better outcome if he had insisted on doing what he thought was best. He was worried, she was troubled, but underneath this, neither really heard the other. They missed the "music behind the words," the non-verbal aspects of communication.

Even if the two people's divergent needs had never been revealed to one another, had they used some of the techniques of active listening and constructive feedback, there might have been a possibility for clearer communication and more comfortable boundaries for both, no matter what the outcome. Some of their uneasiness could have been addressed, and the real underlying concerns may have emerged. As it was, without the establishment of safe mutually acceptable boundaries, Cora did not develop trust in her body or in her caregivers' expertise. She felt ungrounded without knowing why. The good intentions of the staff were not lost on Cora, however. In spite of the undesired outcome, Cora did feel respected and cared for by her caregivers.

The doctor might have addressed both their concerns in the following way, listening empathically to her requests in an attempt to understand and validate her feelings:

"Cora, it's really clear that you do not want a repeat of last time, and you're very determined to make sure it doesn't happen again. I've thought a great deal about your requests and there is much I can work with you on. I'm impressed with the amount of thought you've given to this." (Now the doctor shifts gears to giving her feedback of his own feelings and concerns.)

"However, I'm uncomfortable attempting a water birth for a VBAC. First, I'm inexperienced with water births, and I don't know any physician who practices water birth in the hospital, and honestly, I'm afraid for the baby and for you. I would be comfortable with your laboring in the water with the telemetry unit so we can keep good track of your contractions and the baby. Then you can have the comfort you desire without compromising safety for either yourself or the baby. How does that feel to you?"

Cora might then have felt comfortable stating, "I guess I was a little unsure about the water birth myself. I've heard of people doing it at home, but I'd feel more secure with you making that decision."

If they had had a brief exchange like the above, both the doctor and Cora would have had greater mutual understanding and felt validated. They also would have moved to a more meaningful level of communication, which may have led to uncovering Cora's other concerns about the normality of her body. Now we can see that the whole water birth discussion was not really about the issue of water birth, but about control and deep insecurity within Cora.

When the Caregiver Is an Abuse Survivor

In a society like ours, with a high prevalence of childhood sexual abuse, many caregivers have themselves been abused and can be re-traumatized if a discussion with a client who is also a survivor triggers memories of their own abuse. Such caregivers should have professional counseling available, to help them process their own trauma and avoid projecting their unresolved issues onto the client. Resolution of abuse issues enables a survivor caregiver to provide more empathic care.

Sherril

Sherril, a family doctor, shared her story with us. As a family doctor who attended births, she had an unusually high rate of cesarean sections—44 percent. She started psychotherapy to cope with other troubling events in her life. During therapy, she realized the association of her childhood abuse history with her absolute fear of and avoidance of any aspect of birth that represented pain to the genital area. She also recognized that she might have transmitted this anxiety and fear to her patients. As her awareness grew and her healing took place, she became able to help them have more trust and confidence in their bodies. Her cesarean rate dropped dramatically to 19 percent. As Sherril began to trust the birth process herself, she could separate her past tension and fear related to her own bodily pain from the present reality of normalcy for most of her pregnant clients.

Appropriate Ways to Discuss Abuse Issues

Caregivers may wonder whether and how they should inquire about past abuse if they do not have the experience or resources to help their abused clients. The reality is that even if asked, women may be reluctant to disclose this information for any of a number of reasons:

- Feelings of shame and guilt over having been abused, as if she brought the sexual abuse on herself
- Enforced secrecy. In some cases, disclosure would have meant breaking up her family, whereas keeping the secret kept the family together. In other cases, children were threatened that if they told anyone, dire events would occur—either injury to someone else or themselves. They were warned that no one would believe them
- Anxiety and concern that her family of origin will find out that she disclosed the abuse, and retaliate
- A sense that the caregiver cannot help her with this secret shame or pain, or will blame her, because she believes she deserves to be blamed
- Self-protection of privacy. If her abuse history is noted in her chart, she may worry that numerous people will find out about her secret. She may not wish to talk about it, thinking that avoiding it will make it hurt less
- A wish to avoid the anxiety and discomfort for both caregiver and survivor that are bound to come up if they talk about the abuse

Thus, both the women and their caregivers tend to shy away from discussing abuse, but the issue is too important to ignore. The caregiver should inquire about abuse as a routine part of history-taking at an appointment early in the pregnancy. By avoiding the subject, he or she may miss a major contributing cause of some symptoms and indirectly reinforce the woman's tendency to somatize. (See Chapter 2 for a description of somatization.) Furthermore, avoiding the topic of abuse may imply some unconscious acceptance of violence and ignorance of its impact on health.

It is rarely appropriate to address these questions in acute situations, such as during labor. At such times, if caregivers suspect a background of abuse, they should respond with the type of emotional support most needed at that time—dealing with symptoms, not underlying causes. (For examples see Chapter 10.)

There are several useful ways to elicit disclosure of abuse. In Chapter 3, we explored issues relating to disclosure of abuse from the woman's perspective. Here we will discuss how to ask about abuse and some of the issues from the caregiver's point of view. A caregiver may ask about a history of childhood sexual abuse when obtaining a family and personal history. Some caregivers include questions about abuse on a psychosocial history form. The wording of these questions is important. We suggest the following for a printed form.

Asking about abuse on a printed form

> Please answer the following questions to help us discover if there are potential problems that we should discuss together. This information will be available to the following people. [The caregiver's staff should describe how confidential or how public the record will be. This will help the client decide whether to disclose or not.]
>
> ☐ Yes ☐ No Have you ever been or are you now in a relationship in which you have been physically or emotionally threatened, insulted, beaten, injured, or made to take part in sexual activities against your will?
>
> ☐ Yes ☐ No Would you like to talk about the above question or any aspect of your sex life?

It is not surprising that most such printed forms have the "No" boxes checked, even by women who have an abuse history. (See Chapter 3). If asked to fill out the questionnaire several appointments later, after they have become acquainted with their caregiver, they may feel more willing to answer honestly.

A lack of time or comfort for any in-depth discussion of abuse or sexual issues may also keep the caregiver from asking in the first place. However, when the "Yes" boxes are checked, the caregiver must follow up sensitively and calmly ("I am glad you told me. Sometimes abuse-related issues come up during pregnancy and afterwards. Let's work together to keep that to a minimum."). The caregiver can help with some discussion as described here, or with a referral to a knowledgeable social worker, counselor, or therapist. To ignore her "Yes" answer is to discount the survivor and reinforce an old lesson that she learned as a child: It does no good to tell someone. If the caregiver responds appropriately, it may save time, because many procedures and explanations usually require more time and justification if the woman does not feel understood or trusting of her caregiver.

It is appropriate to ask about abuse, pain, violence, loss or injuries when discussing a client's health and development: significant childhood events and losses; menarche and her related feelings; family of origin; sexual and reproductive history; relationship issues; substance abuse; health complaints; self-destructive behavior; her mental health, her feelings about Pap smears, breast self-exams, and her comfort with vaginal exams.

Asking about abuse face to face

One of the simplest and safest ways to identify a background of abuse is for the caregiver to ask the woman face to face, reassuring her that these questions are asked of all patients. Otherwise, a survivor may feel that there is something about her that indicates that she has been abused. As stated in Chapter 3, the caregiver might begin with a general statement to acknowledge the fact that many women have had difficult past experiences.For example: "Many women have had unpleasant sexual experiences such as being pressured or forced into sex or have been physically abused. Have you ever experienced anything like that?"

While most survivors are cautious when disclosing their abuse history and tend to reveal only part of the story, caregivers must be ready and willing to listen to accounts that are upsetting or shocking. It is most important for survivors to sense that the caregiver is truly open and interested, and will not judge them or overreact. In addition, telling the story, or a part of the story, helps some women begin to understand the connection between their current symptoms or fears and their background of abuse.

Although it is important to inquire about abuse and to handle obstetrical and medical interactions appropriately, a caregiver does not have to be a psychotherapist in order to be therapeutic. For example, it is not necessary or desirable to pressure the woman to disclose more details than she is comfortable disclosing, or to encourage a cathartic release of feelings in order to conduct a satisfactory and appropriate interview. In fact, if the woman feels pressured by the caregiver when she either does not recall or is not ready to reveal her abuse, the relationship will deteriorate.

When the woman does disclose her abuse history, the caregiver should express and demonstrate empathy for her situation, and discuss the abuse only as it is relevant to the birth, always respecting her privacy. Simply having support to talk about the abuse may begin a therapeutic process that the woman may pursue later in an appropriate context.

Caregivers should also acknowledge to their survivor clients the limitations in their expertise, but state that they want to work together to make their childbirths as free from stress and trauma as possible. A woman will be relieved to hear her caregiver say: "I am sorry you had to go through this. If there are some things that come up with the exams, procedures, planning for labor and delivery, or anything else that seems particularly upsetting, please let me know." See pages 243-244 for helpful and unhelpful responses when a woman discloses her abuse history.

The benefit of disclosure is that the client-caregiver relationship is more open and collaborative. Caregivers can also offer women appropriate referrals for more in-depth therapy or support, for example, an incest survivors' group, counselors and therapists, and helpful reading materials.

A question to ask oneself

Survivors may say no when asked if they were abused, even though they may exhibit some or many of the signs and symptoms. They may have no memory of being abused or may not wish to disclose it. In such cases, Barbara Wijma, a midwife, suggests that the caregiver ask him or herself, "Would everything that I see, hear, and feel with this woman seem more natural, understandable, and make more sense if she were in fact a victim of abuse?" If the caregiver's answer to this question is "yes," then the woman's specific needs and worries should be taken seriously and treated respectfully and kindly, without a requirement that she disclose a history of abuse. Although beneficial, disclosure should not be necessary in order for a caregiver to treat a survivor appropriately. (See previous chapters for common symptoms and characteristics present in childhood abuse survivors that may appear in adulthood or the childbearing period.)

A Sample Interview

Here is a sample interview illustrating how the caregiver might discuss the subject of abuse with a client.

Caregiver: I see, Sally, that you have checked "yes" to the question about past sexual abuse (or, Sally, you mentioned there was sexual abuse in your history.) I am glad you told me of this past experience. I want to make sure that my care is comfortable for you. You can help me understand how I can be of the most help.

Sally: Yes, but it was a long time ago. I'm not sure it's all that important.

Caregiver (gently): Let's explore it a bit more because sometimes for people who have been abused, aspects can come up unexpectedly during pregnancy, birth, or even after the baby is born.

Sally (hesitantly): What do you mean?

Caregiver: Some women have discomfort with some procedures, like a vaginal exam, or with changes in their bodies during pregnancy.

Sally: Well, you know, I've always hated vaginal exams...

Caregiver (kindly): Yes, I've noticed that and it's not uncommon for people who have been abused to feel like that. Let's try to work on that together and any other things that come up.

The caregiver's sensitive questioning has reassured the woman that he is aware of her abuse and comfortable in working with her to plan her care. It was not necessary for him to press for details, and he comfortably confined his interests to his area of expertise and the survivor's maternity care needs.

Once the woman has disclosed her history of sexual abuse, it will be distressing to her if she has to do so over and over—each time she encounters a different caregiver. She also runs a risk of extreme disappointment or worse if some of the caregivers in the practice have not been apprised of any individual care plans she and her caregiver agreed upon. Certainly, having multiple caregivers, each with a unique personality and management philosophy, make it very difficult for the woman to establish a trusting relationship with each one.

Melinda

Melinda, a 22-year-old, first-time mother, had a distressing experience with a multi-caregiver practice. Melinda had been sexually and physically abused for years by her older brother who threatened to kill her cat and burn the house down if Melinda told their parents. Her brother died in a motorcycle accident when Melinda was 20; his death freed her to disclose her abuse, but with each telling, she suffered feelings of guilt, terrifying nightmares and a daylong migraine headache.

Her midwife was kind and empathic when Melinda disclosed her abuse, but did not recognize the significance of the disclosure and did not write it in Melinda's chart. Nor did she ask Melinda if she would like the midwife to bring it up at their group's weekly chart conference. At her next two appointments, Melinda saw two different midwives, neither of whom was aware of Melinda's traumatic history. Fortunately, Melinda told the third midwife how stressful it was to have to keep telling her story. The midwife assured Melinda that the other midwives and the hospital staff would be informed immediately, with confidentiality maintained in that the details would not be revealed to others who did not need to know.

Melinda was reassured to know that her care providers were aware of her special needs, especially when the nurse called her by name when she was admitted in labor and said, "I've had a chance to go over your birth plan with your midwife. We will try to do everything you were hoping for. I'm looking forward to working with you."

Practical Solutions for Caregivers to Ensure that Promises Are Kept

One challenge for the caregiver in a busy group practice is to maintain good communication with colleagues. Once a woman has disclosed a history of sexual abuse (often overcoming shame and embarrassment to do so), it must not be forgotten. With her permission, her story should be discreetly told to others in the practice. Her chart should be flagged in some way to avoid embarrassment or humiliation in future encounters.

Michael Klein, MD, a family doctor and his practice group in Vancouver, Canada, have devised a way to share important personal information about clients while maintaining respect and confidentiality. This makes it possible for the client to tell only one doctor, rather than every one, her concerns. Each doctor carries a PDA (Personal Digital Assistant). During prenatal appointments, the doctor enters important personal and medical information disclosed by the client. Before ending the appointment, if very personal information is to be entered, the doctor asks the client to read it, clarify, and help edit it to ensure that it is accurate and includes only what she wants the group to know. Her medical chart may or may not contain this personal information. The doctor then sends it to all the doctors' PDAs. Access is restricted to only the doctors in the practice. When the client calls the doctor on call, or arrives in labor, the covering doctor has immediate and confidential access to this information. The information is deleted when no longer needed.

The software program that they use is Smartlist To Go, available at http://www.dataviz.com.

A second challenge for busy caregivers is to individualize care and treatment for reasons other than clinical ones, such as the survivor's psychological or cultural needs, or even her personal wishes. Her needs may seem trivial or unreasonable. For example, one woman asked that no one use the words, "Relax and this won't hurt so much." Another asked that during vaginal exams, all other staff except the examiner stand at the woman's head, so as not to view her perineum. Another wanted to wear underpants until the second stage. Another wanted bright lights on at all times. Inflexible or inconsiderate caregivers might embarrass a woman who makes such requests, asking, "Why would you want something like that? It doesn't make sense." The sensitive caregiver would ask himself or herself, "Why not?" and agree to these requests. True, it takes a bit of effort for the staff to remember and follow through, but if it means that the woman will feel safer or more respected, it is worthwhile.

Suggestions for Survivors to Ensure Good Communication with the Caregiver

The woman's role in this relationship is as important as the caregiver's. She can contribute to a positive relationship if she can communicate her questions and needs clearly and calmly, using the "I messages" and active listening techniques described in Chapter 7. Even within the context of short appointments and multiple caregivers, good communication is possible when both parties are willing to try.

It also helps if the woman recognizes that caregivers see many people and sometimes forget some important facts about each individual. If she is willing to remind the caregiver of her background of sexual abuse and of what they discussed, rather than interpreting the caregiver's poor memory as rejection, she will be spared much grief.

For labor, the woman and her partner should consider having a doula who is trained and experienced in providing continual emotional support and physical comfort to the woman, and to advise and assist her partner throughout labor. Doulas are available in many communities and are extremely helpful even if there is also a kind nurse and caregiver, because they do not leave and have no responsibilities other than the emotional well being and comfort of the woman and her partner. The doula becomes acquainted with the woman and her special needs ahead of time and can help ensure that those needs will be met. (See Chapter 8.)

A written birth plan, prepared with her caregiver, enables the woman to disclose her past trauma and her requests in writing, so that she does not have to tell these important matters to everyone involved in her care. Childbirth educators, doulas and office nurses, as well as some books (see the Resources: Books) can assist the woman through the initial stages of preparing a birth plan. (See Appendix for a birth plan form that allows clients to disclose fears and most important issues.) Of course, a woman should not be pressured to disclose her abuse history in a birth plan. The decision is hers.

Lastly, sometimes the relationship between a woman and a particular caregiver is impossible. A lack of empathy or interest on the caregiver's part, hostility or suspicion on the woman's part, or simply a personality clash sometimes occurs. If that becomes obvious and persists even with attempts by the woman, caregiver, or both to use good communication skills, the woman (who has the most to lose) should either ask for a third party to mediate or change caregivers if at all possible. A poor relationship rarely improves in labor and can re-traumatize the survivor. (See chapter 3 for discussion of incompatibility between a woman and her caregiver.)

Sometimes both the caregiver and the woman try very hard to ensure a positive birth experience, but unforeseen circumstances or unexpected abuse memories come up and the birth still ends up as a nightmare. Her wounds from the past may be very severe and the efforts made to contain those wounds may be unsuccessful. If this happens, the woman deserves and benefits from discussion with a knowledgeable, empathic person and possibly individual or group therapy. Postpartum debriefing of the birth can often avoid an escalation of painful, traumatic emotional reactions such as nightmares or obsessive thoughts or flashbacks of the birth, or anger with the caregiver. (See Chapter 5.)

The survivor's relationship with her maternity caregiver has features that might trigger negative associations with her past abuse. Caregivers who recognize such associations can usually reduce the likelihood of re-traumatization of the survivor by providing sensitive, respectful, individualized care.

7
Communication Skills

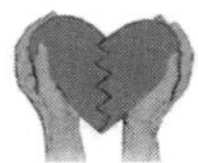

- How do you get people to listen to you?
- I've learned that if I tell him at the beginning of my appointment I have some questions, he's more likely to sit down and talk with me than if I wait until the end
- I just met her in labor, and she acts like I'm trying to hurt her. What did I do to frighten her?

Effective communication in a client-caregiver relationship occurs when directive and non-directive communication are used appropriately. Knowing the difference between them and knowing when to use and not use each is the first step in mastering effective communication. Beyond that, having good listening, questioning, and feedback skills expands the understanding between the parties and lessens the likelihood of misinterpretation.

Directive and Non-directive Communication

How does directive communication differ from its opposite, non-directive communication? Directive communication includes giving information, directing or showing someone how to do something, and giving advice. Directive communication implies that the caregiver is the expert. There are times when expert and knowledgeable information is crucial to care. Most caregivers believe that giving information and advice is paramount, and most women rely on their caregivers for their skill, knowledge and expertise. However, for survivors, the normal ups and downs of pregnancy, birth, post partum, and parenthood are more complex. In confronting confusing emotions and anxieties, they really do not need directive communication. Rather, the major role of the caregiver is to help them express their feelings, understand their concerns, validate their experience, and work with them to find the best way to cope with situations.

Non-directive communication encourages the client to explore her own situation and emotions, and helps her process and resolve her situation. Non-directive communication is very useful when the client has deep concerns, strong feelings, a problem to solve, or conflict over another's behavior. It creates equality between the woman and her caregiver, which helps the woman feel more valid as a person. Non-directive communication includes:

- *Active listening:* listening with empathy (understanding the true content and feelings being expressed by the other person); openness (without interruption, judgment, or evaluation); and awareness (of congruence or incongruence between the content of the message and accompanying non-verbal behaviors, such as facial expression, body language, tone of voice)
- *Unconditional regard* (nonverbal actions that connote interest, acceptance and validation of the other person): open posture; comfort with silence, crying, or anger; a warm tone of voice; head nodding and "mmm hmm," "yes"; avoiding distractions (looking away or at watch, answering phone)
- *Reflecting feelings:* "You are worried about ...;" "You feel discounted because...;" "I wonder if you're feeling ignored by..."

- *Paraphrasing* (restating the content expressed in the listener's own words): "You really want to breastfeed this time"; "You're angry that he never called you back"; "You decided not to return for your appointment."
- *Clarifying* (tentative statements to check the listener's understanding): "If I understand you correctly..."; "I'm not sure I fully understand you, but is this what you're saying?" or "It seems that this is what you're saying ..."
- *Open-ended questions* (that do not have a yes or no answer) instead of closed questions (with yes or no answers): "What are your plans for feeding the baby?" versus "Are you going to breastfeed?" Open-ended questions allow for discussion of concerns, information-seeking, and follow-up with further questions. A yes or no answer to a closed question tends to stop further discussion or make it awkward to follow up.
- *Constructive feedback with the use of "I Messages"* (when the listener needs to express her own feelings or concerns in a non-hurtful way): "When you did or said...[behavior], I felt...[feelings], and now I... [effect]. Example: "When you took that telephone call just as you were about to examine me, I felt insulted and exposed and unimportant, so I got dressed and left."

When to Use Active Listening and Non-directive Communication

It is important to recognize when active listening and non-directive communication should be employed, when it should not, and when it is not possible. In the following circumstances, the effective communicator would put aside usual conversation and "go into active listening mode":

- When the other person has strong feelings, negative or positive
- When the other person has a problem

- When the other person wants to share ideas
- When the other person wants to sort out feelings and thoughts
- When the listener is not sure what the other person means
- When both the listener and the other person have mutual concerns or a problem about something

When Not to Use Active Listening

- If there is really not a problem, but someone only wants information (i.e., "How often are my appointments during the last month of my pregnancy?")
- If the person doesn't have time to talk (the person should briefly acknowledge the importance of the other person's concerns, and plan a future opportunity to talk)
- If one has very negative feelings about the other person
- If the problem is already solved

Barriers to Effective Communication

There are 3 major categories of barriers to effective communication: judgment, giving solutions, and avoidance.

Judgment includes evaluating (positively or negatively), approving or disapproving, criticizing, labeling, diagnosing, blaming, asking "why," interpreting, psychoanalyzing. When people feel judged in any of these ways, they feel inadequate, angry, or guilty. They become defensive and resistant. When a person is praised for making the "right decision" or "knowing what's best," or for being "so much more sensible than those who think they know as much as a doctor," she doesn't dare express ambivalence or uncertainty for fear that she would be judged "wrong." She may also wonder how the listener would or will react when she makes the "wrong decision."

Giving solutions includes advice-giving, ordering, directing, warning or threatening, moralizing or preaching, recommending, excessive or inappropriate questioning. This is a common trap for authority figures, such as doctors and midwives, but it does not allow the woman to fully explore what is concerning her. She feels obligated to take the caregiver's advice or covertly ignore it, either of which shuts down communication.

Avoidance includes becoming distracted; letting the mind wander; dismissing or joking about the person's ideas; rehearsing what to say next; interrupting; avoiding the person's concerns by diversion to other topics; persuasion; logical arguments; lecturing; or minimizing her concerns with reassurance, sympathy, or excusing, before really hearing what she is trying to say. When a person has strong feelings, these avoidance behaviors leave her feeling unheard, misunderstood, discounted, or angry.

Scripts of Conversations Illustrating Poor and Effective Communication

Following are two examples of conversations between Flora (the client), and her caregiver. Both are about the people whom Flora wishes to accompany her through the birth. Flora says she wants to have many people at the birth, but the real underlying issues are about her need to feel safe, and her confusion about how to please various people involved. The first conversation, full of barriers to effective communication, fails to identify underlying issues and angers Flora, while the second uses many of the active listening and feedback skills, and is much more effective and satisfying in addressing Flora's concerns.

In shaded type, we label the barriers, reactions, or active listening skills, which are described above.

Caregiver: Hi, Flora. It's good to see you. I know you wanted to discuss your Birth Plan today, and I really want to hear all about it.

Flora: Thank you. The first thing I want to tell you is the

people we're going to have there. I do have quite a few family members that really want to be there. I have my three sisters, my mother, and my mother-in-law. Then I'd like my best friend, Janie, who has been through all the tough things with me, and of course my husband. Hmm...you don't think that's too many, do you? (anxious, unsure of her own choices)

Caregiver: I sure do. Why do you want to have so many people there? (judges, evaluates, asks why?)

Flora: Well, they all want to be there and they all mean a lot to me. I think they'd feel awfully bad if I leave them out. (becomes defensive, feels disapproval, feels criticized, needs to justify)

Caregiver: Well, it seems to me that your problem is that you just can't say no, and my advice is that it's really too many people and they could distract you. Actually, most people feel birth is kind of messy and upsetting. You should just tell them they should stay in the waiting room. (judges, criticizes, advises, threats, preaches, diagnoses)

Flora: [sitting back and crossing her arms] Yes, but they've all told me that they really want to be there. The hospital has an open door policy so I don't see why I can't have them. They don't think that birth is messy. (becomes defensive and angry, shuts off communication, feels invalidated)

Caregiver: Well, if that's what you want...I guess it won't be a problem. I'm sure it will all work out. Now what else is on your birth plan? (reassures inappropriately, avoids discussion, discounts)

After this interaction, Flora feels angry, defensive, unheard, invalidated, and now entrenched in her desire for this number of people at the birth. The next version of this conversation shows how the caregiver picked up cues of doubt in Flora, explored them sensitively, and, as a result, the conversation came to a very different and highly satisfactory conclusion.

Caregiver: Hi, Flora. I know you came today to talk about some items in your Birth Plan. Would you like to share them?

Flora: Well, yes. First, you wanted to know who's going to be there. I've been thinking about the people to have. My three sisters kind of want to be there. Two of them never had babies. And then, of course, there's my mother and my mother-in-law and my best friend, Janie, who's been with me through all the meaningful things in my life and, of course, my husband. Hmmm, do you think that's too many? (anxious, unsure of her own choices)

Caregiver: It sounds as if you're a bit concerned about how many people ought to be there or if it will be too crowded. (paraphrases, reflects feelings, some content and meaning)

Flora: Yes, and I don't know what they'll do. I mean, I wouldn't want them to get in anyone's way. (feels safe disclosing her concerns)

Caregiver: You're worried that they could be distracting or interfere in some way? (paraphrases, tentative statement, reflects feelings, restates concern)

Flora: Well, you know, two of my sisters, they haven't even had babies and I'm afraid they might freak out or they might just get silly because they sometimes get silly. (feels safe to reveal even more concerns)

Caregiver: So you're worried about how they'll handle watching birth for the first time. It sounds as if you have some mixed feelings about your sisters being there. (summarizes, reflects feelings, content, meaning)

Flora: Yes, and my mother-in-law, too. I'm only asking her because she thinks we always leave her out of everything, but I really don't want her there, I have to admit that. (feels validated and understood, and encouraged to be very open)

Caregiver: You're really not comfortable with your mother-in-law present. But it sounds as if you're not sure how to let her know that. (paraphrases, reflects feelings, starts to define problem)

Flora: I don't know how to say it. I'm afraid she'll be upset that I'm playing favorites and that my mother is getting more than she. Oh, I just wish I hadn't told anybody they could come! (reveals frustration and feeling trapped)

Caregiver: You're in a quandary as to how to set some boundaries around this for yourself. I'm beginning to sense that you know what will be comfortable for you but you're worried about hurting people's feelings or fulfilling some kind of obligation. (summarizes and clarifies, validates concerns, tentative open statement, opens up potential for problem solving.)

Flora: You know what I'd really like? I want my husband there, of course, and Janie, my best friend, and it would be OK for my mom to be there, but I don't know what to do with everybody else and I don't know how to tell them not to come. (realizes what she wants, frames her quandary)

Caregiver: Have you thought of another way to include them without everybody being present? (open brainstorming solutions)

Flora: No. What are my choices? I don't know what else I can do. (asks for advice and guidance)

Caregiver: Sometimes family members come and wait in the waiting room. There's a lovely lounge in that hospital. (offers suggestions tentatively)

Flora: Oh, you mean they could be there but they wouldn't be right in my room the whole time? (clarifies the possible solution)

Caregiver: Yes. (listens expectantly, quietly, avoids advising)

Flora: Well, maybe they could do that, and then if neither my mother nor my mother-in-law got to be there, my mother-in-law wouldn't be hurt because both grandmothers would be out in the waiting room. (creative solution to one of her quandaries)

Caregiver: That's a good point. If you treat them equally, you're not going to have to worry about one of them losing face or feeling that you're rejecting one versus the other. (summarizes)

Flora: Yes, and I can tell my sisters. Actually, the one sister who's had a baby didn't ask me to come to her birth, so why do I have to ask her to mine? She didn't ask my other sisters either so they shouldn't be surprised if I ask them to stay in the waiting room. I'll just have the people I really want during labor. The others can be in the waiting room. They'll be the first to know when the baby is born. I'd love to show them the baby afterwards. I think this will work out. Thank you. (feels relieved, empowered, validated as the decision-maker)

Creative Problem-Solving

When the caregiver and client have recognized a problem and its real meaning for the woman, it is time to begin looking at ways to move forward to some solution. This is where appropriate, open-ended questions help the woman focus her thoughts on possibilities and their consequences.

Creative problem solving includes the following steps:

- The client states the concern or problem.
- The caregiver explores the situation with active listening to understand the feelings, the meaning, the needs being expressed.

Together they

- Re-define the problem.
- Brainstorm potential solutions.
- Evaluate each one in a careful and sensitive manner to see what in reality could work.
- Choose the solution(s).

- Make a plan to implement the solutions.
- Have a plan to evaluate the effectiveness.

Following is an example of well-timed creative problem-solving with a pregnant survivor who had deep fears about a procedure in labor.

Eve

Eve is an 18 year-old primigravida who is pregnant as the result of a rape. She has a history of bipolar illness dating from the suicide of her mother (by a self-inflicted gunshot to the head) when Eve was 12. Eve had been the person who discovered her mother, in a pool of blood. Along with other emotional symptoms she has a phobia of needles—IV's, blood draws, injections. In fact, when she knows she is going to have a blood draw she needs hours beforehand to psychologically prepare herself, and feels weak and faint for hours afterwards. Because Eve was helped by her childbirth educator to communicate her needs to her caregiver, she gained needed understanding and support. This is an exchange she had with her caregiver:

Caregiver: Before you leave, Eve, I would like to get a blood sample and run a hematocrit since it's been quite a while.

Eve: You didn't tell me you were going to do this.

Caregiver: I always check the hematocrit at this point in a pregnancy.

Eve: It's taken me by surprise. I always need time to prepare myself for a blood draw, and I told your nurse about that at my first visit.

Caregiver: We'll do it quickly. It'll only take a moment.

Eve: Please, I'm telling you that blood draws are really hard for me. I need time to 'psych' myself for it. It leaves me weak and faint and I'm no good for the rest of the day.

Caregiver: (shifts gears, uses active listening) It sounds as if blood draws are really upsetting for you.

Eve: Yes.

Caregiver: What would make it easier for you?

Eve: Could I put it off till tomorrow or the next day, so I'll have time to prepare?

Caregiver: Sure, we can do that. But it just occurs to me that during labor we're going to want to take a blood sample or maybe do other procedures that involve needles, so we'll need to come up with a plan that will make this as comfortable as possible.

Eve: Thank you for being willing to help me with this.

Conclusion

Non-directive communication allows the woman to feel heard, validated, and understood. It benefits the caregiver by enhancing his or her understanding of the woman's feelings, and ability to provide highly satisfying care. By promoting mutual trust and equality in their relationship, non-directive communication benefits both people as they strive for positive outcomes, both clinical and emotional.

8
Maternity Paraprofessionals: Childbirth Educators, Doulas, Breastfeeding Consultants, and Massage Therapists

- Our birth class was full of eager beavers. I felt phony and out of place, especially when we were supposed to "share" in small groups. We wound up quitting the class.
- We interviewed three doulas and then met Kate. I didn't even have to mention my abuse to her. She tuned in to me, and seemed to take me at face value. Even my weird birth plan didn't phase her. I felt really comfortable with her.
- I couldn't breastfeed. I had every problem in the book and the baby wasn't gaining. All she did was cry because I was starving her. My breasts let us both down—not surprising. They've caused me all kinds of grief.

How can maternity resource people such as childbirth educators, birth and postpartum doulas, breastfeeding consultants and massage therapists be really helpful to women with sexual abuse issues? How can a survivor work with these people to enhance her childbearing and early parenting experiences? Of course, finding the right people is the key, but not always easy. For survivors especially, acceptable choices may be more limited than for those who have not suffered betrayal, coercion, helplessness, and violation at the hands of others with more power.

This chapter explores how childbirth educators, doulas, breastfeeding consultants, and massage therapists can and do tailor their services to accommodate the varying needs and preferences of clients, particularly survivors of sexual abuse.

Survivors may be uncomfortable in childbirth classes where they are expected to participate in groups, discuss personal matters, and master relaxation while under supervision. Working with a doula requires selecting an unfamiliar person to assist and guide the woman through the ultimate in demanding personal experiences. Asking for help with breastfeeding or household tasks may seem like admitting ineptitude, inadequacy, or failure. It also may mean revealing inadequacy in caring for a newborn. All these challenge the survivor's carefully developed coping mechanisms. The profound changes of pregnancy, birth and post partum disrupt what usually maintains order in her life. It is often tempting to go it alone to avoid the discomforts of getting help.

The Childbirth Educator

Today most pregnant women and their partners attend childbirth preparation classes, and it is likely that every class includes survivors of sexual abuse—both male and female. While the educator does not need to know if a class member has a history of abuse, she needs to know that much of what is routinely taught in childbirth classes can trigger anxiety and resistance in learners with abuse issues. She also has to realize that one in every three or four students is likely to have been molested in childhood. Sexual abuse survivors should be forewarned that some of the material presented in classes may provoke such feelings as anxiety or resistance, or may seem irrelevant. Survivors whose childbirth educators seem unaware of some of the information in this book might share the book with them.

Every educator has stories about reluctant class participants, those for whom the comfort measures do not work, couples who do not work well together, those who are bored, sleepy or downright hostile. They upset the teacher, who feels ineffective or defensive, and who perceives them as difficult, hostile, disruptive, or unusually afraid. And the more dogmatic the teacher, the greater the impasse. She may not realize that part of the problem is with her, that her teaching is not inclusive enough to suit the unique needs of a variety of learners.

The positive side of childbirth education is that a class taught by someone with awareness of abuse issues can be enlightening, ultimately reassuring, and confidence-building. By becoming aware of its potentially distressing aspects, and modifying them, the childbirth educator can transform her class into one that benefits everyone.

In a group setting, it is particularly challenging for the teacher to present topics that may carry an emotional threat to abuse survivors, such as vaginal lacerations and pain, episiotomy, perineal massage, labor complications and interventions, circumcision, breastfeeding, informed consent, sexuality. Furthermore, though it works well for most women, it is anything but relaxing for some survivors to have to practice comfort measures in the usual way—lying on the floor among strangers and trying to relax, under the watchful eye of the teacher, who remains upright.

Childbirth films, especially those that graphically show births, are sometimes disturbing or impossible for survivors to watch.

Reminders to "yield," "surrender," to "open yourself to the pain," from well-meaning educators may inadvertently convey the opposite message to survivors, who have been forced to yield and surrender during their abuse. Advice to "listen to," or "trust your body," "do what your body tells you to do," may lead the survivor to stiffen and go on alert because her body has been a source of pain, damage and suffering; her body has never seemed "trustworthy" to her.

The challenge for the educator comes in trying to present information and comfort measures to a group in such a way that no one feels left out, upset, incompetent, or "judged" by the teacher or group. An open, sensitive and flexible approach takes into account people's different learning styles, relationships with their partners, ways of relaxing, comfort with group activities, and sensitivities regarding emotionally charged topics. The most empathic and effective teachers acknowledge that particular topics, films or techniques may be unsuitable, unhelpful, or inappropriate for some class members. They validate that each woman and her partner are the best ones to evaluate the material and to accept, adapt, or reject the teachings to suit themselves.

When faced with students who seem difficult or challenging, the educator will improve her effectiveness if she can step back and think to herself, "This woman, man or couple is not getting very much from my class. They have a very good reason for their attitude or behavior. It may be early abuse. Although their behavior makes me uncomfortable, I must not take it personally, but I should think about the content of my class and my teaching style as it might seem to someone who has been sexually abused." Once she views all this through the eyes of a sexual abuse survivor, she will be sensitized to broaden her teaching without reducing effectiveness.

Following are specific suggestions for discussing sensitive material in a non-threatening and inclusive way. They will help to establish an open, welcoming, and accepting atmosphere in the class, and make it possible for survivors to benefit. It bears mentioning that these suggestions are valid for all class members, not only abuse survivors.

The educator should acknowledge to the class that there is no single correct way to give birth or to cope with labor, and that she will try to guide each woman or couple in finding their own best way. If she is successful, there will emerge a wide variety of coping styles and birth plans.

When introducing a videotape of a birth, she should prepare the group, "What you will see here is...," and acknowledge that some of the sounds or sights might be alarming or bothersome, and that it is okay to look away or to step out of the room (making sure the path to the exit is sufficiently lit). Afterwards, she should check with the group on how they felt while watching it, discuss any troubling parts, and invite anyone who found it particularly upsetting to speak with the teacher privately. One of the purposes of showing graphic films is to prepare students for the reality of labor, and for them to see how women cope. Such films do raise anxiety in most viewers, and the teacher should be available to process feelings that emerge.

When teaching or demonstrating prenatal perineal massage, she should state that even though the evidence demonstrates that it increases the likelihood of an intact perineum and can reduce the need for an episiotomy, some may find it distasteful. If so, they may prefer not to put themselves through it every day. One teacher normalized some people's negative reactions with "I messages": "When I first heard about perineal massage, I thought it was offensive. As I began to realize, however, that the massage was truly helpful, I decided to teach it. Finally, with positive feedback from my students and further studies that demonstrated its value, I have become convinced. However, I can certainly understand those of you who would rather not do it. The baby will come out whether you do perineal massage or not."

When discussing episiotomy, the educator should recognize that some class members will perceive the procedure as genital mutilation. If episiotomy is routinely performed by local doctors, the educator has a challenging task. After discussing reasons why some caregivers think it beneficial, and research results that support avoidance of episiotomy, the teacher will need to assist those (survivors or no) who want to avoid episiotomy. She should help them strategize ways to communicate their needs and wishes to their caregivers. Active listening and I-messages are usually more effective than producing medical research papers to "prove" that the doctor's practices are wrong. (See Chapter 7 for discussion of effective communication skills.)

Approaches similar to that described for discussion of episiotomy are also appropriate in teaching about other routines that cause controversy, such as intravenous fluids, rupture of the membranes, continuous electronic fetal monitoring.

It is better if the educator does not have or can put aside her own agenda, such as wanting to convince students not to have an episiotomy, or to have electronic fetal monitoring, or to unquestioningly accept her doctor's opinion or routine. When an educator loses sight of her role as educator and becomes an "indoctrinator" (in any direction—natural childbirth, high-tech childbirth, or anything else), students who do not share her bias (and even some who do) will turn away from her. Sexual abuse survivors are often suspicious of authority figures, and may detect and resent attempts at indoctrination more quickly than others, or they may be more easily hurt if they feel misled or betrayed by an authority figure.

As a prelude to teaching relaxation skills, the educator should offer options to ease any sense of vulnerability: "Find a comfortable position. You may prefer to lie on your side, or to sit, leaning against the wall or your partner. You may prefer to close your eyes or to keep them open. Do what makes you most comfortable." Such an invitation avoids singling out those people who may not want to lie down among strangers in a strange place.

A variety of coping strategies allows women to discover the most suitable ones for themselves. While some benefit from tuning in, yielding, relaxing into the pain, and remaining still and passive, this can be unacceptable to some abuse survivors, who may prefer distraction (which is really focusing her attention on something besides the contractions), focusing outward and being physically active during painful contractions. The key will be to help her use rhythmic movement, not sudden, jerky, irregular movements, and to find pleasing voices, sounds, touch, sights or thoughts to focus on. Focusing on specific patterns of rhythmic breathing (slow, light, others) or vocalizing may be reassuring.

The educator should become familiar with local resources, not only for all new parents, but specifically for sexual abuse survivors and for women who have had traumatic births. Resources may include this book, therapists, birth counselors, community mental health agencies, support groups, parenting classes, and self-help books.

Until the educator feels ready to help those who identify themselves as childhood sexual abuse survivors, she should not discuss the subject directly in class. When comfortable with her knowledge and aware of helpful resources, she should raise the topic. For example, in discussing emotions of labor, she might say, "Sometimes a history of sexual abuse comes up unexpectedly during labor and reminds a survivor in some way of her abuse. Some things can be done in advance to help ensure that it won't cause big problems. I'd be glad to talk to any of you privately about this." She should wait until the third or fourth class or until some rapport exists with class members before bringing this up. She might then offer referrals, or may invite the woman to do the Trigger Work (Chapter 10) with her.

The educator should encourage class members to prepare birth plans or letters to the staff, using concise language and good communication techniques (I messages). The plan should include a brief introductory paragraph—a message to the staff—that explains some things about the woman and her partner that will help the staff get to know them as individuals, and also to understand why the birth plan is important to them. It should also include a description of the woman's fears, issues, or concerns. Women who feel comfortable disclosing their sexual abuse history and the issues that have arisen from it usually find staff committed to make the birth as good an experience as possible. No one, however, should feel pressured to reveal any more information about herself than she feels comfortable disclosing. (See Appendix 3 for a birth plan form and Appendix 5 for 2 survivors' stories, along with excerpts of their birth plans.)

Many educators invite students to call and share their birth stories after the baby is born. Many also hold class reunions a few weeks after all the babies are born. Some women or couples will tell stories of disappointing or traumatic births; some may be angry or depressed. The educator should follow up with these people, knowing that some negative birth experiences may result in posttraumatic stress disorder (PTSD), or represent re-traumatization for abuse survivors. (Appendix 6 is a self-assessment for maternal distress after a difficult birth that can be used to explore symptoms of PTSD. See Chapter 10 for guidance on processing a negative birth experience, including the initial phone call and face-to-face counseling sessions. There are also guidelines for self-processing in that chapter.) Using good listening and feedback skills, the educator can validate the woman's perceptions and help her reframe the negative experiences. She should also be prepared to make appropriate referrals to helpful resources, if necessary.

Questions to Ask in Choosing Classes

Because some childbirth preparation classes are better suited than others to the needs of survivors, shopping for the right class makes sense. Beyond the usual questions about costs, schedule and location, the following may help a survivor to decide whether a class is right for her.

- Who sponsors the classes? A hospital, a group of caregivers, a consumer organization, an agency (public health, Red Cross) or an individual teacher in private practice?
- What are the teacher's credentials, training, and experience? Is she a certified childbirth educator? By which organization?
- Does the teacher attend births? Has she given birth? How long has she been teaching?
- How many students are in each class? If classes are large, does she have a knowledgeable assistant?
- What is the teacher's philosophy and approach? Does she emphasize the normalcy of birth and ways in which the parents help keep it normal, or the dangers of birth and the need for interventions to keep the birth from causing harm? Does she support active participation in pain management and decision-making by the parents, or the need to depend on the professionals to make decisions? Does she discuss the risks, benefits, and trade-offs of pain medications, interventions, and cesarean birth? Does she emphasize a particular "method" or approach (Lamaze, Bradley, Birthing From Within, Hypnobirthing, The 3 Rs, other)? Does she promote birth plans?
- How many weeks and hours is the class series? How much time is spent on information sharing and practice of comfort measures? Are postpartum recovery, newborn care and feeding covered?

- Is the teacher available by phone, e-mail, or in person for questions or counseling?
- What kind of follow-up does the teacher have with her students? A reunion after all the babies are born, phone follow-up, none?

After asking these questions, the pregnant woman will have an idea whether she will feel comfortable with the class.

If the Childbirth Educator Is a Survivor

Many childbirth educators are also abuse survivors. Some have successfully resolved or are working on the aftereffects; others have not. The former are often very empathic and effective teachers. However, unresolved abuse issues sometimes interfere with their effectiveness. If, as frequently happens to survivors, her birth experiences were traumatic, old wounds are reopened. Her own unresolved anger and hurt toward her doctor, midwife, nurse or partner may influence her teaching in a negative way. She may feel a need to warn her students about doctors or hospitals. The memories of helplessness, fear, pain or damage may make it impossible to teach about birth in a positive or reassuring manner. Such topics as circumcision and episiotomy may stimulate such negative feelings that she becomes excessively emotional in presenting them. Her attempts to present such emotionally charged issues in an unbiased way may not succeed.

Valid as her feelings are and significant as her hurt is, the childbirth class is not the place to work through these issues. That is not to say, however, that childhood sexual abuse survivors cannot be effective and well-liked teachers. They need to find appropriate ways to meet their own needs. One educator, who is an abuse survivor, realized that she could not be calm or objective about the topic of circumcision, nor could she be respectful to parents who planned to circumcise. She finally realized that neither she nor her students were benefiting. She would be upset before, during and after the class, and would receive poor evaluations as a consequence. She decided to ask a guest instructor to give the talk on circumcision. She explained to the class that as a childhood sexual abuse survivor, this procedure brought up traumatic associations for her. She would leave the class during the discussion.

Teachers with abuse issues need to have a safe place in which to air their concerns. When a childbirth educator announced to a group of fellow educators that she wanted to meet with other "survivor educators," four teachers met with her monthly for almost a year, providing peer support and sharing challenges of teaching.

Of course, high quality psychotherapy will help those educators who find their abusive pasts intruding into their daily lives and disturbing their sense of well-being. As they resolve their issues, they may become especially empathic teachers for all the women in their classes.

The Doula: Mothering the Mother

Laboring women and their babies unquestionably benefit from continual emotional support and physical comfort by caring, experienced, and knowledgeable people. A doula is such a person. Usually a woman, a doula is trained and experienced in providing childbirth support (birth doula) or care of a new family (postpartum doula). Even more important than her training are her warm, nurturing personality and her desire to be with laboring women or new families. The word "doula" is originally a Greek word referring to a household servant, but it has been adapted and incorporated into American English to refer to a woman caregiver of a laboring woman or new mother. Her purpose is to "mother the mother," bringing her knowledge, experience, kindness, and comfort skills to nurture a woman and her partner during this vulnerable and stressful time. The doula does not perform clinical tasks or give clinical advice.

Birth Doulas

Most birth doulas meet their clients (including the partner) two or three times before labor, to become acquainted and to establish how they will work together. They become familiar with the woman's or couple's birth plan and the role they would like the doula to play (how the doula and partner will work together; things that help the woman relax; any fears or concerns). Discussions may include fees, other services offered (for example, childbirth education and counseling, breastfeeding counseling, massage therapy, postpartum doula care), and a plan for keeping in touch.

Birth doulas are on call 24 hours a day and seven days a week, so they usually share call with a partner or work with a backup doula for times when they are unavailable. The couple often meets these doulas, as well.

In labor, the doula's continuous support, tailored to the woman's stated needs and her birth plan, reduces her fear and anxiety. The doula encourages and guides the woman and her partner, helps the woman cope with pain, and helps her get appropriate information before making decisions about her own care. Many scientific trials comparing doula-attended with non-doula-attended births found that the presence of the doula is associated with more favorable obstetric outcomes—fewer cesareans and instrumental deliveries and better newborn outcomes. Furthermore, studies that examined psychosocial outcomes in the mother found that the doula's presence throughout labor is associated with such favorable postpartum outcomes as: less postpartum depression, more positive assessments of her baby; more total breastfeeding on cue; greater satisfaction with the birth experience; enhanced self-esteem; and other benefits.

All these findings are especially significant for abuse survivors, who tend to be particularly challenged by many aspects of childbirth and parenting. Here are specific ways in which a doula's presence may benefit the woman with a history of sexual abuse:

- If distrust of authority figures is an issue, the doula serves as a go-between, tactfully assisting the woman and caregiver to understand each other.
- If abandonment or fears of being alone are issues, the doula's continuous presence and support are most reassuring. The woman's needs and interests are the number one concern of the doula.
- If control is an issue, the doula who is familiar with the woman's birth plan can help ensure that it is followed, by asking each nurse and caregiver if they have had a chance to read it. If it is not being followed, they remind the woman or staff. This allows the woman or her partner to address the problem directly with nurse or caregiver.
- If the doula is aware of the woman's triggers and her personal ("client-centered") strategies, she can assist the woman to utilize her strategies in a stressful situation. (See Chapter 10 for more on triggers and strategies.)
- If the woman permits it, the doula can inform the staff of the abuse and its impact on the woman, with the purpose of helping the staff to understand and respect her needs.
- By having a general awareness of the additional stressors borne by pregnant or laboring women who have been abused, the doula can be ready to adapt her care suitably to reduce the likelihood of re-traumatization.
- By meeting the woman's emotional needs during labor, the doula reduces the woman's distress and anxiety, reduces the associated effect of prolonged labor, and improves obstetric and newborn outcomes.

The search for the right birth doula begins with getting some names of doulas from caregivers, childbirth educators, and friends. The business pages or Yellow Pages of the telephone book may have listings including the words, "doulas," or "labor or childbirth support." Advertisements or listings in local newspapers that are targeted to expectant and new parents are another place to start. Doula organizations such as Doulas of North America (DONA), Lamaze International, the Association of Labor Assistants and Childbirth Educators (ALACE), Childbirth and Postpartum Professional Association (CAPPA), Birthworks, or the International Childbirth Education Association (ICEA) provide information and referrals to doulas. (Website addresses are in the Resources section.) The Internet is a rich source of information about doulas and www.DONA.org contains much information and a listing of DONA-Certified Doulas.

Questions to Ask a Birth Doula

Interviewing doulas usually involves some phone work and a face-to-face meeting. The following is taken from the DONA Website, and is published here with their permission:

- After establishing that she is available around your due date, ask the following questions over the telephone or in person:
- What training have you had? Are you certified? By whom?
- Tell me (us) about your experience with birth, personally and as a doula.
- What are the services you provide as a doula?
- May we meet with you to discuss our birth plans and the role you will play in supporting me (us) through childbirth?
- May we call you with questions or concerns before or after the birth?
- Which care providers have you worked with? In which hospitals have you attended births?

- When do you try to join women in labor? Do you come to our home or meet us at the hospital?
- Do you meet with me (us) after the birth to review the labor and answer questions?
- Do you work with one or more backup doulas (for times when you are not available)? May we meet them?
- What is your fee? Do you work on a sliding scale? Is any part of your fee refundable if you do not attend the birth? Does health insurance reimburse for doula services?
- May we have a list of previous clients for references? Be sure to call these references to gain insight into this doula's services.

When you and your partner meet the doula, pay particular attention to your personal perceptions:

- Is she kind, warm and enthusiastic?
- Is she knowledgeable?
- Does she communicate well?
- Is she a good listener?
- Is she comfortable with your choices or does she seem to have her own agenda?
- Do you feel comfortable with her?

You may want to interview more than one doula to find the right one for you.

Once the woman or couple chooses a doula, they may schedule one or more meetings to establish more personal and specific aspects of the doula's role, for example, how the doula and partner will work together; specific fears or personal concerns of the woman and how the doula may help with those; the woman's pain medication preferences and other items in her birth plan. This is when abuse issues might be brought up, if the woman wishes to do so.

It is not necessary for the woman to disclose her history to the doula, though she may decide to do so. In fact, the woman can disclose only what she wants her doula to know about her. The doula's role to serve the woman as the woman wishes. She is also there to assist the woman's partner as they wish.

Postpartum Doulas

Postpartum doulas are trained and experienced in the support and care of families with a newborn baby. They usually work with the family in their home for a few hours a day to full-time for one to several weeks. Some provide overnight help. Their usual tasks include advice and help on infant care and breast or formula feeding. They help the new mother to rest, care for older children, run errands, prepare nourishing meals, and do light house-keeping. They are trained to identify problems in the mother's recovery, her emotional state, or in the newborn, and can provide referrals, if necessary.

Survivors sometimes feel uneasy at the thought of having a relative stranger, who is an authority figure, in their homes, observing them and doing better at some of the parenting tasks. Others appreciate the doula's support and guidance, especially if they have no experience with babies or breastfeeding, or if they are having emotional difficulties, as described in Chapter 5. If a woman is interested but unsure, an opportunity to meet one or more postpartum doulas for an interview (with no obligation to hire that person) will help her decide if she will be comfortable with a postpartum doula.

The woman can get names of postpartum doulas from her caregiver, childbirth educator, hospital, or from newspaper advertisements, from Doulas of North America (DONA), or from the National Association of Postpartum Care Services (NAPCS), Childbirth and Parenting Professional Association (CAPPA), and Birthworks (Website addresses in the Resource Section).

Choosing a Postpartum Doula

Once the woman has names of postpartum doulas her first contact will probably be by phone or email. She can get the basic information on training, experience, credentials, and fees.

A prior interview of more than one postpartum doula will give the woman and her partner some choice and an opportunity to compare the doulas. There is usually no need for the woman to disclose her abuse history unless she wishes to do so. However, postpartum doulas who are aware of the impact of childhood sexual abuse on post partum may be more empathic than others. Such a doula can be especially helpful if the new mother is struggling with abuse memories, post-traumatic stress disorder, or other issues, along with the usual demands of post partum. Questions similar to those asked of a birth doula (above) are appropriate, but should be tailored to postpartum care of new parents and baby.

The woman may want to interview more than one post-partum doula to find the right one.

Postpartum doulas have had training and experience in helping women who are breastfeeding, and some are certified lactation consultants. They should be sensitive to unique stresses for survivors caused by breastfeeding. Complex or challenging problems with breastfeeding may be handled best by a breastfeeding consultant. The next section covers some of the potential stressors and some helpful solutions.

The Breastfeeding Consultant

A breastfeeding, or lactation consultant is a woman (often a nurse, childbirth educator, postpartum doula, or a lay woman who has breastfed successfully) who is trained and experienced in all aspects of breastfeeding. Many are certified by the International Lactation Consultant Association (ILCA) or La Leche League International (LLLI). (See the Resources Section for addresses.) Breastfeeding consultants recognize the benefits of breastfeeding to baby and mother, understand the physical processes and emotional aspects. They also are experts in correcting the problems and challenges that sometimes interfere with the successful initiation and continuation of breastfeeding. Their theoretical knowledge, practical skills, and experience equip them to find the best solution to almost any breastfeeding problem, or recognize those rare situations in which total breastfeeding may not succeed and provide appropriate solutions.

How to Find a Breastfeeding Consultant

Many hospitals have breastfeeding consultants, who can help new mothers. Some also follow up with home visits or at least a telephone consultation. Some pediatric or family medicine practices have a breastfeeding consultant, as do some public health departments and Women, Infants and Children (WIC) programs. Private breastfeeding consultants practice independently. The latter are often listed in the telephone book, and are well known to many childbirth educators and caregivers. As with all caregivers, one breastfeeding consultant's personality and style may be more appealing than another's. The woman should not feel stuck with one consultant if she is uncomfortable with her. It is appropriate to seek another one if available.

Breastfeeding consultants' fees are often covered by health insurance, especially if a doctor or midwife has made a referral.

How a Breastfeeding Consultant Helps the Abuse Survivor

Even without realizing their client's background, breastfeeding consultants frequently assist abuse survivors with feeding problems. A history of sexual abuse can play a role in many of the common problems associated with breastfeeding, such as inadequate milk supply, sore nipples, inability to recognize the baby's feeding cues, and dissatisfaction with breastfeeding. Other complications of early abuse, such as postpartum mood disorder, low self-confidence, and diminished ability to cope with stress, may also impair breastfeeding.

(See Chapter 5 for more on how early sexual abuse may influence a woman's feelings about breastfeeding and her ability to do so.)

Many abuse survivors are committed to breastfeeding. Some see it as the best mothering they can give their children. Others see that successful breastfeeding constitutes another personal triumph over their abuse. Common problems in early breastfeeding, however, are sometimes especially challenging, because of their abuse history. Many women at the outset are highly motivated and determined to succeed, but once they actually begin to breastfeed, may feel unexpected ambivalence. For example, although they believe deeply in the benefits to the baby, the requirement that they freely share their breasts with someone else, even their baby, may be unsettling or even sickening.

Consultants should be aware of how an abuse history may manifest itself during breastfeeding. If a number of symptoms are present in the new mother (as described in Chapter 5), the breastfeeding consultant should recognize the possibility of sexual abuse. Even if it turns out that the woman has not been abused, individualized care and advice will still be appropriate. The consultant does not need to ask the woman if she has been abused, even though the woman might choose to reveal that information. The consultant's response to such a disclosure is critical to a positive, problem-solving relationship. (See Chapters 3, 6 and 7 for a discussion of disclosure and appropriate ways to respond.)

Breastfeeding consultants who are most helpful to survivors are those who are flexible, creative, patient, sensitive to the mother's concerns, and able to see the whole picture. A consultant who has a single agenda, who believes that nothing less than total breastfeeding is acceptable, and that all women can and should breastfeed may do more harm than good. One with poor listening skills, or who handles a woman's breast without permission, or who has little concern about modesty, will likely irritate or offend. If so, the woman might seek another breastfeeding consultant, or give feedback.

Amelia

The following story shows how a creative and sensitive breastfeeding consultant helped Amelia find a solution to her abuse-related difficulties with breastfeeding.

Amelia came to resent night feedings. She hated being awakened and being required to allow her baby to suckle at her breasts. In fact, she felt nauseated during nighttime feedings and she devised ways to avoid them. She tried awakening the baby for a feeding just before she went to bed. She mixed her milk with baby cereal to make thin gruel and fed it to her baby in a bottle with a large-holed nipple, in hopes of filling him up enough to sleep through the night. She tried ignoring his cries until he would fall back to sleep. She placed him a crib in another room and shut the door between them so she would not hear him. None of these things worked. Amelia, tired and frustrated, resented her baby even more. She became very worried about how this desperate issue was affecting her feelings about her baby.

When her baby began losing weight, Amelia was referred to a thoughtful and sensitive breastfeeding consultant. Although Amelia did not disclose her own history of nighttime abuse by her father, the consultant recognized the possibility. Realizing that Amelia's relationship with her baby was in jeopardy, along with her baby's well-being, she helped Amelia work out a plan in which her husband would sleep in the baby's room and give the first night feeding with a bottle of expressed breast milk. Her husband would then come to their bed and set the alarm clock for 2 or 3 hours after the feeding, at which time Amelia would awaken and take the baby into the living room for a feeding.

This solution worked fairly well. The alarm clock was more acceptable to Amelia than her baby's demands. Sometimes the baby awakened before the alarm went off but Amelia resented those times less and less, probably because her needs to have her concerns treated empathically and respectfully were met. She was taken seriously and was aided in finding a solution that worked for her family. The baby thrived and Amelia's resentment gave way to deep attachment. Amelia appreciated the validation and creative problem-solving by her breastfeeding consultant. She breastfed for 16 months.

Women who are committed to breastfeeding but who find it painful or reminiscent of their abuse sometimes pump their milk and feed it to the baby in a bottle, as a way to feed their baby without negative associations.

Other women find it impossible to share their breasts with their babies and cannot bring themselves to pump milk. For them, the benefits of breastmilk do not outweigh the disadvantages of a strained relationship. These mothers can be shown the value of holding the baby close while formula feeding and making feeding time a time of warmth, love and joy.

The breastfeeding consultant who has good rapport with the woman and who sees as paramount the goal of a loving relationship between mother and baby, will recognize the rare occasions when a history of abuse complicates breastfeeding and prevents its success. She will use creativity and sensitivity to help the woman find the best of all options.

Massage Therapists and Body Workers

By Guest Author, Carole Osborne-Sheets,
author of *Pre-and Perinatal Massage Therapy*

Traumatic birth experiences and sexual abuse assault a woman's body as well as her emotions. When both tissues and feelings need to heal, bodyworkers and massage therapists can be ideal facilitators. They specialize in touch methodologies combined with education of their clients on the structure and function of the affected body parts. Their professional skills increase their clients' awareness and understanding of the connection between their feeling states, memories, and physical experience.

Appropriate bodywork helps pregnant survivors in these ways:

- reduce anxiety and pain;
- reach deeper relaxation states;
- improve body awareness;
- embody positive touch experiences;
- resolve and discharge unproductive traumatic memories and feelings;
- physically and emotionally prepare for childbirth and mothering.

Women with a traumatic touch history often cope by numbing themselves. They have steeled themselves against pain and humiliation to the point where they continually shut out much physical awareness. To armor effectively, such a woman clenches her jaw and throat and freezes her diaphragm to diminish both breath and feeling. Tension in other muscles, especially in the chest, inner thighs, abdomen, and pelvic floor often complete her defense.

Relaxation of these areas can be extremely difficult for such a defended woman.

Bodyworkers skilled in working with abuse survivors can gently and patiently help decrease this muscle tension and improve overall relaxation ability. The one-on-one nature of body therapy is ideal for individualized breathing instruction while coaxing chronically tight respiratory muscles to ease their grip. Appropriate deep tissue and other therapeutic techniques melt painful pelvic and leg tension. This can be especially helpful with fearful women who are unintentionally resistant to vaginal exams or anxious about birth's inherent "letting go."

Consciously directed bodywork helps reacquaint the woman with her body. Modulations in depth, direction, duration, rhythm, speed, and intensity of touch create a rich influx of information and corresponding responses and awareness. This heightens her perception and stimulates new body understanding and awareness. In this safe environment for self-exploration, the bodywork client can gradually rediscover numb, neglected, or tense body areas. As they work together, the client can practice distinguishing what she experiences as positive and negative touch. Because the client controls the pace and nature of the work, she can alter the experience, stopping altogether if desired. This also helps to improve her ability to communicate her awareness and feelings.

Some survivors, rather than numbing themselves to their pain and hurt feelings, become hypersensitive to touch and exhibit a low tolerance to pain. During bodywork or massage, such clients sometimes flash back to traumatic events that flood them with piercingly intense memories, body sensations and feelings. Productive processing of this type of experience requires a practitioner who can help to defuse these memories by assisting the woman in staying with her sensations while encouraging emotional expression. Active resolution can begin to come when unsaid words and sounds or decades-old gestures and actions slip out. After the feeling and sensation states normalize, touch and dialogue are critical to help the client assimilate the intense experience.

Lessons learned in this type of somato-emotional integration directly improve women's birthing experiences. Discharged of some of their traumatic energy, such memories have a less present impact, improving both baby's and mother's prenatal and birthing outcomes. Their resolution also helps women to anticipate and recognize threatening or negative triggers and to develop skills for avoiding or responding to those situations in new, more empowering ways.

Reva Rubin, RN, former nursing professor, has documented her conclusions about the positive impact of appropriate touch during pregnancy. From extensive clinical observation, she has concluded that those women who receive warm, responsive, supportive physical contact prenatally and during labor tend to interact with their infants similarly. Positive physical contact, therefore, might facilitate disruption of the repeating abusive cycles so prevalent in the families of the sexually abused.

Many abuse survivors appreciate bodywork alone or as an adjunct to other forms of counseling. For best results, pregnant women and their healthcare providers should seek a practitioner who is educated and experienced in trauma survivors' special needs. In addition, comprehensive training in the safety concerns of prenatal massage therapy is also essential. Practitioner referrals are available (see Resources list). To help the woman or care provider to choose, they should ask practitioners for a resume, including their education and experience, professional references, and/or a consultation prior to beginning therapy to ensure a feeling of safety and confidence with that individual.

Conclusion

Childbearing women have access to valuable services from a number of paraprofessionals. Sexual abuse survivors will benefit more from the people who provide these services if those people are knowledgeable about the impact of early abuse. Careful selection of these people and knowledge of their areas of expertise are important factors in maximizing the benefits they can provide.

9
Self-Help Methods to Prevent and Manage Distress During Childbearing

- During the prenatal exam, I panicked and had a flashback to smells, sounds, and the same body sensations from my childhood bedroom.
- I don't know what's wrong with me. When I felt the baby move, I was overcome with intense feelings of sadness. It was hard to stop crying.
- Every time I imagined giving birth I felt unusual tension, my heart beat faster, I almost couldn't breathe.

Anxiety, fright, panic, uncertainty, helplessness, inability to act, and distrust can catch the survivor unaware and throw her into distress and despair. Other people perceive her reactions as inappropriate and exaggerated. This chapter offers a variety of self-help techniques to recognize and allay these automatic reactions, or to prevent them in the first place. The techniques fall into these general categories:

- *Exploring and transforming symptoms* to discover what they can tell the survivor about her real needs and how to meet them

- *Stress management strategies*, mental and physical activities that ease tension in the body and relax the mind and reduce the likelihood of being overwhelmed by unexpected physical and emotional reactions
- *Safety exercises*, which provide a way for the woman to feel emotionally safe during this period
- *Self-nurturing and self-care activities* to help the abuse survivor maintain her sense of self-value
- *Emotional safety techniques*, to help the survivor discover the importance of emotional safety and tailor techniques to her specific needs
- *Grounding techniques* to help the woman feel more fully in the present and avoid being re-triggered to past memories
- *Containment tools*, which enable the survivor to contain or diminish the emotional flooding that often accompanies flashbacks or remembered events
- *Panic attack management skills* to recognize and remain centered during these frightening episodes
- *Anger management techniques*, to facilitate the release of anger in appropriate harmless ways
- *Breaking out of old patterns or beliefs*, ways to help survivors recognize self-damaging reactions and develop different and more useful ways of responding

The goals of these techniques are to empower the woman, to avoid being re-traumatized by medical procedures or childbirth events, and to avoid feeling discounted or demeaned. She learns to safely protect her boundaries, deal openly with concerns and feelings, problem-solve appropriately, and avoid potential distress. By developing a sense of control rather than powerlessness, the woman can achieve a healing childbirth experience. These techniques can be used in conjunction with psychotherapy or other healing methods.

Fundamental to her success in mastering many of these

techniques is to separate past experiences and responses from the present. Reacting to stressful new situations, such as pregnancy, birth, or post partum, the survivor may at times be flooded with negative emotions and body sensations without any awareness that they are rooted in her childhood abuse. Automatically reacting to a stressful event in the same way she did as a child is a set-up for re-traumatization. By recognizing when her feelings and responses are related to early abuse, and mastering new ways to avoid reverting to these old patterns, she can stay grounded in the present and bring her adult self to these situations. Then the survivor is less likely to be overwhelmed or feel helpless when stressed.

When Are Self-help Methods Not Useful?

There are situations when self-help methods are not appropriate, adequate, or useful. For example, if a survivor is facing issues that are potentially dangerous to herself or others, or if she has a mental illness that is best managed with medications and/or psychiatric care, then embarking on a self-help path is not advisable. If at any time, one is triggered by feelings she cannot manage on her own, she should consult a qualified professional until she achieves stability.

The Concept of the Inner Child or Child Self

Success in using many of the self-help techniques depends on understanding the concept of the "inner child" or the adult's "child self." When upsetting circumstances or strong reactions occur in adulthood, the woman may feel and think very much as she did at a younger age, when she was being abused. She may have difficulty distinguishing the needs of her adult self to be calm, and to communicate effectively from the reactions of her child self (to fight back, to clam up, to dissociate). For the abuse survivor, the childhood feelings were largely trauma- and fear-based, and self-protective.

Nora

Nora was vivacious, outgoing and friendly. She laughed a lot, often inappropriately at her own expense. For example, when describing to her co-worker the distressing and painful birth of her first child—an attempted out-of-hospital birth that ended with a transfer to the hospital, an epidural, Oxytocin, episiotomy, and a vacuum extractor delivery—she emphasized the foolishness of trying to labor without drugs and laughed that she could have thought it was a good idea, but "now I know I'm a wimp—bring on the drugs!" She laughingly characterized herself as screaming and writhing as if she were dying. Her co-worker expressed concern for Nora, who laughed it off. In fact, the whole experience had been terrifying for Nora, but the only way she could talk about it was to cover up her terror with humor. This old pattern had begun during her childhood.

When she was a child, her uncle, who lived in the same household, frequently forced her to perform oral sex. She was helpless until he let her go. She could not avoid him. He told her she was asking for it and threatened that no one would believe her if she "tattled" on him. She felt completely discounted and powerless, and learned to act as if nothing had happened. She repressed memories of the abuse.

She carried the feeling into adulthood that she—the real Nora—did not matter. It became a pattern for her to cover up her true feelings by deflecting personal conversations away from herself, not allowing herself or others to take her seriously. When she laughed at herself, even in distressing circumstances, her friends took her cues and laughed along with her, which reinforced her feelings that she didn't matter, and that she had no "real" friends.

After the sudden death of her uncle, which plunged her into depression and guilt, she began to remember him as cruel and disgusting, and began to recall the abuse. She entered psychotherapy. With help, she began to realize that her reactions to his abuse and his threats had become ingrained in her and were expressed in self-damaging ways. She was stuck in the only survival techniques available to her as a child. Now, as an adult, she learned to identify situations in which her "inner child self" responses backfired and brought more hurt on herself. She worked on separating the past from the present, and replacing her old patterns with more adult expressions of her true feelings. She found people to be more empathic and supportive than she ever knew, and began to feel worthy of their caring.

As Nora found, a survivor can learn to recognize these inner child responses and master appropriate ways to separate them from her present circumstances. She then gains a sense of internal safety and self-confidence.

Exploring Symptoms

During pregnancy survivors can learn to explore and understand the meaning of distressing emotional reactions and physical symptoms that have no apparent organic cause. Of course, the woman should check with her medical caregiver to rule out any physical problem that requires medical attention before trying self-help activities.

Communicating with the Symptom

Sometimes, a woman can focus on a particular painful or problematic area with the intention of allowing it to reveal what she needs in order to relieve the pain or distress. She allows herself to relax in a quiet place and to imagine the painful part "talking to her" or imagining it in a position of comfort, and then, imagining what gets in the way of this comfort.

Learning about symptoms using imagery

- Allow yourself to become as relaxed as possible in a position of comfort. Take a deep breath, release tension, and close your eyes.
- Imagine yourself in a place of safety or with a guide or helper.
- See the painful or problematic part in your imagination.
  - If that part had a color, what color would it be?
  - If it had a shape, what shape would it be?
  - If it had a temperature, what would it be?
  - If it had a texture, what would it be like?
  - If it had a sound, what sound would it make?
  - If it had a message or a voice, what would it say?

Learn as much as possible about the meaning of this symptom or discomfort.

Transforming the symptom

Now, imagine what the symptom or discomfort would be like if it were better.

- Taking your time, imagine what color, shape, temperature, texture, and sound it would have.
- If it had a message or voice, what would it say or want you to know?
- Imagine changing it gradually to make it better.

Practice this to develop the skill of shifting the symptom to a more comfortable state should it recur, or to make the changes in your life that will alleviate the distress.

Carol

Carol was troubled by almost constant back pain for months during pregnancy. When she did the above exercise, she imagined a big bag of bricks preventing her from releasing the pain. The message was that she was carrying too much work in her life right now and her back was saying, "Let me rest." She "listened" to this "request" and began to "remove" the bricks, literally by reducing her workload and obligations and figuratively, by using imagery to lift off the bricks one by one until the load was truly lighter. Her pain diminished.

Using Art to Understand and Transform Symptoms

By drawing or using other art forms to create images or symbols of the symptoms, women can also gain insight into their meaning.

- Draw the symptom symbolically or with colors.
- Draw the symptom all healed.
- Draw, in some symbolic way, what the symptom needs to get better.
- Draw or represent symbolically any obstacle to healing.
- Develop a symbol or drawing of overcoming the obstacle.
- Re-draw the symptom healed, adding any new aspects of the healed symptom that evolved, such as more strength, etc.
- Imagine, if desired, stepping into the healed drawing and sensing the comfort of the healed aspect.

Catherine

Catherine used this technique for her leg pains. She drew a picture of her legs, using colors of flaming red, tinged with black. She then drew the colors of her legs all healed. The colors changed to blue and green, tinged with yellow. Next was a drawing of what she needed to do to change the pain colors to the healed colors. She drew stick figures of pushing her mother's hands away. Her mother had been her abuser. She then drew a series of small drawings that showed the colors changing to health. Every time she felt some leg pain, she recalled the healing colors and the pain diminished.

Non-dominant Hand Drawings

A number of survivors have found non-dominant hand drawings (scribbles, words, doodles, shapes, colors) illustrative of their inner child's or inner parts' worries.

By first accessing these, and then using the dominant hand's response (through drawings, colors, words, shapes, or symbols) the survivor's adult self can respond, providing comfort, validation, or other aids. Developing non-dominant hand to dominant hand communication, an inner dialogue can take place, which can accentuate healing hitherto unrevealed concerns.

Exercise

Move into a reflective quiet state and gently ask yourself how you are feeling right now, perhaps before going to see a care provider for a prenatal exam (or any other situation that has evoked some distress).

- With your non-dominant hand, using any medium you prefer, place on paper some symbol or representation of how you feel. (Draw a picture, design, scribble, doodle, shapes, colors.)

- If you have a connection with an inner child part, let that part express itself in this way.
- Now with your non-dominant hand, jot down any words that express the feelings that accompany your designs. Use as much paper as you want. Don't let an inner critic stop you.
- Continue to play with your drawings; make as many as you wish.
- When you have finished, review with your adult mind what you have expressed.
- Using your dominant hand in your adult state, draw designs, colors, etc. that represent ways to heal, help, and resolve those worries and feelings.
- Add words, ideas, or solutions to help. Allow your adult self or wise protective self to give comforting messages, holding, kindness, and understanding to the part that has been hurting.

Self-Care

Survivors need to recognize their changing needs during pregnancy and identify the activities and people that help them feel more nurtured.

Self-nurturing activities are extremely important for all women during the perinatal period, but especially for the survivor whose memories of abuse may be evoked and create anxiety and strong reactions. These needs are grouped into 5 categories—emotional, physical, social, mental, and spiritual. Survivors can make a list that addresses these areas as a self-help exercise.

This should be a relaxing activity without pressure to add more to one's life, but rather to examine the quality of one's life right now. One woman began to take stock to discover what could ease any demands to help her relax and add more pleasure to her life. Her focus was on her emotional and social needs. She realized she wanted more emotional sharing with her husband, more affectionate holding and talking. Socially, she wanted to plan some fun but quiet activities, too, such as going to a movie or having new friends over (a couple with a new baby who had moved into the house next door). She wanted her husband to be more available for joy and fun.

Another woman realized that she had some important physical needs. She noted that she needed to rest more each day; she wanted a massage once a week; she had to say no to tasks at work that felt too strenuous (such as evening meetings). She also gave herself permission to let go of more of the household tasks and to engage her husband's help. In this case, he was most eager to participate, wanting her to feel better.

Still another survivor addressed her mental and spiritual self-care needs. She recognized her desire to spend some time writing poetry, a creative activity that she once loved but hadn't given herself time for in a long while. Spiritually, taking some time to meditate and commune with an inner spiritual figure was extremely important to her.

This process validates the importance of nurturing the self—of re-parenting, in a way—and becomes an internal realization of the importance of giving TLC (tender loving care) to the self. For one woman as for many survivors, the self-nurturing exercise helped her become aware of her needs, and facilitated her sensitivity to the nurturing needs of her unborn child. By recognizing these different levels of need, the survivor in some way is sending an internal message to the unborn infant that its mother can take care of herself and the infant, too.

For each survivor, the simple act of thinking about different needs is a way to validate them. However, these concepts are intended only as ideas for ways to take care of herself, not to add pressures on herself. Survivors can simply choose one or none, but find their own way to meet some heretofore unrecognized needs. One woman realized that sitting in her garden for a few minutes every day gave her immense pleasure and a sense of peace. For another woman, taking a warm, soothing bath helped her feel comforted and nurtured.

Survivors may make a sheet with the following categories or other categories of their choice.

Ways to Nurture Myself

- Activities I enjoy
- People that I enjoy
- Places that I enjoy
- To nurture myself emotionally I....
- To relax myself physically I....
- To stimulate myself mentally I....
- To inspire myself spiritually I....
- To gratify my social needs I....

Once her list is complete, she may prioritize it in order to manage her choices without pressure.

Maintaining Emotional Safety

Throughout this book we address methods to help the survivor gain a sense of external control and safety. This section describes ways for women to gain a sense of internal control and safety.

As we have seen, many survivors, even though they may have no conscious memory, have emotional and sensory access to the memory of themselves as a child being abused. Often the distressing feelings they experience in the present moment are reactions to those memories from childhood. During particular events related to childbearing, some survivors appear to regress to that earlier emotional state, and to experience the same state of trauma they experienced as children. Feeling threatened, they may react, but may be unaware at a conscious level of the origin of their response.

Some emotional or physical symptoms may also represent aspects of the child self that need to communicate to the adult self. It is helpful for the survivor to learn how to listen to the needs or fears of her inner child self that are being retriggered by something in the present. She also needs mechanisms to remind herself that she is in the present and safe, as well as methods to reduce distressing emotional or physical symptoms.

Karen

Karen's story illustrates how she learned some methods to alleviate her severe anxiety and pelvic pain during pregnancy, and others to create safety for her child self. Even before pregnancy, Karen suffered from chronic pelvic pain and constipation, probably as a result of the extreme tension she held in her pelvic area. In therapy, Karen had learned to communicate with her inner child self and realized that her pelvic tension and pain stemmed from the rigid body position and breath-holding she would maintain as a child during sexual abuse by her father. The penetration felt like an "ice pick." As she neared term, she sensed a growing fear related to the pain of labor.

Listening to her inner self, she realized that her fear was about how to handle pain in her pelvis and the birth canal. Although it upset her, Karen felt somewhat encouraged that she was learning ways that she could listen to the meaning of these symptoms. She could now understand that anxiety and tension were related to her past trauma. The symptoms were like a "teacher" for her, reminding her that she now needed to prepare as an adult for labor. She also needed to keep her inner child self safe as the adult Karen explored ways to be more secure during labor. She was a perfect candidate for learning self-help comfort measures, while remaining open to using effective medications for pain relief. Her new plan gave her hope. It consisted of three goals: 1) to feel safe; 2) to stay relaxed; and 3) to have a variety of methods, either non-pharmacological or medical, to relieve discomfort or pain during each stage of labor.

Karen, now in her adult state, could explore and practice with her partner and doula numerous methods for pain relief. She first learned ways to reassure her inner child. Using her imagination she visualized a "safe place" in an imaginary playroom with her beloved grandmother where her inner child could safely stay during this period. She then learned relaxation methods, such as relaxation breathing, muscle tension releasing exercises, and visualizations. She used the imagery of stepping into cool water, feeling a comfortable numbing sensation. She also visualized her cervix opening like a beautiful tropical flower, and her tissues and ligaments becoming supple and stretchy.

She practiced position changes with her partner and learned about medications and epidurals. She was encouraged to accept an epidural, as a way to take care of herself. She learned that a light epidural might not sufficiently block the pain in her perineum, and explored the possibility of increasing the block late in labor as the baby was coming down the birth canal. Since Karen could now confront this fear and tension and approach the pain of labor differently, her anxiety and pelvic tension decreased, and her confidence grew.

A survivor might ask her inner child; "What would help you feel more comfortable, or more safe?" "What do you need from me?" She may receive or sense an answer or have some insight to help this inner part of herself trust that she will be O.K.

Surprisingly, listening to her inner child may be a reminder to the survivor to be more nurturing of herself as an adult. In a sense, by listening to her inner child's needs, she will probably also recognize some important nurturing or self-care needs of her own.

Three Levels of Emotional Safety

For the pregnant survivor, the concept of internal safety has three levels of meaning. The first represents how the adult self can create an internal feeling of being safe. The second means creating a safe place for her inner child self. The third means creating a sense of safety around her baby. Using her imagination and employing her senses to visualize a place or situation of safety, the survivor experiences much of what she would feel if she were actually in that situation. As she imagines and visualizes such an activity, her brain sends messages to all parts of her body to act as though she were actually in that experience. For example:

- Imagining being in a peaceful place can actually reduce stress hormones and put her *adult self* — her body and mind — into a physically relaxed mode.
- Imagining a safe place for one's *inner child self* as well as for the adult self creates a healthy separation from distressing memories or current triggers.

- To create a sense of safety for the *baby*, women may visualize an aura, light, or energy surrounding the baby, or use some other symbolic way to imagine their baby is being held in safety. They may talk to the baby with reassuring messages, or pray for their baby to create a sense of safety.

While some people use their imagination for creating images of safety, others use art and drawings or music. Still others start by writing down the attributes of a safe place, a person, or good feelings and then imagine experiencing them.

One can also begin by using open-ended, self-reflective questions, or enjoy letting ideas or images appear in her mind, follow them for a while and see which ones feel right.

"When I am safe, I..."

"Images or places that help me feel safe"

"In what situation or scene do I feel most comfortable?"

"If I could surround myself with safety, calm and peace, what would it be like?"

"What would I like my baby to know?"

Other Sources of Safety

Power animals or symbols

Helpful people

Strong structures

Inner guides (a wise part, an inner healer, an inner loving or protective part or an inner power)

Spiritual figures

One woman often retreated from expressing her needs. When asked to think about what animal, person, or symbol represented a strong voice for her, she thought of a beautiful, powerful panther. Applying this image to a real situation, she could visualize herself becoming stronger and more able to say what she needed to say.

The "safe place" exercise

A survivor may use her imagination to think of an environment that creates a feeling of safety, calm, and peace. Perhaps it is a time of enjoyment and comfort at a beach, in a garden, in a special place in nature, or in a favorite place in their home, or even a lovely memory from the past, but most importantly as a sanctuary where one feels protected, relaxed and safe. Some survivors choose to include a special person with them. This person might be from their present or past. In these reveries, if the survivor develops a scene where all the sensory connections with the environment are intensified, it enhances the safe place exercise and makes it easier to recall at other times.

Developing special place imagery can help during labor as a reminder to feel both safe and relaxed. This visualization works well along with some stress-releasing mechanisms such as relaxation breathing and muscle tension-releasing exercises (described later in this chapter).

Some survivors create a sense of safety by imagining themselves inside a large pink bubble, surrounded by light, choosing only what or whom they allow to enter, and keeping distressing feelings or memories outside. The choices are as varied as the women.

Containment

Containment is a mental process designed to keep fears, intense feelings, or abuse-related memories from overwhelming the woman and preventing her from functioning effectively. Containment strategies figuratively remove, reduce, or put aside the distress when it is triggered, until a better time when the survivor can deal with it.

Sara

Sara, who recalled abuse that began at age ten, was having such painful Braxton-Hicks contractions around her due date that she panicked at the prospect of labor.

After several hours of distressing contractions, at the suggestion of her midwife, she called a therapist. During a session with the therapist, she had, for the first time, flashbacks of abuse at age four. She was shocked and saddened by these memories, but it was clear that with the birth so imminent, this was not the time to explore the new memories or do intensive psychotherapy. The therapist helped Sara come up with a containment strategy.

With Sara's permission, the therapist recorded the session, so Sara could listen to it later. The therapist asked if she could think of a place where her "self" as a frightened little girl (represented by the tape) could be safe until there was a better time to tend to her. Sara thought of a small desk at home that had a locked drawer. The therapist suggested that she place the tape there with the promise that "Little Sara" would be safe and cared for until the time was right to help her heal. Sara's contractions subsided for several days, after which she went on to have a normal labor.

Madeleine

Madeleine, who had been abused as a teenager, was a single mother with an unwanted pregnancy. She had very little interest in the pregnancy, and almost no support system. There were few positive life experiences that she could draw on to help her feel safe or empowered. The counselor wondered if she had any fairy-tale characters that she particularly liked or any literary or TV heroines. She replied that she liked the story of Cinderella. Madeleine was encouraged to imagine that she was a princess living in a special castle where she was very comfortable and safe and every wish was granted. She was the most important person in the castle and was well protected. She had many beautiful and surprising things there and they were only for her personal use. Around the castle was a large moat that contained a big iceberg. Whenever Madeleine felt any fear, she was to send it into the iceberg where it would eventually melt away. After a few weeks of using this imagery of a safe place as well as a container for her anxieties, a surprising change occurred. Madeleine began to feel very close to her baby and much of her fear subsided. She began to take an interest in self-care and planning for the birth.

Containing or putting a shield or imaginary boundaries around upsetting feelings or memories is one way to temporarily reduce the distress connected to them. In highly stressful situations these strategies can allow the woman to safely postpone dealing with them until a more appropriate time.

After "containing" their feelings, both Sara and Madeleine were able to practice mental and physical relaxation exercises that continued to reduce stress and give them a greater sense of control.

Other Examples of Containment Techniques

One woman contained her fears by imagining herself placing them in a locked safe. Another imagined sending all her fears, memories and angry feelings on a big jet across the country, in order to keep them out of the birthing room. Another woman put her distressed and hurt self in the arms of the Virgin Mary, which gave her an enormous sense of comfort. One woman imagined that these flooding and panicky feelings were like water from the garden hose; she could turn the nozzle and control the amount of water, turning down the discomfort. Another survivor imagined that she had a radio and could immediately turn down the volume as soon as the sound or feelings got too loud. This gave her a sense of instant control of overly strong emotions. Still another survivor imagined putting all her memories and fears into a big quilt, folding the quilt, placing it in a large trunk, and locking the trunk until she was ready to open it and deal with them.

Eight Step Visualization to Reduce Symptoms

Often it is not possible for a woman to use the relaxation or visualization exercises she has learned in preparing for birth until she has safely "contained" the enormously distressing flood of feelings or memories or other anxieties. A good example of a distressing fear that may trouble a survivor is of vomiting during labor.

Many survivors have heard of vomiting during labor and worry that this could happen to them, especially if they have vomited frequently during pregnancy, as Lois had.

Lois

Lois is a survivor of early sexual abuse, who felt sick and vomited every time she was abused by her stepfather. She did not recognize the connection between the vomiting after being abused and the vomiting during labor that she feared. She only knew that some women in labor do vomit occasionally while others vomit after every contraction. Her doctor tried to reassure her, pointing out that constant vomiting is very rare, she knew it was unpredictable, and worried that she would vomit uncontrollably during labor. She planned to use mint tea, acupressure and medication if needed, but she also wanted to use guided imagery techniques.

Most people do better with visualizations if they have someone to guide them the first time. After becoming familiar with their own images of comfort, they can more easily call them up during labor or other stressful times. Visualizations work better if practiced a few minutes a day for a number of weeks beforehand. The images presented here are specific ones that Lois came up with. Other survivors will discover and use their own.

The following is a script for an eight-part visualization exercise that survivors (or their guides or counselors) can use for various symptoms or concerns. Here, it is geared toward Lois' specific concerns.

1. Imagine yourself relaxing and moving to a safe and peaceful place.

Let yourself move into a very comfortable position...take a natural and cleansing relaxing breath...enjoy letting every out-breath be a relaxing breath. Gently close your eyes...take a little tour of your body, and notice any tension. As you take the next breath in and then breathe out, let the warm air melt the tension away. In a naturally easy way, let an image of a very peaceful place come into your mind...a place where you feel completely safe and deeply relaxed. Perhaps this is a place you have visited or imagined before or one that just comes into your mind now. Allow yourself to go to that place...following a gradual stairway or a lovely path. Let yourself gently drift or walk to this pleasing place. Perhaps you might like to count mentally backwards from ten to one as a way of deepening your relaxation as you move to this place of refuge 10...9...8...7...6...5...1. When you find yourself there, just nod your head as a sign to yourself that you have reached this sanctuary. Enjoy experiencing yourself there with all your senses. You can bring to this place any aspect of comfort you like. If this is in nature or a special room or a garden, enjoy all the colors, and all the pleasing shapes. Breathe in the freshness of the air, the special aroma...helping you become more relaxed. Let the sounds you hear be comforting sounds for you... and whatever sounds you hear inside or outside, let them invite you to go deeper into a peaceful reverie...and take all the time you want to become even more comfortable. If you would like or if it would be helpful, you might imagine a special safe place for any younger child part where this part can be completely comfortable...and very protected. You can bring in a "helper" or older safe part to be with your younger child part if you wish. (By "child part," we are referring to your inner child, or a part of yourself as a child, that was hurt and defenseless. By "older part," we mean a protective, mature adult part of yourself that can understand the real situation.)

In this part of the exercise, Lois imagined herself in the top room of a beautiful tall white tower where she was very safe and comfortable, with wide windows, a beautiful view of lush valleys and hills, very fertile lands, and, in the floors below, all her younger child selves were safe and taken care of.

2. The next step is to ask questions of the symptom, by using direct communication with the part of the body, or a part of the self that knows its meaning, or by communicating with an inner guide.

Imagine that in your special place there is a path...or a corridor...from where, in the distance, you see a special being coming toward you. This is your special guide. Some people see the guide...others hear the guide...still others somehow sense the guide's presence. This guide can be a spiritual guide, a special person, a part of nature, an inner healer or advisor.... When you have some awareness that your guide is there, just nod your head to reaffirm for yourself the guide's presence.

3. Now, take some time to ask questions of your guide...and listen very respectfully, keeping yourself open for receiving messages and information from the guide.

The messages may come in an unusual form. They may be in images...or sounds...or words...or smells...or thoughts...or just as a sense of something. Try to be receptive to new ways of gaining understanding of the meaning of the discomfort, symptom or fear.

Ask yourself questions, such as the following:

- What is the purpose of this symptom?
- Is there something from the past or present that I need to know about at this time ?
- Does my stomach want to tell me something? What might it be that I can't stomach? (Lois asked this question in relation to her fear of vomiting.) Other women might inquire about other bodily or emotional reactions.

As Lois asked these questions, she realized an association of vomiting to the "sick" feeling she would always have after being abused. And she wondered if the contractions imitated the tension she felt in her stomach.

4. After receiving insight from your inner guide, ask for ways to contain or separate the old fears from the current situation.

Maintaining the state of reverie, Lois visualized placing these old feelings and fears into a big mountain of snow. She developed a series of affirmations she could repeat to herself in labor:

- "I can separate the past from the present."

- "I can keep these sensations of nausea and my fears separate from myself; they can stay frozen in the deep snow for now and someday they will melt away."
- "I am safe here."
- "Labor is giving life and breath to my baby."

5. Ask the guide if there is anything else you need to do to help yourself (in labor).

Lois's guide smiled and reinforced her choices of comfort, containment, self-talk, and herbs. She also discovered that she wanted her sister to be with her in labor.

6. Ask the guide to kindly make any necessary physiological adjustments to reduce the symptom.

In Lois's case, she asked for the hormonal changes necessary to release tension from her gut and stomach.

7. Now, imagine yourself in the future with the symptom gone and handling the event as you wished.

Lois imagined the labor going well, and if any twinges of nausea came up, she could easily recall the comfort of snow and safety.

8. Gently bring yourself back to the present, counting up mentally but slowly from one to ten, taking time to become comfortably alert.

After the exercise, Lois felt more relaxed and confident. This visualization, along with the other strategies, worked well for her in labor. Nausea was not a problem. It is sometimes helpful to ask someone to read these relaxation exercises, such as the "Safe Place," out loud to the survivor, or make a tape, CD, or add music for use during the relaxation sessions. There are also many alternative health supply stores and websites that sell relaxation tapes.

Staying Grounded in the Present

Survivors need a technique to keep themselves in the

present or stay relaxed when they begin to feel overwhelmed, tense, or out of control. What is important is finding a method that is personally meaningful. Here are some examples:

Physically feel yourself walking, feet firmly on the ground, or feel the chair, the bed, and the earth beneath you.

Look at objects nearby; name them, look at their color, their shape, their purpose, how they feel.

Choose an object to focus on—a person's face, a picture, a flower—or hold someone's hand.

Carry a special object in your pocket as a reminder of the present—a special stone, a small picture (the ultrasound of the baby perhaps), a crystal, or some other meaningful thing.

Try exercise, dancing, yoga, or moving to music to release tension.

Draw a picture of your body, naming and validating each part, using beautiful colors.

Communicate with someone special.

Women have found that when they acknowledge or express their feelings and find a way to handle them constructively, they feel more in charge.

The image of water is self-soothing for many survivors. Carol combined her safe place sanctuary near a gentle stream with visualizing her distressing thoughts as leaves or little pieces of driftwood. She would watch them drifting toward her, observe them from a different perspective, and see them float away downstream.

Developing Cues As Reminders for Staying Centered or Relaxed

Cues are quick and simple ways for survivors to steady themselves in moments of stress. Cues should be created when in a state of relaxation or while visualizing a place of comfort or safety. The survivor imagines a symbol for her relaxed state. This symbol becomes her cue to recall the feeling of comfort and safety, or to anchor her. The cue might be a soothing word, an object, an image in her mind, or an action such as clasping her hands or two fingers together. Eventually the cue itself evokes the positive feeling since the comfort feeling is related to the cue. A cue can simply be the image of a sunny playroom for the child self, as it was for Alice. For another woman, visualizing the image of a spiritual figure helped evoke the feeling of safety.

Panic Attacks

Panic attacks are among the most frightening and discomforting events a person experiences. It is not unusual for survivors to continue to suffer from them long after the trauma ceases. These attacks often come on suddenly, in association with a reminder of the trauma, or sometimes "out of the blue," when the person is in no true danger. Feelings of dread or helplessness burden the person who has frequent panic attacks.

Panic attacks cause physical symptoms such as a rapid, pounding heartbeat, tight chest and shortness of breath, sweating, clammy hands, faintness, dizziness, trembling, shakiness, "butterflies" in the stomach, feelings of choking, and tingling in the fingers. Psychological symptoms include a desperate need to get away, fears of dying, suffocating or going crazy, and feelings of unreality.

The Physiology of Panic Attacks

In a panic attack, the body's survival mechanism (the "fight or flight" response) is mobilized, just as when a person is truly in danger. During a "fight or flight" response, adrenaline (epinephrine) a major stress hormone, is secreted rapidly in large quantities to enable the person to flee danger or fight off an attacker. Adrenaline increases blood pressure and heart rate, allowing more blood to be pumped to the muscles to temporarily increase one's strength, speed, and stamina. It mobilizes glucose for added energy. Respiration is altered to enable increased uptake of oxygen. The person becomes extremely alert, more easily startled, and ready to act. This physiological response is beneficial when one is truly in danger.

During a panic attack, however, there is no real danger, and the response is not appropriate to the situation. The physiological and psychological reactions are triggered during normal everyday circumstances. Panic attacks may begin either with symptoms of physiological arousal or by fear-producing thoughts and beliefs. They then escalate to catastrophic interpretation and full-blown panic. One of the most distressing symptoms of panic attacks for the victim is feeling as if she cannot get enough air, or that she will suffocate or faint. These are symptoms of hyperventilation, which accompanies about 60 percent of panic attacks.

The hyperventilating person feels that she cannot get enough oxygen, and she gasps and gulps air. In actuality, however, just the opposite is true. She is overbreathing, actually taking in too much oxygen and breathing out too much carbon dioxide. Without a proper balance between oxygen and carbon dioxide levels in her blood, her body cannot use the oxygen she has, and she will feel very uncomfortable and afraid. She sweats, has a rapid heartbeat, feels weak, dizzy, and develops numbness and tingling in her lips and hands, and even muscle spasms in her hands. The goal in controlling the symptoms of hyperventilation, then, is to allow a build-up of carbon dioxide. When levels of carbon dioxide normalize, the frightening symptoms disappear.

The techniques one might use to build up her carbon dioxide levels include holding her breath; breathing into a paper bag or her cupped hands; or slowing her breathing while prolonging her out-breaths. Although it seems to be the opposite of what she wants to do, her symptoms will subside within a short time when she uses these techniques.

The goal for handling panic is to defuse the physical arousal symptoms as well as to intervene and change the scary thoughts of negative self-talk or distorted beliefs. The suggestions below can be useful for someone who suffers from panic attacks. She should try to do the following:

Recognize her own early warning signs of anxiety and panic such as rapid heartbeat, butterflies in her stomach, tightness in her chest, dizziness, muscle tension, rapid breathing, and sweaty palms.

Recognize the catastrophic interpretations she typically makes about herself in association with these symptoms. She should immediately stop these statements and change them to coping and realistic ones.

Develop regular practice of deep relaxation methods such as deep, slow, abdominal breathing, progressive muscle relaxation, or calming imagery to create physiological relaxation and to counteract the stress response.

Develop and practice a cue such as a calming word (peace, calm, relax), a comforting image (a peaceful scene, a lake, trees), or a physical action (putting thumb and two fingers together or touching the back of her hand). She can associate this cue with relaxation and use it as a signal to decrease her anxiety and reverse the conditioned anxiety response.

Recognize the types of situations or triggers that may initiate a panic attack.

Learn to acknowledge her own feelings, especially sadness, anger, and fear, and find safe ways to deal with them, or safe people to share them with, in order to dissipate their emotional power.

Identify the distorted untrue thoughts she says to herself that magnify and escalate her anxiety. These are thoughts that typically accompany her panic symptoms as well as thoughts that inappropriately strengthen the self-defeating core beliefs.

Develop and rehearse positive, realistic, coping. self-talk statements in order to shift her thinking from fear-producing thoughts to fear-reducing thoughts. Write these on a card.

Practice methods that keep her grounded in the present and counteract the imagined fear-provoking thoughts, actions, and scenes.

Learn to combine and practice several techniques when panic seems insurmountable, and remember that panic attacks are time-limited and will pass within a few minutes, as the oxygen/carbon dioxide balance is restored and adrenaline is absorbed

Examples of Negative Panic Statements and How to Reframe Them

Statements such as "I'm going to die," or, "I'm going to have a heart attack," in reaction to heart palpitations; or, "I can't breathe," when feeling tightness in the chest; or, "I'm going to pass out," in response to dizziness; or, "I'm going crazy," "I have no control," when feeling as if she is losing control or wanting to escape – these can all be changed to reality-based statements, such as the following. "This is just a panic attack. No one dies from a panic attack." "Even though I feel like I can't breathe, I am getting all the oxygen I need." "I will hold my breath for a few seconds or breathe into a paper bag. It will get better very soon." "Even though these feelings are not pleasant, I've handled them before, and I can handle them now." "I can take all the time I need in order to think slowly and to relax." "This not an emergency. I can do my relaxing breaths and allow this to pass." "These are just thoughts, not reality." "I can say 'Stop' to those scary thoughts, realize that I am scaring myself, and breathe so as to restore my oxygen/carbon dioxide balance and send calming hormones to my brain and body."

If during labor she equates the pain or pressure of the baby coming out with the thought or belief that she is being raped, she can change that thought to: "Although this pressure is reminding me of my abuse, I am really safe here, and this pressure and stretching are the baby coming out to greet me." "I can focus on my baby." If she starts to have the negative thought that the pain of contractions will make her writhe and lose control, she can change it to: "All I have to do is keep a rhythm (breathing, moaning, tapping, swaying, stroking, or counting) through each contraction, and this will help me stay in control and keep me from being overwhelmed."

Stress Management

Many classes for the public offer techniques to promote body awareness, relaxation, and self-calming (yoga, meditation, prenatal exercise, and stress management). Pregnant survivors may want to explore such classes, and join those that are appropriate.

Stress-reducing activities include physical and mental actions that alleviate tension. Becoming aware of tension in the body, of where the breath is, and of any anxious thoughts are the first things to do to overcome stress.

Underlying most self-help activities is the power of the mind to create images and thoughts. Much of what survivors are plagued with are negative thoughts and images. Although imagery and visualization have been used throughout human history, we now have greater understanding of the benefits of using them to help bring healthy changes into our minds and bodies. In athletics, medicine, psychology, education, and business, creative imagery has been applied to reduce stress and to enhance performance as well as to envision ways to solve problems and fulfill one's potential. It is no less useful for abuse survivors.

Using Deep Relaxation for Immediate Relief of Stress

For immediate relief of stress, take a few deep, slow breaths in the following manner:

Let your body become loose and relaxed, like a rag doll, arms and legs loose, shoulders sagging, head and neck loose, hands open, palms up. If you have been breathing shallowly or rapidly, on your next exhalation, make an long "sssss" sound through your mouth, until there is no more air to exhale. This automatically leaves more room in your lungs for the next breath to fill them with oxygen.

Now begin slow deep breathing, saying to yourself, "I am taking a deep, slow breath through my nose, while counting to 4 slowly, 1...2...3...4..., and exhaling fully and completely through my pursed lips." Try to make your out-breath longer than your in-breath. Continue this type of breathing for about 3 or 4 breaths. This practice may bring some immediate relief, after which you can continue with a more involved relaxation method.

A variation to the above relaxation technique:

With eyes open or closed, as you prefer, breathe slowly and evenly as described in the above exercise.

Look at or imagine some object and focus on it, staying in the present. Continue the breathing.

Wink first with one eye and then the other.

Imagine an inner smile and let your face smile.

Imagine a place of comfort and safety.

See this place and imagine being there in your mind's eye. Take a big breath in and let it out.

Imagine yourself in that scene using safe self-talk: I am safe; I can breathe; it's O.K., I'm not going to die.

Use the above statements with the rhythm of your breathing, in this way: On the breath in, repeat in your mind, "I am safe, I can breathe, I am alive"; on the breath out, "I am letting go, I am OK, I am releasing."

Using Relaxation for Stress Management

Practicing relaxation techniques on a regular basis helps to reduce one's overall stress level, and promotes long-term health benefits. There are many tried and true methods to produce deep relaxation. They all have physical and mental components. One of the oldest methods is called Progressive Relaxation, and is based on the concept that muscles will become more relaxed after they have been actively tensed. This entails tensing and then relaxing groups of muscles, starting with the hands or feet, and eventually working through the entire body. We suggest tensing and relaxing each muscle group two times before moving to the next group, in order to strengthen your awareness of the difference between tension and relaxation.

How to Do Progressive Relaxation

Before you begin, choose a time and place where you will not be disturbed.

Recline or sit in a comfortable position.

Close your eyes and breathe in a relaxed manner as you scan your body for any tense areas. Also notice areas that are relaxed. Take three relaxing breaths and enjoy the sensation of the air filling you up and flowing through your body. Take another deep breath and let the exhalation be a releasing, letting-go breath. If it is difficult to take a deep breath at first, it may be easier for you to start directly with deep muscle relaxation. Some people like to start the progressive relaxation at their feet and work up the body; others start with the hands and arms, work up to the head and neck and back through the body. We will begin with the feet. The goal is to tense the groups of muscles comfortably, avoiding strain, but producing enough tension so that you can feel the release when you deliberately let go.

Begin by focusing on your feet; as you breathe in, tense the muscles in your feet (by bringing your toes up and bending your feet back, not pointing your toes, which causes foot cramps) and hold your breath and the tension for a few seconds, and then while exhaling completely, release the tension in your feet, allowing them to relax completely. Then breathe in a deep cleansing breath and breathe out fully and completely, letting the relaxation continue....

Now, focus on your legs and any tension you may be holding there. When you are ready, breathe in while you stiffen your legs, and then let the tension go as you breathe out. Complete another full breath cycle.

And, as you breathe in, squeeze your buttocks tightly, hold for a few seconds, and then let all the tension go on the exhalation. Continue up through your body, becoming aware of your abdomen next, and any tension you are holding there. As you are ready, inhale, tense this area, and release the tension along with your exhalation, beginning to notice those small differences between tension and relaxation. Continue to breathe in and out, feeling more and more calm and peaceful.

Now, as you breathe in, stiffen your entire back, hold it for a few seconds, and then release your tension as you breathe out. Notice the comfort that comes when you release tension in your back.

As you breathe in, clench your fists and stiffen your arms, then release them as you breathe out.

Now shift your focus to your chest and shoulders, an area where much stress and anxiety may be held, and tense this area as you breathe in, and once again, release the tension and your breath fully and completely. Then take time to inhale and exhale gently, easily, and peacefully.

And now, focus on your head, neck, and face, and as you breathe in, tense all those muscles and let all that tension go, releasing the stress and tension from your face, head and neck. As you continue to breathe in and exhale, imagine releasing that stored tension from your mind, feeling more at ease, quiet, and calm.

After any relaxation exercise, take the time to gently and slowly return to full present alertness, feeling refreshed, replenished, renewed, and confident.

Variations in Progressive Relaxation

If there are areas that seem particularly difficult to relax, allow yourself to take the time to tense and release those areas two times, noticing that the second time releases even more tension or tightness. It can also be abbreviated after you are comfortable with it, by using the breathing while focusing on larger groups of muscles, such as the legs and feet, buttocks and trunk, the arms, and the head and neck.

As they do this exercise, some people imagine breathing in soothing colors, and breathing out negative colors.

The exercise can also be done in a more passive manner by simply focusing on these areas of the body, noticing any tension stored there, focusing on the tension, breathing in, and as you breathe out, releasing the tension simply with your breath and mentally releasing the tension without using the actual tensing of the muscles. You can imagine the tension melting away,

Adding the imagery of a safe or special place can enhance one's sense of peace, comfort and safety, again reducing the anxiety.

Remember that you can re-enter a state of relaxation by using your cue as a signal to your mind and body to return to this state. This is discussed in the earlier section, "Developing cues as reminders for staying centered or relaxed."

One survivor learned to recognize the physical symptoms of anxiety, such as fast heart beat, cold sweaty hands, change in breathing. She learned to reverse these physical reactions by taking slow deep breaths and imagining beautiful colors and music flowing through her with each breath out. As she would become physically calmer, she would send any intrusive negative thoughts (related to never being valued and fearing that her baby would not love her) just flowing out of her with the colors and the music, and give herself calming and realistic messages of safety.

Another abuse survivor imagined white light flowing through her abdomen surrounding her baby.

Releasing Hurtful Emotions Through Creative Expression

When a survivor finds herself preoccupied with hurtful emotions or memories, she needs tools and techniques that allow her to express and release these feelings without harming herself or others. Without this ability, she becomes stuck in disempowering or self-damaging thought patterns. Here are useful techniques for releasing such emotions:

Writing in a notebook or diary helps some people. Putting distressing feelings on paper (to be read by no one) helps her distance herself from them.

Creating a written dialogue between herself and her abuser or imagining that she is sitting in front of and speaking out loud to her abuser gives her an opportunity to finally tell that person what she has never been able to say.

Expressing troubling feelings through art may also help. It is not necessary or even desirable that she have artistic ability, only that she can represent in some way–colors, shapes, doodles, scribbles, stick figures, patterns–what she is feeling. Paper and pencils, crayons, pastels, charcoal, paints, or clay are good tools for artistic expression.

Other actions include writing letters that she will not send, or recording her spoken thoughts and feelings and putting them in a secure place.

Doing any of these exercises only once may not be enough to gain full benefit. After doing them several times, the intense feelings begin to defuse and abate. At the same time, the survivor clarifies her present feelings and her real needs. She might explore different aspects of her experience on different occasions. For example, at different times, she might express "what you did to me," "how it left me feeling," "how I feel about you now," "what I wished you had done," "what I still need from you," or other messages. There begins to be a pattern of internal brainstorming, which can lead to appropriate problem-solving. This process helps the survivor understand the meaning of her abuse in her life and what she truly wants. After completing the written or art activities, some survivors find that ripping up the paper and throwing it away seems to lift the heaviness.

Other activities that can help one deal with distressing feelings include reading the words of others—inspiring writings, poems, spiritual messages—praying, and listening to music.

Anger Management

Anger is a normal, healthy reaction to abuse, as is fear. Survivors have very good reasons to be angry, but expressing anger is risky. It may bring on further abuse, abandonment, or retaliation by others. It may mean losing control of one's behavior, abusing others or harming oneself. It may be displaced from the perpetrators onto others (spouse, obstetrician, midwife, therapist, friends, coworkers, authority figures in general, or one's own unborn or newborn baby) who have done nothing to deserve the anger.

The fear of losing control often leads survivors to stifle their anger, but depression, which may invlove the numbing of all emotion, might replace it. Conversely, anger may fester until it becomes distorted into violent rage, or converted into debilitating physical symptoms (somatization).

The strong emotion of anger causes a physiological response similar to the "fight or flight" response, described earlier. As with other forms of emotional distress, physical illness and extreme behavior result when anger is unexpressed. An important step in the survivor's recovery, therefore, is to acknowledge and validate her anger, and to learn effective ways to release it in a harmless way. Because anger has a powerful physical component as well as an emotional one, it is necessary to find ways of releasing that tension through breathing, movement, or strong physical actions.

There are numerous techniques for releasing anger. They should always be done in a safe place and in such a way that the survivor feels in control and is not overwhelmed by the force of her feelings. It is important to her sense of control that she give herself a short and specific length of time for the exercise, planning a few minutes for anger-release activity, and then time to close it down by taking some deep full breaths and letting herself become calm again.

Releasing techniques include punching pillows or yelling into them; screaming without disturbing anybody; running, stomping; kicking a ball; throwing rocks outside in a safe place, like a pond, onto a pile of earth, or in a field; or ripping up things like rags or telephone books. With each punch, stomp, throw, kick, or tear, she recognizes that she is getting rid of some distress.

Another way to release and defuse anger is to effectively communicate one's feelings to people she needs to understand her. As preparation for a real interaction with a person toward whom she is angry, it helps to say out loud, in private, what she feels, imagining that person sitting in a chair and having to listen to her. Or, she may write a letter (that she plans not to send), expressing all her anger and frustration, using any words that help release these powerful emotions. After she defuses forceful negative feelings through one or both of these exercises, it becomes easier to say what she wants, face to face to her partner, caregiver, or others, using constructive feedback and "I-messages" (as described in Chapter 7). The real goal is to communicate strong feelings and gain validation of her experience by effectively expressing herself without hurting anybody else.

A counselor or friend might help a survivor make a list of things that made her angry, and to whom she would like to say these things. Doing so enables the survivor to remain calm and in the present when discussing important concerns with people who need to listen to her and understand. It will be very important that she not lose her temper or react inappropriately in potentially charged situations. For example, during a prenatal appointment, when she wants to ask her doctor to modify his or her usual obstetric management to accommodate some of her abuse-related fears; or, after the birth, if she is distressed by incidents during labor and wants to review them with her doctor.

Breaking Out of Old Patterns

So much of a survivor's life experience is coping with triggers that cause distressing reactions that she would prefer not to have. Recognizing these reactions and patterns of behavior, and designing new, more appropriate responses helps the survivor feel more in control and positive about herself.

Survivors, as is true of many other women during the perinatal period, are quite likely to construe remarks about them as negative or hurtful, even though the speaker intended the remark to be a compliment or a neutral observation. For example, a friend remarked to a pregnant survivor that she certainly didn't look pregnant. The friend believed she was complimenting the survivor. That night, the pregnant woman dreamed that something was wrong with the baby, and woke up thinking that she was defective or that the baby was not growing. The friend had no idea that she had activated this negative self-perception in the survivor.

Once the survivor recognizes situations that cause negative reactions or behavior patterns, she can begin to change her reactions to more positive ones, by following the steps described below.

How One May Change Negative Patterns and Reactions

Recognize the negative comment or situation.

Describe her behavior and self-negating reactions.

Identify her bodily sensations.

Recognize the emotions she is experiencing.

Understand her negative self-defeating core beliefs.

Develop ways to change thoughts, emotions, and behaviors.

The following table includes examples of scenarios that may cause negative reactions, along with the underlying negative beliefs of the survivor that may prevent her from reacting more positively. The far right column offers alternative responses to consider if similar circumstances recur. It helps to make a chart to be able to distinguish exactly what is happening. Then, solutions may not seem so insurmountable. A survivor can notice these disparaging remarks or negative self-talk or behaviors and explore ways to reframe their meaning or change her perspective and responses. Over time her attitudes may begin to change and she will develop more self-esteem.

Reframing negative reactions to more positive ones

Negative Situation	Negative Inner Response	Emotions, Bodily Sensations	Core Beliefs	New Response
You don't look pregnant	Is something wrong with the baby? Am I normal?	Fear Anxiety	I am inadequate	I look great I'm just right
You look huge!	I'm huge The baby is too big	Embarrassed, Worried	I've always been overweight	I'm giving the baby the nourish-ment he needs. I'm perfectly healthy
Every time I go to the clinic, I have many questions but am afraid to ask them	Fear of speaking up	Anxiety, clamming up, tension, fear, embarrass-ment, anger	I have no right to ask for what I want. No one cares what is important to me.	I have a right to ask for what I want. Even if the doctor is rushed, I can trust he wants to meet my needs.

How A Survivor Can Make Changes:

Practice cues or a method to relax and calm herself.

Recognize when her fears are magnified and develop reality statements instead.

Rehearse the new behavior ahead of time. Role play with a friend.

Use imagery to see herself changing her behavior or her reactions.

Give herself positive coping self-talk statements

Self-Talk

The following ideas are additional methods to be used whenever unexpected feelings flood the psyche. First, by paying attention to the feelings and acknowledging them, one can begin to strategize ways to control them. Sometimes, repeating significant phrases or positive self-talk is helpful: "I know these feelings are from the past. I can recognize them. This is now. I am here. I am not a child anymore. That was then. I am safe now. I can put them in a safe place until I can work with them." During labor, using rhythmic and repetitive phrases, as "My body knows just what to do," My baby knows just what to do." "My baby takes the pain away," can also contain frightening feelings. These sorts of statements can be put on cards to be carried around and repeated as needed.

Strategies Involving Other People

A trusted person—friend, relative, doula, counselor, therapist, or partner—is a valuable asset during potentially stressful times and can help a survivor remain centered and contain her distress. This trusted person may help in any number of ways.

For example, a childbirth educator visited the doctor with her student who was an abuse survivor; the educator remained with the woman as a witness and for moral support. She said very little. The woman felt more secure in asking questions, and was glad to have someone who would give feedback and discuss the appointment afterwards. Another woman, at a difficult time in her therapy, was recovering intensely painful memories. She felt she needed extra support between appointments. She and her therapist made an arrangement that she could call and leave a message on her therapist's answering machine every time she felt distressed. The therapist was not expected to call the woman back, unless there was an emergency. Simply knowing that her therapist was there and would hear the message was enough to help the woman release her anxiety.

A doula asked her survivor client, who had a great deal of anxiety, to call her after each visit with her midwife. These structured phone visits allowed the woman to feel that she was not imposing on the doula, and they became a good opportunity for the woman to express any concerns or ask questions that had come up since the appointment. On two occasions the woman was quite upset, and her doula realized that she had misinterpreted some things her midwife had said. She suggested that the woman call her midwife back for clarification. These calls also helped the doula know better how she could support her client.

Another pregnant woman, who suspected that her husband was having an affair, needed someone to talk to. She did not want advice or judgment. She asked her friend to be available for listening only, to allow her to air her feelings and frustrations, and to hold her hand if she became emotional. Her friend agreed, and was relieved to play this role instead of bearing the responsibility of having answers for this difficult quandary.

Conclusion

The self-help techniques in this chapter address a broad range of challenges for the survivor. They utilize a number of different strategies to increase her sense of personal safety, enhance her understanding of her own needs, and show her how to make some changes to promote her well-being. It is not expected that every technique will suit every survivor, but readers are encouraged to carefully consider, adapt, and apply those techniques that seem promising.

Mastery of self-help methods is essential to a survivor's well being. When combined with a strong support network, excellent maternity care, and counseling or therapy as needed, much healing is accomplished.

10
Birth Counseling

- Even though I've had two years of helpful therapy, and thought my abuse issues were behind me, the birth film in childbirth class brought up some of the old stuff again.
- When I saw the machines, cords, and all the equipment in the hospital, I got scared just at the thought of being tied down.
- I just don't want to be discounted. I'm afraid I'll clam up and not be able to speak for myself when I'm in labor.

Birth counseling is short term and goal-oriented. It consists of exploring psychological issues related to childbearing, and developing strategies to prevent adverse effects or reactions that might otherwise ensue. The counseling techniques in this chapter seek to validate the woman's issues; build her self-esteem, confidence, knowledge, and feelings of control; and devise appropriate strategies for dealing with her issues as they arise. Counseling can be useful during pregnancy, between births, during post partum, or even years after childbirth. It can help women to:

Identify and work through anxiety or concerns about the upcoming birth

Process and come to terms with events of a previous disappointing or traumatic birth

Identify mood disorders that sometimes occur post partum and apply useful counseling approaches to promote healing

Explore other emotional issues related to childbearing, such as breastfeeding, sleep, and relationships between the woman and her partner, her own parents, her baby, and others.

In this chapter, we will describe a number of counseling techniques:

Trigger work—identifying and strategizing for those events and features of childbirth that may lead to an adverse reaction, such as panic, dissociation, helplessness, anger, bodily tension, "holding back" in second stage

Dream exploration, using the "Dream Interview Technique"

Counseling after a traumatic birth

Using Counseling Methods As Self-Help

Although it is usually more successful when the woman works with a skilled and knowledgeable counselor, there may be no such person available, or the fees may not be affordable. If so, we encourage women to work on their issues themselves, or with an empathic partner or friend.

Advantages of Doing This Work Without a Counselor:

For a woman who has trust issues, it might be best to rely on herself.

She can do this work at her own pace.

It is less costly than working with a counselor.

When there is not a counselor available, a woman can gain insight into her own issues and devise some worthwhile strategies.

Disadvantages:

The woman's lack of clinical knowledge and experience with childbirth and choices in care are limiting.

Emotional reactions to potential stressors may be upsetting or even damaging, especially when there is no qualified person available who can assist the woman in dealing with them.

A lack of counseling and communication skills in the woman and/or partner may lead to unnecessary misunderstandings and misinterpretation during the self-counseling process.

Without help, early defense mechanisms, once helpful in protecting the woman from emotional pain, may interfere with her ability to gain new insight and to form less distressing patterns of thought and behavior.

This chapter can be used by the woman herself, one who is working with her partner or friend, or one who is working with a caregiver or counselor. In addition, Chapter 9 contains other self-help measures, and there are some useful self-help books that guide the reader through exercises designed to help gain personal understanding, clarify and express concerns and plan self-help and healing strategies. (See the Resources: Books for some titles.)

We strongly suggest that the woman have a trusted partner, relative, friend, doula, or caregiver with whom to share these exercises as well as what she feels and learns in the self-help process.

Working with a Counselor

If the woman decides she would like a counselor to help her address birth-related psychological concerns, she needs first to find the right person.

Ideally, anyone who counsels childhood sexual abuse survivors in birth-related issues should have: 1) an extensive knowledge about birth or easy access to someone with such knowledge; 2) good communication skills; 3) knowledge about sexual abuse; 4) the time necessary for short-term focused counseling; 5) the ability to stay within the limits of the counseling role, by assisting the woman where possible, recognizing when the woman's needs exceed the counselor's abilities, and referring appropriately for therapy; 6) and, for those who are also physicians, midwives, or doulas, the ability to separate the "counseling" role from the other "caregiving" role (in order to avoid a conflict of interest). For example, a physician who is listening to a woman's fears about an intervention that he or she usually uses may find it difficult to listen to her concerns openly without bias.

As long as they meet the criteria listed above, many health care workers can provide the counseling, for example: maternity care professionals (doctors, midwives, nurses), mental health professionals (psychotherapists, perinatal social workers, other social workers, nurse practitioners, and licensed counselors), and experienced birth paraprofessionals (childbirth educators, doulas, and others).

The counselor must be able to openly and clearly put aside his or her own beliefs, practices, and reactions when listening to the survivor client's concerns. The purposes of the counseling are to discover and elicit the woman's feelings and fears, and to find ways to alleviate them.

This chapter is a practical guide for birth counselors, clients, and caregivers. It contains useful techniques for helping troubled childhood sexual abuse survivors to achieve a sense of mastery and a feeling of being understood and respected. Even if caregivers do not plan to actually do the birth counseling, many methods described here will be helpful in clinical dealings with their clients or patients.

The Setting for Counseling

A private, comfortable, undisturbed setting (free from interruptions by people coming and going, phone calls, pages) establishes a feeling of safety for the client. It helps to have adequate but not extremely bright lighting and a comfortable temperature; pillows for the client to make herself comfortable; a choice of chairs or couches that are not so low that a pregnant woman has trouble getting out of them; a box of tissues within easy reach; a choice of beverages available; the counselor's business card, notebook, pencil, forms, and any resource books, audio or video tapes that the counselor might want to use for herself or show or loan to the client. The client should be told where the bathroom is, and invited to use it whenever necessary.

Opening Comments

Once the client is greeted and comfortably settled, the counselor begins by asking if the client would like her to describe her usual approach to birth counseling (if that has not already been done before the appointment). Of course, the client should already know how long each appointment lasts, how many appointments it usually takes, the costs and arrangements for payment. (Some counselors include the cost as part of a childbirth education series or a doula's service. Some counselors are in private practice and charge an hourly fee. Some counselors work on the staff of a clinic.)

The counselor who is not a psychotherapist should clarify her or his qualifications and the limits of her or his expertise, and describe the counseling as it applies to the client's stated needs. For example, "I am a counselor, not a therapist, and my qualifications are that I know a great deal about birth, I'm a good listener, and I have extensive experience working with pregnant women who have been sexually abused" (or, depending on the client's reason for coming, "with women who have had disappointing birth experiences," or "with women in their childbearing years"). "Usually in one or a few appointments we can accomplish the things I can help with. I also can make referrals for more extensive psychotherapy, if desired and needed."

The psychotherapist who is offering the birth counseling should differentiate between the goals of birth counseling and the goals of psychotherapy. For example, when birth becomes imminent, it may be appropriate to postpone work on healing from past traumas and work on immediate concerns relating to the upcoming birth.

Establishing Trust

Part of establishing trust from the beginning is making sure the woman knows that she is in control of what she wishes to reveal, and can stop the discussion or take a "time out" whenever she would like. The counselor should check periodically on how the client is feeling in order to reinforce her sense of control.

Information Gathering

The counselor should first explore with the woman any present circumstances and concerns. She and her counselor can begin by exploring how she feels right now. For example, the woman who arrives 10 minutes late for her appointment may need to be sensitively listened to while she expresses her anxiety about that, before she can even focus on her feelings about pregnancy and birth.

Helen

Helen was upset because she arrived late. The counselor, reassuring her that the lateness didn't matter said, "What's important now is to take some time to get settled. How about taking a moment to catch your breath, sit back, and get comfortable?" After a pause, "How are you feeling right now?" Tears came to Helen's eyes, and in a rush of words, she described a fight with her husband and getting lost on the way to the appointment. After expressing her feelings, and being listened to with empathy, Helen could finally relax enough to focus on the issues that brought her for counseling.

Other relevant areas to touch upon include present circumstances, such as: her relationship with her partner; her family; her support circle (friends, acquaintances); her work situation; financial situation (if appropriate); her home situation; how the pregnancy has been thus far; and what she sees as stresses currently in her life. They explore not only factual information, but more importantly, her feelings about these issues. She is in control of what she'd like to tell her counselor and can guide the direction of the counseling.

The counselor should listen intently and be non-directive at this point (see Chapter 7). Simply by providing a listening ear, the counselor can help relieve distress and help the woman discover more clearly for herself her real concerns. Unless the client is really reticent, unclear, or the counselor is not following her, the counselor should not interrupt to ask questions or discuss specific points. Instead, the counselor should take notes (having assured the woman of confidentiality) and place a check mark or star in the margin to note a comment or event that the counselor feels is potentially significant. Then when appropriate, the counselor may go back to the marked comments for further discussion. Discussing present circumstances usually gives the counselor some clues as to what to ask about the client's family of origin, significant events of childhood and adolescence, and more. If the woman is veering away from the topic, she may be avoiding distressing issues. The counselor can use sensitive clarifying responses to help the woman keep on track, such as, "I have a question about something you said a moment ago."

Abuse History

The counselor does not ask about the client's abuse history unless or until such a disclosure is made. Frequently a history of abuse is known before the first appointment and is the reason for the woman to seek counseling. But sometimes the woman comes because of birth-related fear, anger, or other strong emotions. A connection between these emotions and early abuse may be made as they work together.

Once the abuse is disclosed, the counselor should ask for a brief description. It is not necessary to get more information than the client is comfortable disclosing. One way to ask is: "Ann, I know you are concerned about how your past abuse might come up during childbirth. Would it be all right to tell me something about the abuse? I don't need a lot of details but it would help if you could tell me the relationship of the perpetrator to you, how old you were, how long the abuse went on, and something about what the abuser did. Also, it would help me to know whether you ever became pregnant as a result of abuse and whether there were other types of abuse (physical, psychological, verbal abuse, or neglect), whether anyone else knew about the abuse and tried to stop it or to help you. Knowing these things might help us as we explore the impact of your abuse history on your pregnancy and birth."

Another way to take the abuse history is to ask the woman to write out her story (in as much or as little detail as she wishes) and the impact she believes it has had on her. She can then e-mail or mail it to the counselor before the appointment. This method saves time for the busy practitioner and may be a useful exercise for the woman.

After the history, the counselor might ask how the woman believes the abuse affected her then and now, and if she has ever been in therapy; if so, how helpful it was. By asking in this way and encouraging the woman to disclose only what is comfortable for her, she feels safe and the counselor does not overstep her boundaries. The answers to the above questions will provide many clues to both the survivor and her counselor as they work together to understand and resolve troubling issues.

Deirdre

28-year-old Deirdre (a primigravida with a history of sexual abuse), came for counseling about her birth plan. For prenatal care she was attending a clinic staffed by competent, caring midwives and nurse practitioners. When her counselor asked how everything was going, she described becoming increasingly uncomfortable with each clinic visit, especially when she had to remove her clothing for an abdominal check, and also when her midwife gave her a hug at the end of the visit. In exploring her discomfort, she recalled that a female high school teacher had initiated her into sex. She had been "trapped" in that relationship for four years, unable to say or do anything to stop it until she left school. She had much shame, guilt, and fear from that experience, and understandably began to dread the clinic visits where female fingers would probe and touch her.

Having someone listen to her without judgment and with compassion allowed her to express strong feelings of shame along with sadness and anger. She wept as she said that it was the first time she had ever been able to tell anyone. Her counselor calmly listened, acknowledged the pain that comes in recalling the abuse, praised her courage, and checked to see if she felt okay talking about it. She said she felt relieved to talk about it.

All that the counselor needed to know was the general information on Deirdre's present concern (the "stress" caused by the clinic visits) and something of her abuse history. The counseling helped Deirdre make the association between the abuse history and her present mistrust of her care providers, and then to begin to separate her teacher's actions from those of her current female caregivers. It was enough to help her resolve this conflict. (There is more of Deirdre's story in Chapter 11.)

Counselors' Responses to a Client's Disclosure of her Sexual Abuse History

Talking about her abuse history, especially for the woman who has never done so, may cause strong emotional reactions (tension, shame, guilt, anger, crying) or somatic or physical reactions (nausea, trembling). The birth counselor must be comfortable with such emotions and convey this by maintaining an accepting, calm, caring attitude, and by validating the woman's experience with appropriate responses.

Sometimes, especially for counselors or caregivers who are unfamiliar with the realities of sexual abuse, survivors' disclosures of their abuse are most upsetting or even difficult to believe. Furthermore, the listener may feel so disturbed that he or she becomes preoccupied with the graphic images, and have disturbing dreams and visceral or emotional reactions. This is termed "vicarious traumatization." When this occurs, the counselor or caregiver should consult with his or her more experienced colleagues for guidance in gaining a healthy perspective.

Finally, some professionals do not believe the survivor's claims of having been abused. They label such claims as "false memories," which can be devastating to someone for whom it has taken great courage to disclose such experiences.

Following are examples of non-helpful and helpful responses when a woman discloses her abuse history. They are adapted and expanded from *Counseling Survivors of Childhood Sexual Abuse*, by Claire Burke Draucker.

When a woman discloses her abuse history, what does the listener say?

Non-Helpful Responses

Shock/disgust: "Oh, my God. That's horrible. What kind of person would do such a disgusting thing to his own child?"

Identification: "How did you get through that? I don't know if I could have survived so much abuse." Or, "I know how you feel, because it happened to me, too."

Vicarious traumatization: "I feel sick just listening to your story. I can't stop thinking about it."

Anger/rage: "Every time I hear something like that, I want to lock up every abuser and throw away the key."

Disbelief: "Are you sure that happened? It was a long time ago and you were awfully young."

Blame: "Why did you agree to have sex with him? Why didn't you tell your mother? Why did it go on for so long? Why didn't you make him stop or run away? Why didn't you tell someone? Why did you let him do it?"

Minimizing: "Since it's all over now, and you feel you've resolved it, why don't we focus on concerns you have today?"

Intrusive interest: "What exactly did he do? How did you react? Did you respond?"

Pity: "You poor thing. You must have suffered terribly."

Rescuing: "I'll make sure that this won't cause you any more problems."

The non-helpful responses such as shock, identification, or anger may be intended to be supportive by the naive counselor, but they actually make the woman feel she's upsetting her counselor, or that she must protect her counselor from the truth! This demoralizes the woman, adds to her shame and makes her reluctant to tell her story. Other non-helpful responses, such as disbelief, blame, minimizing, or intrusive interest may seem to the inexperienced counselor as a voice of reason and perspective, but to the woman they are a realization of her worst fear—not being believed. Such responses or the fear of them have silenced her in the past and will reinforce for her that no one understands or believes her. Responses such as vicarious traumatization or rescuing indicate that the counselor has not established appropriate boundaries.

Helpful Responses

Calm concern: "I'm glad you've shared your experiences with me. It's important, because sexual abuse can continue to have an impact, even in adulthood."

Acknowledge difficulty of disclosure: "I imagine it is hard to tell me these things. It takes a lot courage and I respect you for it."

Reinforce client's control of disclosure process: "It can be very helpful in our work together if you can share your sexual abuse experiences since they may relate to your current concerns. However, I don't need any more detail than you are comfortable disclosing."

Acknowledge feelings: "Sometimes, when people talk about their abuse experiences it brings up very strong feelings. How are you feeling right now?"

Assess well-being: "Do you feel unsafe or fearful in any aspect of your life?"

The helpful responses reassure the woman that her counselor can handle her story and that the woman has a strong and capable ally in her healing process. Every woman should know that if she ever senses her counselor is responding in a non-helpful way, she should say so (using "I messages" in Chapter 6). "I feel bad that you find it hard to believe me. Others didn't believe me either." "When you keep asking me for so many details, I feel uneasy and wonder why you need to do that." If the counselor does not relieve her discomfort, the woman should remember that she is in charge of what is revealed and has the right to sensitive empathic care. The woman also should remember that she may discontinue the counseling if it does not meet her needs.

Specific Counseling Techniques for Specific Problems

Now we turn to counseling approaches for two of the most common issues that bring childhood sexual abuse survivors to birth counselors: fear over the upcoming birth and processing a disappointing or traumatic birth.

Fear over the Upcoming Birth

We have explained in earlier chapters how and why childhood sexual abuse survivors often fear labor and birth. They often welcome an opportunity to discuss and alleviate their fears in a counseling situation, especially if they are reassured that the counseling is intended not to bring up new memories and greater fear, but to deal with existing fears by clarifying them and developing specific ways to keep them in check.

Dawn

Dawn found herself becoming increasingly anxious after taking the hospital tour, during which the leader dismissed many of her questions with such answers as: "It's up to the doctor"; or "That won't seem so important once you get into labor"; or "We only do what is best for you and your baby." She couldn't sleep. She felt her own needs were insignificant, that she was powerless. She also wondered why she was upset while no one else on the tour seemed to be. She came to dread going to the hospital. In childbirth class, her teacher recognized Dawn's anxiety by the questions she asked: "Why do they...?"

"Do I have to...?" "How can I make sure...?" Dawn was relieved and grateful when the teacher asked her during a refreshment break if she had some uneasiness about the upcoming birth and offered to meet with her so they could explore Dawn's concerns and figure out how to deal with them.

When they got together in a counseling setting and Dawn described the anxieties she had felt ever since the tour, her teacher (now in the counseling role) listened carefully and, using good communication skills, acknowledged Dawn's discomfort. Dawn was troubled by what she labeled as her own overreaction to the tour. The counselor asked if she had ever had similar feelings before (powerless, insignificant, more upset than others). Dawn thought, and answered quietly and hesitantly, "Yes, when my brother used to make fun of my breasts and grab them. I couldn't get him to stop, and when I told my mother, she said, 'He doesn't mean anything by that. He likes teasing you. If you just wouldn't get so upset, he'd stop.' "

After the connection was made between her abuse and her current anxieties, they were able to go on with "Trigger Work."

Working on "Triggers"

By "triggers" we mean specific actions, events, or other factors that cause undue anxiety, fear, or reactions such as resistance, anger, or tension. They may also bring up memories or flashbacks of early abuse. Before exploring the triggers, the counselor and the woman work together to develop techniques to use during the sessions and also during labor to alleviate the anxiety that may come up. These include stress management, containment, and increasing the survivor's sense of safety (described in Chapter 9).

From working directly with childhood sexual abuse survivors, we have developed the list of triggers and the approach described here.

Components of "Trigger Work"

Counseling on triggers usually requires two to five sessions totaling approximately four to five hours, and consists of these four components:

1. Preliminary work: discussion of present stressors, abuse history, and explanation of the counseling method (30 minutes to 1 hour).

2. Exploration of things that make the client feel safe; how she responds, whether successfully or unsuccessfully, when worried, afraid, or in pain. (30 minutes)

3. Identification of client's triggers and the "personal meanings" (that is, what it is about each trigger that upsets her) (1 to 1 and a half hours)

Brainstorming strategies to either avoid those triggers that can be avoided (such as wearing a hospital gown); reduce the impact of triggers that cannot be avoided (such as strangers entering the room); or deal with those that are inevitable (such as a baby emerging from her body) (1 and a half to 2 hours)

We have found that the times allotted are realistic for most clients, but both client and counselor must be willing to revise the time frame if needed.

The counselor explains the process clearly to the client as follows:

"Now that you have shared with me some important things about yourself and your abuse history, our next step is to take a good look at the upcoming birth and anticipate areas that may be distressing for you. First I'd like to find out what things, techniques, or people help you feel safe. I'd also like to know how you usually react to fear and pain. It will help to know these things as we strategize ways to deal with your fears around birth. We can then go over the list of triggers that includes events that occur during labor, procedures that are often done, and the attitudes and actions of the people involved in your care. Because this approach requires that I use graphic and rather blunt language in describing the possible triggers, you may feel uncomfortable or anxious with some of them, and that's exactly what we want to happen, because, once we know the things that distress you, we can do something about them. I will make checkmarks on my list by those items that cause you discomfort. These are your triggers. Together we will analyze what it is about each trigger that is uncomfortable for you (the personal meaning). After we go over these potential triggers and their personal meanings, we'll develop some strategies for dealing with these triggers. Does all this sound okay with you?"

We have designed the form, "Strategies for Specific Triggers " to use for this work (Appendix 3). It allows space to record the following: 1) techniques or things that help the client feel safe; 2) her usual way of reacting to or coping with pain and fear; and 3) her triggers (from a list of 25 common triggers, and others), their personal meanings, and strategies for avoiding the triggers or minimizing their negative effects.

As stated above, the counselor graphically describes each potential trigger. The woman listens carefully, picturing herself in the situation described by the counselor, and notices what feelings, if any, it brings up. If she has an adverse emotional response, she tells her counselor, who places a checkmark by that "trigger," and asks, "What is it about this trigger that makes you feel uncomfortable?" "Does it remind you of a feeling you have had before?" This is how they explore the "personal meaning" of the trigger for the woman. The counselor fills in the "personal meaning" box for each trigger.

After all her triggers and personal meanings are identified, "themes" usually become evident and the strategies will follow a pattern, and be easier to devise. Common themes include:

- control and loss of control (over what is done to her, or self-control over her own behavior and reactions), fear of restraint;
- pain, injury, damage to, or invasion of her body;
- vulnerability and dependency on others (partner, friend, doula, care provider) for protection and safety;
- distrust of strangers, authority figures;
- shame, humiliation, being judged on body appearance, behavior, weakness, secretions, "mess;"
- exposure (modesty, people staring, looking and feeling inside).

Even though the act of discovering triggers and their meanings causes some stress and anxiety, the woman usually finds it highly reassuring. For a person who simply knows she's afraid but not what she's afraid of, it is a significant accomplishment to identify more specifically what bothers her and why. As one woman said, "Now, at least, I know my demons. I feel better. This has brought them all down to size."

At the end of this session, it is also important for the counselor to be reassuring: "There's a lot we can do to handle these triggers. I look forward to tackling them with you at our next appointment." The next appointment(s) will consist of problem-solving and brainstorming strategies to keep the triggers from causing undue distress in childbirth. Time between appointments gives the woman and her counselor a chance to separately review her triggers and think about appropriate strategies.

Sometimes, during the first appointment, a trigger will be so upsetting to the woman that she cannot wait until the next appointment to plan a strategy. If so, strategies must be devised right then, for the woman's peace of mind.

The woman and counselor should meet again at least a week later, ready to plan strategies to avoid, minimize, or deal with the woman's triggers.

If the Counselor Is Not a Birth Professional

The counselor's knowledge of childbirth and birth management is extremely helpful in developing realistic and appropriate strategies. If he or she has little or no training or experience with birth, the counselor will be handicapped in providing critical assistance. We recommend that such a counselor use the time between appointments to consult a maternity nurse, childbirth educator, experienced doula, a midwife or doctor, to present the woman's triggers and their personal meanings. The counselor would ask, "How can we realistically help my client avoid or minimize these triggers?" A flexible, patient-centered, and creative maternity care expert can be most helpful.

When they meet again, woman and counselor, using good communication skills, can then consider strategies and how the woman feels about them.

The Role of the Partner

Should the woman's partner accompany her to the counseling sessions? This important question often comes up and should be considered in light of the realities of their relationship.

It is obvious that if the partner is abusive, he or she should not be there. The woman may be afraid or unable to attend the appointment by herself, because her dominating partner will not allow it. In fact, a woman in such a situation is unlikely to find an opportunity to work on these issues unless she is free from the abusive partner.

An unsupportive partner may discourage a woman from getting help with her abuse-related distress over the upcoming birth, which may keep her from seeking counseling. The counselor might try to inform both the woman and her reluctant partner of the purpose and practical applications of trigger work, and may be able to recruit the partner into a supportive role.

Many partners, however, are very supportive, protective, and interested in helping. Abuse survivors often feel dependent on such a partner and may want him or her there for protection from the counselor (a stranger whom she has no reason to trust), and from anxiety over the abuse that is the object of the counseling. The partner can reassure the woman, hold her, and regulate the depth of introspection and the amount of information revealed.

If coming alone is unacceptable to the client, then there is no choice but to include her partner.

Sometimes women have withheld from their partners some of the most sordid aspects of their history out of fear that it would cause their partners to leave them. In that case, the presence of the partner, especially during the discussion of the woman's abuse history and when identifying triggers and their personal meanings, is likely to present a barrier to complete openness between client and counselor. The less the partner knows about the abuse, the greater the barrier he or she presents. Furthermore, an overprotective partner may prevent the counselor from discussing potentially distressing events, by promising that he or she will not allow them to happen.

The counselor must modify her methods and expectations accordingly.

Paula and Craig

Paula, a 32-year-old primagravida, was referred to a birth counselor for exploration of triggers and strategies for the upcoming birth. She wanted Craig, her partner, to attend with her. Craig, a loving, attentive, and protective man, had given up his business, which had kept him away from home for long periods every day, to start a home-based business that he and Paula could operate together. The reason was Paula's fear of being alone. Craig knew that Paula was an abuse survivor, and that she could trust very few people. In fact, he shared Paula's distrust of physicians and other authority figures.

During the counseling sessions, Craig sat with his arm around Paula, who gave a sketchy account of her childhood abuse. She expressed anger at previous male doctors who victimized her when she was helpless (during an abortion, a D&C operation, and vaginal exams) and her fear that if she were transferred to a physician's care, she would be "messed with." Whenever she became upset during these accounts, Craig held her and said, "I won't let them do anything to you," or "You know that won't happen as long as I'm there."

Toward the end of their last session, Craig had to leave momentarily to get something from the car, and immediately upon his leaving, Paula revealed much more about her history: "He doesn't know that I've been raped by six different men. I've been beaten up, too. I've never had someone decent like Craig. He's so good to me. I don't want him to know all this. If he knew the truth, he'd either try to kill them or he'd leave me. I can't let him know."

The counselor had been aware that the dynamics of the relationship between Paula and Craig would limit the effectiveness of the trigger work, and in this brief moment she had with Paula alone, could not hope to add much to the work they had already done. She merely restated Paula's trust in her husband and added that Craig probably found it personally rewarding to feel so important to someone he loves. At some time in the future, she hoped that Paula and Craig would find the opportunity to work with an excellent psychotherapist who could help them maintain their strong bond while Paula addressed these unrevealed aspects of her abuse.

In this case, the presence of the partner was essential to the client's willingness to address her fears, but it limited the depth of the work that could be accomplished by client and counselor. This is one of the realities a counselor accepts. She takes the client where she is and helps her get to where she wants to go.

How to Describe Triggers

The art of this counseling lies in the counselor's ability to describe potential triggers truthfully, in a graphic and realistic enough way to elicit an emotional response, only in those clients for whom they really are a trigger. The counselor should not exaggerate to the point that anyone would find them offensive or frightening. Both over-description (exaggeration) and under-description (minimization) by the counselor would hinder the trigger work. The key is not to interpret a trigger for the client, but to give her enough of a description that she can feel whether it strikes her negatively, and is actually a trigger.

Consider the following example of how not to describe the first trigger on the list (Appendix 3), "Changed appearance (make-up, hair style, clothing)." The italics denote exaggerated or value-laden language that makes the description overly negative, and would lead anyone to perceive it as a trigger.

"First of all, you realize, don't you, that you're going to *look your worst* in labor. If you wear make-up, it'll probably be *smeared all over* your face; if you don't put any on, you're going to *look horrible*, the way you do first thing in the morning. Your hair gets messed up and stringy and sweaty, and of course *they make you* wear one of those plain ugly gowns that *gapes in the back* and doesn't protect your modesty at all. And think of *all those strangers* who'll see you like that."

Such a description, though not inaccurate, carries enough editorializing to upset anyone, because it goes beyond a negative description of the trigger to a negative and subjective interpretation. The counselor is leading the client, not allowing the client to interpret for herself.

On the other hand, the well-meaning but over-protective counselor who is afraid of raising anxieties may be inclined to reassure the client by sugar-coating the triggers, by under-describing or qualifying everything she says. For example:

"You won't look the same as usual when you're in labor, but I think women in labor are beautiful. Your hair might be a little messy, but whose wouldn't be? They give you a special very practical gown to wear, so you don't have to mess up one of your own."

All the qualifiers, meant to allay anxiety, block the client in her efforts to truly explore the personal meaning.

Here is an example of how to describe the trigger without exaggerating or minimizing it:

"When in labor you will not look the way you usually like to be seen. For example, if you're wearing make-up, it is likely to get smeared; you sweat more, and your hair will be messy. Every woman is given the same style of hospital gown, which makes you look like every other woman in labor. The gowns also are designed for easy access to your perineum (for vaginal exams, washing your perineum, and delivering your baby). It's sometimes difficult to remain covered in front of the various people that will see you. As you picture yourself in that situation, what do you feel?"

This last approach will be the most successful in eliciting triggers. The woman for whom this is a trigger will probably picture herself as being exposed, ugly, stripped of her identity. The woman for whom this is not a trigger may interpret sweat and mess as no surprise and the hospital gown as a practical measure.

All the triggers on our list have been drawn from our conversations with childhood sexual abuse survivors before childbirth or after a disappointing or traumatic childbirth.

No woman finds all the items to be triggers, but most survivors will find some or several to be triggers.

Following are some points that should be made when describing each trigger, to ensure that the client has enough of a picture that her reaction truly reflects her comfort or discomfort. The descriptions include information-giving and anticipatory guidance. The amount of detail given, of course, depends on her knowledge and experience. With each description, she is asked to imagine herself in that situation and describe how it makes her feel. Please note that the italicized words highlight potentially disturbing aspects of each trigger.

1. Changed appearance (make-up, hairstyle, hospital gown). See above discussion for how to describe this potential trigger.

2. Nakedness/exposure of her perineum and buttocks

Many women *take off their gowns* in labor; they get hot and forget their usual modesty or sense of decorum.

Even if partially clad, your buttocks and perineum are *easily exposed* for the convenience of the caregiver.

3. Secretions (blood, mucus, amniotic fluid, feces)

Laboring women are *not in control over all their body fluids*. They often do not wear sanitary pads in labor. As a result they sometimes *soil or stain bed pads,* or *fluids drip down their legs* or onto the floor. While pushing the baby out, they may also push out *feces.*

The nurse or midwife *cleans up the secretions* and replaces the bed pads.

4. Body positions

Women often are asked to move into positions that might feel *undignified, revealing, or embarrassing.* Some of these positions, such as *on your back with your knees spread,* or on your *hands and knees,* mean a lack of eye contact with people in the room, or inability to see what they are doing around you or to you.

5. Hospital environment

The hospital is unique in that it has busy uniformed personnel, numerous machines, and an aura of illness, crisis, efficiency, mystery, and its own *smells and sounds.*

Past experiences with hospitals sometimes are recalled when you enter the hospital in labor.

6. Blood draws

If the woman has never had a blood draw, she might need an explanation of the procedure, as follows: At least once during labor, you are likely to have your blood drawn for various tests. The nurse or a specialist in blood draws (phlebotomist) applies a *tourniquet above your elbow,* has you clench and unclench your fist several times, cleans an area around a prominent vein in your forearm, and *inserts a hollow needle.* She then attaches a test tube to the needle, fills it and one or two more with *blood.* She removes the needle and applies a bandage over the *puncture site.*

There is some *pain* associated with the blood draw.

If you watch, you will see *blood flowing from your arm* into the test tube.

Some women have veins that are difficult to locate and to *puncture*. It sometimes takes *several attempts*. They are said to have *"poor veins."*

7. Intravenous fluids

The procedure is much like a blood draw, except that a *tube (catheter) is threaded through the needle in your vein*, the needle is removed and the tube is taped in place. At the other end of the tube is a plastic bag of fluid containing water with electrolytes (salts), possibly dextrose (sugar), and possibly medications.

The bag of fluid hangs from an IV pole, either attached to the bed or on wheels. If you walk, *you are connected to the pole* and must push it alongside you.

The *sight of an IV catheter* bothers some people.

Changing gowns and rolling over in bed, are complicated by the tube in the arm.

8. Vaginal exams or artificial rupture of the membranes

Some women have trouble with vaginal exams. *Lying on your back with your lower body exposed* and your *legs spread* is the usual position.

The procedure ranges from *uncomfortable to painful.*

Your job is to relax while *objects* (speculum, vaginal swab, ultrasound probe, electronic monitoring devices, amniohook, and others) or *examining fingers* are *inserted into your vagina.*

If your caregiver ruptures your membranes with an *amnihook during a vaginal exam*, it will cause an *uncontrollable* flow of a *substantial amount of fluid from your vagina.* To many women, it feels as if they have *lost control of their bladders.*

9. Connection to lines (tubes or wires)

Procedures such as induction or augmentation of labor and epidural anesthesia require *3 to 9 lines or tubes* connecting your body to machines (monitors, blood pressure recorders) or containers (IV bags, bladder catheters and bags for urine, oxygen supplies, and others).

Such attachments *restrict your freedom* to move in bed and get out of bed. They mean that the nurse and caregiver must take more responsibility to keep the machines and the labor running smoothly and to monitor your baby, and *you must play a less active role.*

10. Restriction to bed

It is quite likely that you will be *lying in bed in pain* or *kept there with lines,* while others—authority figures and loved ones—move in and about freely, or stand by the bed.

11. Pain with labor contractions and with birth

The *pain of labor* rates as some of the greatest pain a woman is likely ever to experience.

Pain is felt in your uterus, your low back, and your vagina.

12. Pain-related behavior

The inevitability of pain and its intensity may cause you to *lose control* over your behavior, or to *panic at your helplessness* during the pain.

13. Expressions of pain

Grimacing, crying out, moaning, thrashing, clenching your fists, tensing your body, not responding to directions or instructions, *struggling* — these are ways you might express your pain, especially if a lot of fear is involved.

Sometimes, the intensity of the *pain is too great* for you to remain calm and in control, or not to show the pain.

14. Pain medication "trade-offs"

Narcotics promote relaxation between contractions and reduce pain at the beginning and end of contractions. They do not remove all pain. You are *less alert and less able to think clearly.* Side effects, especially if you are chemically sensitive, may include *hallucinations, frightening thoughts or reactions.*

An epidural, depending on the medication used and the concentration and dosage, reduces the pain markedly. An epidural may leave you with *intense sensations in your vagina,* or *remove all sensation and ability to move* from the waist down, or anything in between.

With an epidural, it is necessary to have intravenous fluids, continuous electronic fetal monitoring, frequent blood pressure checks, and an epidural catheter in your back. You may also require Oxytocin to speed up contractions, a bladder catheter, an oxygen mask, and other medications. You may not be allowed to have anything but ice chips. *Forceps or vacuum extractor are more likely* than with no epidural. These additional interventions *keep you in bed,* and though free of pain, you are *more helpless in moving and more dependent* on the staff and your partner to take care of you, your baby and your labor.

15. Relationship with your doctor or midwife

Comfort with your caregiver and trust in his or her skills and judgment are indications of a good relationship. A feeling of being respected and heard by your caregiver is desirable.

Some clients express a *gender preference* for their caregiver yet the group of caregivers includes both males and females. You have *little control over who is on call* when you go into labor.

Being able to *share your abuse history with your caregivers* and what you need in order to feel safe and cared for is a sign of a very good relationship.

Some caregivers have *routines that they prefer to follow* with their maternity patients regarding such procedures as intravenous fluids, electronic fetal monitoring, rupturing the membranes, episiotomy, and others. Do you know your caregiver's routines? Are you comfortable with them?

16. Strangers (nurses, unfamiliar caregivers)

It is rare that a woman knows the nurses who will care for her. There are usually *several strangers* involved because of shift changes, coffee breaks, and staffing requirements.

If your doctor or midwife is one of a group *you may have a stranger in charge of your care* during labor. This person has your chart to review but may not have discussed your case with your primary caregiver.

17. Behavior of caregiving staff toward you

Some nurses and caregivers are quite matter-of-fact about *entering your hospital room without knocking*, seeing you *partially or fully undressed, touching you, being with you when you urinate*, or doing procedures (checking temperature, blood pressure, position of monitors, discharge on your bed pad, fullness of your bladder) *without asking or warning you.*

Vaginal exams are often treated casually. If you react with tension or resistance, the examiner may say, "Relax and it won't hurt so much (or take so long); I'm only touching you; you're making it harder on yourself."

If you express a preference for care that is not customary in that hospital, the caregiving staff may respond with *lack of cooperation, ignoring your requests, questioning your judgment, or hostility.*

If you disclose your sexual abuse history to your nurse or caregiver, she or he may be *embarrassed, uncomfortable, unable to respond* in a way that would put you at ease.

18. Issues with your partner, family, friends, or doula

Sometimes there is an *unspoken fear or worry* that loved ones or members of your support team may be *unreliable, disappointing, judgmental, or undependable.*

Feelings of *dependency on your partner or other support people*—to protect you—are sometimes accompanied by *doubts about their adequacy or commitment* to meeting your needs.

19. The actual birth

(If she has seen a graphic birth film or slides) In the film (slides) you saw how the *vagina bulges and stretches open as the baby pushes on through.*

Many women feel the stretching of their vaginas as a *burning, splitting sensation.*

Sometimes this stretching is gradual and *takes hours*; sometimes the baby almost pops out in only a few contractions

20. Pushing effort, sounds, and pain

During the second stage you may feel an *intense involuntary reflex* urge to push that comes and goes during contractions. Your reflex response is to strain, sometimes letting out a *bellow, a roar, or a grunting sound.* Your pushing effort may surprise you with its strength. You may also *push out some feces.*

If you do not have an urge to push (from anesthetic or for no clear reason) you may *be told to hold your breath and strain hard and long,* in an effort to push your baby out.

The pain associated with the baby coming down and out varies from no pain or a good feeling to *extreme stretching or acute searing pain.*

In many hospitals, the nurse and/or caregiver implore you to hold your breath and *chant "push, push, push!"* They may count to 10 while you push. They may become very directive, insisting that you *follow their orders* of when to push, when to breathe, when to rest.

21. Episiotomy or tearing

Just before birth, some caregivers *surgically cut the perineum to enlarge the vagina* to spare you the last few contractions. It is sometimes done with local anesthesia. If not, anesthesia is given (several injections in the perineum) after birth before the perineum is stitched back together.

Many caregivers *do not ask or tell you* about the episiotomy before doing it.

Though rarely felt when it is done, the episiotomy usually causes *pain for a week or more* afterwards.

Many caregivers who do episiotomies believe that without one, the *vagina and perineum will be overstretched and weak.* They believe that *sexual pleasures of male* and female are diminished without an episiotomy. [Authors' note: Scientific research indicates that these assumed benefits do not result from episiotomy. In fact, if an episiotomy is done, it is actually more likely to extend than if she tears spontaneously. Episiotomy does not prevent overstretching and weakness, nor does it enhance sexual pleasure. Because it does shorten the delivery by a few minutes, it does sometimes benefit a baby in distress.]

A *tear, or tears, of the tissue in the vagina or perineum* sometimes occurs (in approximately one half of births), without an episiotomy. The *tissue stretches* to a point and if it *cannot stretch enough,* it then splits open to allow the baby through.

Some tears are small; others are large enough to *require stitches.* All episiotomies require stitches.

22. Forceps or vacuum extractor

If the baby's head does not move down with your pushing efforts, either forceps or a vacuum extractor may be *inserted into your vagina, grasping your baby's head.* The doctor *pulls* while your uterus contracts and you push. The doctor's added efforts usually bring the baby down.

Instruments are used if the *baby's head is large* for your pelvis, in a position or angle that makes for a poor fit between head and pelvis, or if your contractions or pushing efforts are deemed *inadequate.*

The *vagina may be bruised* and an episiotomy is more likely in an instrumental delivery.

23. Immediate postpartum procedures

After the birth, your caregiver *inspects the vaginal canal* to determine if and where stitches are necessary. This involves *spreading your labia, shining a light into your vagina, swabbing any bleeding area* with a gauze pad and *looking in.*

If you have not been anesthetized, this procedure is *painful, as the vagina is now very sensitive.*

Before stitching (if you have not been anesthetized earlier), the caregiver *injects your perineum and vagina* in several places. The injections sting, but within minutes, numb the area.

The stitching process should be painless, but occasionally an unanesthetized area is stitched, causing *stinging pain.*

The nurse will palpate your abdomen frequently during the first hour or two after birth to check the firmness of your uterus. A firmly contracted uterus keeps you from excessive blood loss. If it is not firm, she *vigorously kneads your uterus,* which usually causes it to contract. This may be *quite painful.*

24. Cesarean section

This operation is considered necessary if there are *insoluble problems* with the baby's or mother's health and well-being, if labor progress stops and does not respond to measures to speed it up, or if the *baby seems stuck* and won't move down.

You will be anesthetized, probably with a spinal or epidural, which *numbs you* from your breasts to your toes. Or you might on rare occasions receive general anesthesia, which causes *loss of consciousness.*

You are *unable to move your legs or roll over,* so 3 or 4 staff members will place your body on rollers and slide you between your bed and the delivery table. You cannot help move yourself. Your legs are *strapped together* onto the table, so they won't fall off.

A drape is placed between your head and lower body so that you cannot see the surgery or the surgeons and they cannot see your face.

One or both arms are usually strapped to boards that extend out from each side of the table.

Everyone in the room, including your partner, *wears a mask.* You may have an *oxygen mask on your face.*

You may feel some *pressure and pulling sensations* (though you should feel no pain) during the surgery.

The surgeons often discuss unrelated matters with each other *as if you are not there,* such as other patients, sport events, vacations, good restaurants...

After the surgery it is common for women to *feel nauseated and to tremble* for a period of a few minutes to an hour. There are medications to stop those reactions, but some may make you *groggy.*

Your first contact with your baby occurs after the baby has been checked and found to be healthy. The baby is wrapped so that you see only the face. The nurse *frees at least one of your arms* so that you can touch your baby, but *you will not be able to hold the baby* until later. Your partner may hold the baby close to you.

The first feeding takes place one or two hours after the birth, when you are in your bed. If groggy from post-operative medications, you may be *unable to do the first feeding or to remember later that you did it.* The *nurse might grasp your breast* and put it in your baby's mouth.

Your partner may have more time and cuddling with your baby than you in the first days after the delivery.

25. Holding and suckling baby

After the birth, the *baby is removed to a warmer* for a while, to be checked over by the nurse or doctor, cleaned up, given eye treatment and a Vitamin K shot, weighed, have blood drawn to check blood sugar, and when deemed okay, wrapped up in a warm blanket and given to the you. It may be a *half hour or longer before you get to hold your baby.*

Once you get to hold your baby, you have the opportunity to put him or her to your breast to suckle. This first feeding usually takes place while you are lying almost flat on the bed, so it may be difficult for you to see. *Your breasts are exposed, you may feel awkward, strangers may be watching, or your baby may not seem interested.*

Your baby opens his or her mouth wide, locates your nipple, and latches on and *sucks on your nipple, possibly very suddenly and strongly.*

Personal Meanings for Triggers

When the description of a potential trigger elicits a negative emotional reaction from the client, the counselor notes it on the form. The next step is to figure out why. What is it about that trigger that is personally upsetting to the client?

The reasons for each trigger (the personal meanings) are different from one woman to another, as different as the women themselves, but they are often directly related to their abuse experiences.

The personal meanings provide a basis for developing strategies to avoid or minimize the triggers. Although strategies that will help with each trigger differ from one woman to another, as one gains experience, one realizes that some triggers are successfully handled with one of only a few strategies. For example, for women who are troubled by the anonymity or exposure or ugliness that come with the hospital gown, wearing their own gown or long T-shirt during labor is an easy solution. These are the "easy triggers." Others require creative cooperative effort to develop highly individualized solutions.

The counselor patiently seeks the underlying associations that make each trigger upsetting to the client. Such efforts should reveal vital insight into the specific effects of her abuse. The first time the counselor asks, "What is it about this trigger that is upsetting?" the client, who has probably never thought about this, may not be able to answer. Or she may give a rather shallow or general answer, such as, "Who would actually like being in the hospital?" or, "Any doctor who does episiotomies practices genital mutilation," or, "There is too much done for the convenience of the doctor, and not enough for us patients."

Questions such as, "Does this event, action, or trigger remind you of anything that has happened to you before?", or "Have you ever experienced anything similar?", or "Describe your feeling when you were picturing that trigger. Have you ever had such a feeling?" will help the client get to a deeper level of personal meaning. It is at this point that the client may connect the trigger with other events in her life, in which she had a similar psychological reaction.

The content in the Table, "Sample Responses to the Triggers," on the next page is taken from our client records to illustrate the variety of personal meanings a counselor may encounter. Strategies for those triggers are listed in the right-hand column. Some are widely applicable to many clients, while others are specific to a single client's unique fears.

Once the triggers and personal meanings have been discovered, then client and counselor work together to brainstorm strategies that are acceptable to the client. The strategies have several purposes: to devise a meaningful birth plan; to instill a realistic sense of control and optimism in the client; and to help ensure that her abuse history does not adversely influence her experience of labor and birth.

Sample Responses to Triggers

Trigger	Some Women's Personal Meanings (in their words)	Various Strategies
Changed appearance (make-up, hairstyle, clothing)	• I want to be beautiful in labor. That gown is awful. • My identity is tied up in looking my best. I feel vulnerable when I don't look attractive.	• Wear own gown or long T-shirt. • Figure out how to tie hair up to look good. • Paint nails, wear minimum waterproof make-up. • Look at photos of laboring women. Try to see their beauty & power. Try to reframe for yourself
Nakedness/ exposure of sexual parts of body	• I'm so fat; I don't want people to see and talk about my disgusting body. • I don't want people staring at my private parts. My father used to stare at me naked. • I've always doubted my femininity and played it down, but in this pregnancy I'm relishing my body. I like being a woman! But I'm not myself. These feelings are so new they scare me. • If I become sensual, I'll worry about being judged by my husband. He inhibits me.	• Try to keep covered. Enlist help with this from loved ones. • Wear sports bra in labor and underwear beneath gown. • Put in birth plan that you want to remain covered as much as possible. • Discuss feeling and being sensual with partner. Allow him to take a break if he is uncomfortable. Have others present who are comfortable with it.
Secretions (show, blood, amniotic fluid, feces)	• It's filthy. I have to be clean. I take 3 showers a day. I always cleaned up and washed the sheets after my cousin or stepfather raped me. • The blood scares me. Blood means something is wrong. Will it freak me out? Will I be gross? • Dad was into anal penetration. I'd die if I saw my stool. • Husband will pass out if I smell up the place. How disgusting!	• Clean up after myself. Change my own bed pads. • Reframe perception of blood as healing blood – a sign that your body is working well. • Wear a pad in under-pants 'til delivery • Self-administered enema in early labor.

Trigger	Some Women's Personal Meanings (in their words)	Various Strategies
Body positions (hands and knees, squatting, on back with legs pulled up and spread)	• On all fours, my backside will be out for everyone to see as soon as they walk in. • People coming at me from behind—I can't have it. • Compromising, humiliating. I've been like that in the past for someone's sexual needs. • On hands and knees–it's like being a helpless animal. I need my hands to be able to fight people off. • On my back, with stirrups, especially, I can't get up & leave. I'm pinned down.	• Kneel facing foot of bed or leaning over a birth ball to keep hands free. • Keep a sheet over lower half of body. • Avoid compromising positions. • Plan to push in upright sitting position or on side
Hospital environment smell, machines, sounds, uniformed personnel)	• I've been to the emergency room with nausea, panic, & pain; had to wait; it was scary • The hospital tour made me feel sick. I wish I could have the baby at home, but I'm scared of that too. • I've had medical fears as long as I can remember • Open doors, lack of privacy, people wandering in & out; it isn't safe.	• Tour hospital; separate maternity care from psychiatric emergencies. • Bring in flowers, music, own pillow, etc. • Take hospital tour, more than once, if necessary, to get used to it. • Keep door shut.
Blood draws, amnio-centesis	• Contact with blood & guts; • Needles make me feel faint; • I've passed out with blood draws. • Needle phobia since childhood. • Invasion into and taking something out of body. Some of the sex I've had felt like that.	• Distraction; talk with nurse; partner engage me and talk me through. • I may choose to "check out" for awhile. • Look away. Think of something else. • Have a dry run at clinic. Nurse does every-thing except needle stick. Explains every-thing. Counselor there to help client describe feelings, and devise coping techniques (counting slowly, lying down, having a friend there).

Trigger	Some Women's Personal Meanings (in their words)	Various Strategies
Intravenous fluids	• Sensation of fluid going in. It's staying there, implanted in my body. • Seeing needle coming at me. I've had to be held down. They got angry at me.	• Use same as for blood draws • Cover IV site with wash cloth or sweatbands. • Birth plan – ask to avoid IV unless medically necessary.
Vaginal exams, Rupture of membranes with amnihook	• Foreign objects in vagina • I'm a big baby. I cry with a Pap smear. • "Piece of meat" feeling. It's like a rape. They force your legs apart and tell you to relax. • I'm very deep inside. Doctors jam their fingers in and push on my uterus just to find my cervix. I scream.	• Ask for as few as possible. • State needs (go slow, explain what you're about to do; let me tell you when to go ahead). • Let me cry if I need to. • Be gentle • Put needs in birth plan.
Connection to lines from body (monitor, IV, continuous blood pressure, bladder catheter, epidural...)	• Invasion, whether breaking skin with needle or knife, catheter in private parts of body; • I don't want to be tied down. I have to be able to get away. • Reminds me of being pinned down by my father while he tickled & molested me. I was helpless. • Puts me on guard. • No catheter! I had bladder infections all through childhood (from the abuse). The catheters were as bad as the abuse. I had to be held down.	• Be sure to be up and moving, even with IV & monitor, to show that you are not helpless. • Talk about how you feel. • Have partner, doula remind you that you know how to handle flashbacks. That was then; this is now. As as adult, you understand more now and do not have to be frightened. • If you need a catheter, ask to be anesthetized first.
Restriction to bed	• I don't like lying there while everyone stands above me. It feels like the victim position. • I'm not sick. I want to be strong. • I have to stand up & move when I'm in pain. I can't lie there and take it.	• Item for birth plan • If bedrest is necessary for health, ask questions to understand reasons & choices. • Think of ways to move in bed and visualizations to use as alternatives to being out of bed.

Trigger	Some Women's Personal Meanings (in their words)	Various Strategies
Pain with contractions	• I'm a wimp when it comes to pain. I even go crazy with menstrual cramps. • I was shocked by how much it hurt before–chaos, fear. • Just because I was a girl, I had to put up with abuse. Now as a woman I have to put up with labor pain. It's so unfair.	• Have a game plan for coping. • Ask partner, doula to make suggestions, not ask you what you need. • Master self-help relaxation & comfort measures. • Have a doula for comfort & reassurance. • Plan on an epidural.
Pain-related emotions (panic, loss of control, shame at behavior	• Loss of control seems unbearable. • I'm a control freak. I learned a long time ago not to let things get out of my control. If I fall apart, you might as well knock me out. • Last time, I got bitchy & numbed out & had hallucinations of being violated.	• Recognize what you can control (response to contractions) and cannot control (the contractions themselves). • Master acceptable self-calming ways to respond to contractions. • Tell nurse of tendency to panic. • Develop ways you and partner or doula can recognize and control panic • Consider pain medications. • Have partner or doula check in: "What was going through your mind during that contraction?" If distressing thoughts, they provide more emotional support.

Trigger	**Some Women's Personal Meanings (in their words)**	**Various Strategies**
Expressions of pain (grimace, cry out, tense or writhe)	• I'm afraid they'll criticize me for the way I handle the pain. • I'll bite my tongue and pass out before I'll show pain. My uncle never knew how bad he was hurting me. • I'd hate to scream or swear at my partner. He's not inflicting it. I have no right to do that, but I used to scream during the abuse. • I might laugh to keep me and everyone else from freaking out.	• Express pain in a purposeful way. Sing opera loud; complain about pain; put a rhythm to moaning or moving. • Be sure nurse reminds me I can have pain meds, so I don't have to ask, because I won't ask. Shut door to room. • Partner or someone else, in a firm voice, stops her from being abusive or swearing. • Or assures her in advance that he will not take it personally. • Tell partner if you're starting to freak out. Let him or her interpret your behavior to caregivers. • Consider an epidural to regain composure.
Nausea/ vomiting	• I always vomited after I was abused. I always do now when I'm scared. • Vomiting is the ultimate in being out of control.	• Separate vomiting during labor from vomiting after abuse or when afraid. Use "self-talk," containment, visualization (See Chapter 9). • Sip mint tea, use aromatherapy, acupressure • IV fluids to prevent dehydration with vomiting • Medications to ease vomiting

Trigger	Some Women's Personal Meanings (in their words)	Various Strategies
Pain medication "tradeoffs": Narcotics: (groggy, sleepy, less pain, more relaxation) Epidural: (pain relief, numb, can't move much, need more interventions)	• As an addict, I can't take any drugs. It'll throw me right back into hell. • I hate being foggy. I have to stay alert. An epidural will help me keep my composure. I don't want to feel a thing down there. • An epidural makes me helpless. I can't do anything for myself. I have to be able to flee.	• Item for birth plan – no narcotics. • Clearly state preferences re epidural. • Learn about other pain relief measures (bath, massage, relaxation, breathing, etc.) to use instead of or before an epidural.
Relationship with caregiver (gender, familiarity, trust, expectations, confidence)	• I'm really counting on my own doctor; I don't trust any of the others. • I can't have a man doing a vaginal exam • I have to nag to be heard in their busy practice. I annoy them because I'm demanding. • Last time I thought I was going to die, and no one came to help me • My doc's fine on the touchy-feely stuff, but I worry about her medical competence. She's almost too reassuring. • It almost scares me. They're letting me run the show. Maybe I intimidate them. I almost wish they'd say no to some of my requests.	• Find out just how available your own doctor is. Tell how you feel about backup doctors and learn options, if any. • Ask doctor to share birth plan with backup docs. • Have a doula for reassurance, continued presence, and assistance with communication. • Ask caregiver if your requests are within reason for safety. Are they realistic?

Trigger	Some Women's Personal Meanings (in their words)	Various Strategies
Strangers–(nurses, unfamiliar caregivers)	• Have you ever felt as though you don't count with anyone? That's what I'm afraid of with with the nurses. I'll be nothing to them. I seem to be a totally forgettable person. • It's such a gamble. What if I get a bitchy nurse? I can get pretty bitchy too, if I have to.	• Write preferences in a birth plan, so you are not a stranger to the nurse. • Practice maintaining eye contact when talking with authority figures. • Review feedback techniques in Chapter 7 • Choose a doula so a busy or unfriendly nurse is not so important. • When calling hospital in labor, request a nurse who is supportive of natural childbirth, even if you want medication. She may know more about emotional needs.
Behavior of caregiving staff toward you (respect, control, asking before touching, individual treatment)	• All these people with their own agendas. They don't really want to help me. • I don't want to feel I'm being a chore, with all my demands. • I've seen people robbed of their dignity in a hospital situation because a nurse is disrespectful.	• Consider disclosing abuse history to staff to help them understand your needs. • Tell charge nurse if there is incompatibility with a nurse. • Try not to be the cause of poor relationship with nurse.
Issues with partner, family, friends, doula, (disapproval, abandonment, unreliability, inadequacy, disagreement, trust, dependency)	• If I make too much noise, my partner will just walk out. • My alcoholic mother is coming to the birth. I can't stop her. • I think my doula wants me to go natural. I don't want to let her down.	• Discuss fears of abandonment or disapproval with partner. • Don't call mother until after birth. • Clarify pain medications preferences with doula. If uncomfortable with her response, switch doulas. • Have only those people at the birth whom you feel have something positive to give you.

Trigger	Some Women's Personal Meanings (in their words)	Various Strategies
The actual birth, baby bulging perineum, emerging from your body	• I want to think of this as a miraculous thing, but I'm afraid it will feel like rape. • I can't picture myself giving birth. • I'm afraid I'm going to hate the baby for doing this to me.	• Think of the baby as your ally — taking the pain away. You can push the pain out with the baby. • Talk to the fetus about your fear that you'll blame him, and explain that it is not about him, but that the fear is rooted in your memories of abuse. • Try to separate rape from birth (See ch. 9 on self-help).
Pushing effort, the sounds and the pain	• It's so animal. • I don't want to be so out of control. It is so involuntary; you grunt, and make horrendous noises. • It's as if you become your vagina. • I can't even watch videos of a birth.	• Think about how well animals give birth. • Warn loved ones I may make primal sounds.
Episiotomy/ tearing	• I feel bad for my body that it has to hurt like that. • Purposefully cutting my genitals vs. a tear happening. A tear is better, but I hope I don't get either. • Episiotomy is mutilation of females by males.	• Prenatal perineal massage • Hot compresses to perineum while pushing. • Select a caregiver who does not do many episiotomies. • Talk honestly with caregiver about these feelings.

Trigger	Some Women's Personal Meanings (in their words)	Various Strategies
Forceps or vacuum extractor (VE) delivery	• Ghastly. Any instrument in vagina is like a terrible punishment because you won't push your baby out. • I'll have to be knocked out for that. It's like a giant rape. • I will probably dissociate, just leave my body.	• Choose caregiver who tries to avoid these. • Do things to prevent forceps & VE: use alternatives to epidural in early labor or throughout; move about in labor; use gravity positions to facilitate delivery. • In birth plan, state desire to avoid these. Perhaps disclose abuse and tendency to dissociate. • Accept that it may be necessary and that you will need to have support from partner – being held, distracted, encouraged to push, or to "go away."
Cesarean section	• They tie you down. It's the ultimate ravage. • Part of me wants a cesarean so I can spare my vagina. • Memories of ritual abuse with sharp instruments. I lay there the same as for a cesarean. • I'll just have to deal with it – probably afterwards. I can't imagine me having a cesarean.	• Read about cesareans so you know something of what to expect. • Have partner and doula present if possible. Let them help you with self-calming measures. • Keep at least one arm free. • Ask anesthetist to keep you posted on how much longer, explain what's happening and reassure you; and check on the adequacy of the pain relief.
Holding, suckling baby (wet with secretions, blood)	• Slimy baby – ugh! • I'm afraid I will feel nothing for the baby. I don't feel much now. I might not want to breastfeed.	• Ask to have baby wiped off and wrapped before you hold her. • Give yourself permission to need time before falling in love with baby. Honor your feelings. Have partner hold baby at first, if you don't wish to.

Trigger	Some Women's Personal Meanings (in their words)	Various Strategies
Postpartum (inspecting, stitching vagina, fundal massage)	• It's the "penetration thing," especially if a male does it. • Inflicted pain is worse than labor pain in some ways. It's more victimizing.	• Ask caregiver to be gentle; describe what is being done. • Hold or look at baby during procedures. • Remember to continue breathing techniques; may need intensive coaching.

The counselor will be most effective if she or he has a broad knowledge of available options in childbirth, and of usual management practices in area hospitals and among local caregivers. A creative and open-minded spirit is the key to finding suitable strategies.

Themes usually emerge in the course of discovering the personal meaning, such as: a need to remain in control or fear of losing control; distrust of authority figures and strangers; shame over her body; feelings of being judged; a need to show no pain; fear centered on vaginal pain and damage; expectation of being treated as an object. By recognizing the themes, both client and counselor are helped to devise appropriate strategies.

Client-Centered and Caregiver-Centered Strategies

Some strategies are client-centered; others are caregiver-centered. Client-centered strategies are self-help measures that the client and her support people devise. Some insightful clients consult the filled-in trigger form and write their own synthesis of what they have learned. They may share it with their partner, doula, caregiver, and other people who will be at the birth.

On the other hand, caregiver-centered strategies require the cooperation of nurses and midwife or doctor. They should be discussed with the caregiver or included in the birth plan, Using I-messages (see Chapter 7), the client can express her triggers as fears or needs, then ask the staff to assist her with the strategies. Such requests as knocking before entering the room, introducing themselves by name, washing their hands where she can see them doing it, and heeding the client's preferences regarding pain medications, procedures, and interventions are included in caregiver-centered strategies.

Case Where the Strategy Was Worse Than the Trigger

Sometimes a possible strategy is actually worse for a client than the trigger!

Ellen

Ellen was particularly distressed at the prospect of excreting bloody mucus and expelling fecal material as she pushed her baby out. The thought of other people—strangers as well as her husband—seeing and smelling this horrified her. As she and her counselor discussed the "personal meaning" for this trigger, Ellen revealed that she had always felt her body was filthy inside and out, and she finds bodily fluids, excretions, and smells to be repulsive. She is fastidious about cleanliness. She bathes once or twice a day, uses deodorant, feminine deodorant spray, and perfume to prevent detection of any bodily odors. During menses she changes her pads constantly. Her abuser had inserted objects into her vagina and anus and she fantasized that they were filthy and that parts of them were still there—she could never get clean enough.

Such feelings can cause a woman to "hold back" during the second stage, that is, contract her pelvic floor muscles involuntarily. When her counselor proposed as a strategy that Ellen self-administer an enema in early labor, Ellen replied, "I can't do that.

I'd rather poop all over everywhere than do that to myself!" She was dismayed and hopeless until her counselor calmly normalized her fear: "Self-administered enemas are a problem for lots of people. Let's forget that as a strategy. There are other ways to deal with this trigger." The strategy that felt best to Ellen was to disclose her worries about passing some feces to her caregiver and ask that her caregiver cover her perineum and anus with a disposable hot compress. Any fecal material then could easily and inconspicuously be wiped away and thrown away with the compress, which would quickly be replaced.

In summary, birth preparation counseling for the sexual abuse survivor consists of these steps: Discussion of her present circumstances and abuse history; identification of what makes her feel safe and secure; listing of ways in which she usually reacts to fear and pain; identification of triggers and their personal meanings; planning strategies to avoid, minimize, or deal with triggers; preparation of a birth plan to inform and elicit cooperation and support from nurses and caregivers.

The Birth Plan

A birth plan is a letter to the nursing staff and caregiver, in which the woman and her partner tell something about themselves, their fears and concerns, and their preferences for the care of mother and baby during labor, birth, and afterwards. It includes preferences for normal labor and a healthy baby, but also considers the "unexpected"—a difficult or complicated labor, a cesarean birth, and problems with the baby. (Appendix 4 is a form that can be used as a guide for women or couples to prepare their birth plan.)

Abuse survivors should consider disclosing in their birth plan the fact that they were sexually abused and how this has affected their feelings about the upcoming birth. This is particularly helpful to the nurses and caregivers whom the woman has not met. For many abuse survivors, however, openly disclosing such personal information would be too uncomfortable or risky. Alternatively, they might clearly state their fears and concerns, and the kind of help they need from the staff (the caregiver-centered strategies described above).

Appendix 5 presents case histories of two women, including their abuse histories, their triggers and strategies, their birth plans, and accounts of their birth experiences. One of the women, Joanna, is a well-educated artist (whose history and birth story we told in Chapter 4), who had had the additional benefit of years of psychotherapy, and the other, Sherry, is an unsophisticated teen. As can be seen in the summary of their birth plans, both were able to effectively describe their needs.

Birth plans are introduced and described in detail in *Pregnancy Childbirth and the Newborn* by Simkin, Whalley and Keppler, or Simkin's *The Birth Partner*. (See Appendix: Books.)

The Dream Interview

Sometimes, when a client requests birth counseling because of high anxiety that she can't really put into words, the counselor might ask her to dream about it. Before going to bed the client reminds herself to dream about whatever is bothering her, in order to understand it better. Then if she dreams anything, she writes down whatever she recalls—even if it is only a few fragments. E. Sue Blume recommends that she keep pencil and paper by her bed, and write down details without even opening her eyes or turning on a light; this helps to keep much of the dream from disappearing from her consciousness. The recalled material becomes the subject of a counseling session.

Dreams express emotions or thoughts that are not available to a person at a conscious level. They provide coded or disguised messages, which when decoded, add to the dreamer's self-understanding and clarify some vague feelings or questions.

Birth counselors can use a dream interpretation technique—the Dream Interview—pioneered by Gayle Delaney, PhD, author of *Living Your Dreams*, and applied specifically to pregnancy-related dreams by Eileen Stukane in *The Dream Worlds of Pregnancy*. This technique is one that Delaney devised for lay people. One of the greatest appeals of the Dream Interview technique is that the dreamer does all the hard work and provides much of the symbolic meaning. She also is to a great extent in control of the amount of self-knowledge that will be gained from the dream. The birth counselor normally does the interviewing, but the client's partner, close friend, or relative, or even the client herself may do it. The interviewer facilitates the search for meaning with simple, non-leading questions. The interviewer is also the note-taker and may tentatively suggest a hypothesis for a possible interpretation, for example: "I wonder if there's a connection between your upsetting dream about pregnant women dying and some of your worries about how your life will change when the baby is born, a recognition that your life as you now know it will end?" The dreamer is the real authority on the meaning and whether it feels "right." Also, she can regulate, consciously or unconsciously, how much she learns from each dream. The Dream Interview technique does not deal with dreams in the depth and detail that many psychotherapists might achieve. (Chapter 11 includes discussion of dream work as done in a psychotherapeutic setting.)

Dreams have many layers of meaning. A dream about having a baby boy, for example, may be taken literally as a message that the baby is a boy, but the Dream Interview, by delving deeper, may reveal that the dream about a baby boy is a way of expressing what it might mean to the dreamer to have a boy. By exploring questions like, "Why a boy, not a girl?" or, "Does the baby remind you of anyone?"or, "How do you feel in your dream as you see or hold the baby?" much more insight might be gained.

The Technique, Step by Step

One way to work with dreams is for the client and counselor to plan in advance to do a Dream Interview at the next appointment. If so, the counselor asks the client to ask herself, before going to bed to dream an answer to a specific question, such as, "Why am I so worried about the birth?" "Why do I feel so different from the other pregnant women in my childbirth class?" "Why am I uneasy with my caregiver?" "What kind of a mother will I be?" She needs to expect that the answer will come in clues, or as metaphor to be deciphered, and that one dream may not give all the answers. She should write down all that she remembers of her dream. Most of the time, however, dreams are unplanned, and the client will report that she had a disturbing dream, and it seems to be important to discuss it right then (although the counselor should give the client a choice of adding an appointment to their counseling in order to finish the trigger work). The counselor asks her to give her dream a title and relate it as described below.

Before the dream is told, the counselor prepares to take notes. One helpful way is to fold a sheet of paper down the middle; write the dream on the left and use the right half to make notes on the client's answers to the counselor's questions.

The counselor asks the client to give the dream a title and to relive it—to describe it in the present tense, as if it is happening now. The reason for using the present tense is that the client relives rather than recalls the dream, and, in doing so, is more likely to reexperience some of the feelings associated with it. The counselor tries not to interrupt with questions, except when something is unclear. She takes notes as the story is told.

When the client is finished, the counselor asks general questions:

What do you think this dream is about?

Literally, is it related to anything you did or felt recently?

How do you feel about these recent events in your life that were related to your dream? Notes on these answers might go on a separate sheet of paper.

Then, the counselor asks seemingly naive questions about each person, object, place, color, and feeling mentioned by the dreamer, such as:

- Describe the man. Does he remind you of anyone in your life?
- Why green? What does that shade of green remind you of?
- Who are these people? Whom do they remind you of?
- Describe the place. Does it remind you of any place you have ever been?
- Why a snake? What are your experiences with snakes? Does it remind you of something?
- Describe the way you felt when...? Have you ever felt that way? Please describe it.

Thus, the dreamer supplies much of the symbolism and meaning. The counselor writes notes on the answers on the right side of the page opposite the description of it in the dream recall.

The next step is to find the meaning(s) of the dream. "What is this dream telling us?" The counselor may have some clues, but before mentioning them, may have other questions based on the client's previous answers. These might confirm or reject the counselor's hunches about the dream's meaning. For example, "You mentioned that the dress you are wearing in the dream is the one you wore on your first date with Jim. Can you tell me more about that first date? And about Jim?" "You said the group of people was like a church congregation. Tell me more about them and the church. Do they remind you of any church that you know?"

The counselor asks the client if she can understand the dream's meaning any better now. The counselor might offer a tentative hypothesis, if the client has no more to offer, and if the counselor has picked up some possible interpretations. She asks (does not tell) the client if it makes any sense. It is very likely that they both will gain new insights and greater depth of understanding. One impressive effect is that most clients feel much better after a dream interview, and marvel at the creativity and cleverness of their own unconscious minds in forming dreams, even the frightening ones. They also appreciate the new awareness they have gained.

Laura

Laura, age 21, single and pregnant, came for counseling six weeks before her due date. She had many fears – that the baby would be abnormal, that she would blank out during labor, and that "the baby could never come out that way." She planned to have a friend with her during the birth. In an effort to clarify her fears, the counselor asked Laura to try to dream before coming to her appointment. Here is a condensed re-creation of the notes of her Dream Interviews:

Dream #1 Title: The Disturbing Dream

Laura's description	*Counselor's questions* and client's answers
I'm in a delivery room, lying there with my legs in stirrups.	*Describe the room more.* Pinky-maroon walls—my favorite color. My room as a kid was that color.
The delivery room has a long mirror in front, standing on the floor. The only other thing was the bed. There's no one in the room. It is painful. I'm screaming, but no one comes.	*Describe the pain and the screaming.* It's a draining pain; I'm not crying over the pain. I'm not yelling loud; I'm not saying anything; no one hears it.
Suddenly a contraction. I push and push. I see the baby's head in the mirror. I'm giving birth alone.	*How does it feel to push? What or who does the baby look like?* It's natural to push and painful, but that's not why I'm screaming. It's the fear and being alone.
Next thing, the doctor is holding the baby, stillborn. I awaken crying.	*Describe the MD and your feelings.* He has a thing over his face, dark hair, a blue gown on. He's holding the baby out front.
I know there's a problem and no one is telling me. I don't see any hands or eyes on the baby. The MD keeps saying, "It's stillborn. It's stillborn."	*Tell me what you feel.* All I can do is cry. I feel lost. There is no one to console me.

Does this dream remind you of anything in your life?

At age 16, I had an abortion. The doctor in my dream is the abortion doctor. I did it alone. Only my aunt knew. No one else knew. I would always wake up crying night after night for a long time after the abortion. I've always felt guilt whenever I see a baby. When I got pregnant accidentally this time, no way could I do that again.

The counselor's questions had been basic and simple, but extremely important in getting to the deeper meaning of the dream. Ostensibly the dream is expressing the client's fear about being alone and giving birth to a stillborn baby, but with the counselor's questions about the color of the delivery room, the stillborn baby, and the doctor, it becomes clear that the upcoming birth is triggering memories of her traumatic abortion and the unresolved sadness and guilt that she feels.

Laura had another clearly related dream the same night that made further advances in her understanding of her fears:

Dream #2 Title: So Weird—Nothing To Do With Baby

Laura's description	*Counselor's questions* and Client's answers
I'm not pregnant in the dream, but I am at the end. I have long hair. I'm getting ready to go out. I'm in front of the mirror. The mirror is on the back of the bathroom door.	*Will you tell more about your hair? Where are you going? How do you feel?* My hair is like it was when I was 16. I'm flipping it around; I'm going out for the evening with my friends. I don't know where. I'm happy.
My friends are with me. They're jumping around in the bathroom being silly. We're going to hang out at the mall.	*Who are the friends? Do they remind you of anyone in your life?* No specific ones, three or four people.
I have my little white dress on.	*Can you tell me more about the dress?* It's sheer in a couple of layers, tight around the waist, really short with a full flurry skirt. Not what I usually wear. I was a tomboy.
I start throwing up little white worms with red eyes. My friends start screaming. I keep throwing up—thousands of them. I'm looking at them.	*Can you tell me more about the throwing up?* I turn around onto my hands and knees. The worms are gross, slimy, disgusting. My friends are standing over me, screaming, "Oh my God," going crazy, freaking out over the worms. I feel disgusting and dirty.
Next, I'm lying there pregnant. I wake up. I've been holding my waist while throwing up. When I stopped throwing up "It's over."	

What is this dream about?

> I was on my own quite a bit when I was 15 or 16. I got pregnant the first time I had sex. The guy was 23, giving me drugs and drinks. I said no to the guy; he took advantage of me. He thought I was saying yes. He had sex with me on my hands and knees. I was sick afterwards. It was my fault. I was disappointed in myself—so irresponsible. It totally ruined my first time with sex. I felt disgusting and dirty. I couldn't tell anyone. For a week afterwards I told my Dad I was sick. That's the pregnancy that I had an abortion for.

These dreams provided much rich imagery. The counselor, through her questions about Laura's hairstyle and dress, was able to establish that this dream was related to something that happened at age 16 or earlier. Laura's friends, who freaked out in the abortion dream, were not around for her in the birth dream, described earlier. The counselor, in thinking about a tomboy in a white sheer dress, thought about purity, virginity, communion dress, bridal gown, not drinking, drugs, rape, and pregnancy. The fact that Laura was a "tomboy" for whom a dress like this was out of character, tells us that what she did was not "the real her." She was not one who partied and asked for sex. Her formerly high opinion of herself was shattered. She was to blame. The counselor wondered if that irony represented the difference between past expectations of herself—fun at the mall with her friends—and reality—rape, self-disgust, loneliness, and pregnancy. The tie between the hands and knees position for throwing up the worms and the rape while Laura was drunk led the counselor to wonder if the worms might represent sperm, but Laura did not think so.

These dreams led to more discussion in which Laura revealed that she was raised by her father who left her with a baby-sitter when he was working. She was abused by the baby-sitter's husband from ages 4 to 9. During the abuse she would stare at the ceiling and memorize it. There were no threats. It all seemed "natural." At age 13, she realized it had been wrong. She "went crazy and had bad dreams about it." This dream may have touched on the earlier abuse as well (the white dress may have been a "little girl dress.")

Today she hates vaginal exams, and needs the "doctor to talk to me." She prefers a female midwife for the exams. Laura and the counselor completed the trigger work, identifying many triggers and planning strategies. As it all turned out, however, Laura never labored. At two weeks beyond her due date, her bag of waters broke, she had a herpes lesion on her labia, and her baby was delivered by cesarean section, which, Laura said later, "...was fine with me. I was lucky. I'm glad I didn't have to go through labor."

After the cesarean birth, Laura stated that the dream work helped her understand that her abortion had destroyed her sense of self-worth and had led her to self-blame, a sense of aloneness, and a belief that she deserved to be punished. The interpretation of her second dream the same night showed her that she was not to blame for the pregnancy and the abortion. She began to forgive herself.

It may be that Laura unconsciously desired a cesarean with no labor. The abdominal delivery avoided associations with her abortion, her dead baby, and her vagina, the source of much pain. The cesarean may have protected her from what might have been a re-traumatization. At this time in her life, a cesarean was psychologically safer than a vaginal birth. The counselor suggested that Laura enter psychotherapy when she feels ready to address these deep psychic injuries.

In summary, the Dream Interview is a useful technique for identifying unknown issues, unblocking the client who has trouble putting a name to her fears, and enlightening client and counselor on relevant past experiences.

Counseling after a Traumatic Birth

If care providers know that the client has a history of trauma and are aware that such a history increases the likelihood of Post-Traumatic Stress Disorder (PTSD) after childbirth, they may be able to prevent PTSD by individualizing their care. (See the "Self Assessment of Maternal Distress After A Difficult Birth," Appendix 6). Asking a woman to think about her childbirth-related distress helps both the woman and her counselor to know the degree of her distress, and how it is affecting her. This provides a good basis for discussion. After birth, other measures may minimize the likelihood of PTSD.

Immediately after birth

Even if the doctor, midwife, or nurse has only a few minutes while on break or on rounds, a few well-chosen and well-timed words may reduce the chances of PTSD.

For five minutes or less, the nurse, midwife, or doctor might visit the woman and say, "I'm on a little break and only have a couple of minutes. I wanted to stop in and see how you are...." "Your baby is adorable." "I just want to tell you what I found to be so special about you during your challenging labor. When you were still at 4 cm. after the third exam, and said, 'Baby, unless you obey us and come out soon, you're grounded until you're in school!' we could not believe your great attitude. And then you got up and walked some more. I was really impressed. You should be proud of yourself."

Relating an example that is complimentary to her will add a positive note to her birth experience. As she mulls over the events of her childbirth, the compliment and respect from an expert help reframe a potentially negative experience to a more fulfilling one.

The doula who attended the birth might do something similar in a phone call within 2 or 3 days after the birth, with the promise of an opportunity to go over it together in detail within a few weeks.

Follow-up Interview

A follow-up appointment several weeks after birth allows for more detailed processing of the birth because the woman, having had time to adjust to the new baby and early motherhood, may now feel ready to focus on her child's birth. This visit can occur at the four- or six-week check-up with the doctor or midwife, or at a mutually convenient time for the new parents and their birth doula.

Postpartum doulas and childbirth educators also sometimes process the birth experience with the woman.

Goals of this postpartum meeting are to assess the woman's perceptions of the events of the labor and birth, validate them, or fill in gaps in her memory or understanding; answer her questions; assess her emotional state for signs of anxiety or trauma; and help her resolve any distressing aspects. Such a meeting can possibly avoid recurring emotional reactions leading to PTSD. Sometimes, having a chance to process the troubling events with her caregiver is all she needs to come to resolution. If, however, she has unanswered questions, feels she or her baby was in danger, believes she was mistreated or taken beyond her limits, or feels angry at her caregivers, her negative feelings may worsen and become seriously debilitating. She might benefit from counseling or therapy.

Other Counseling Methods to Help Resolve a Disappointing Birth Experience

If the woman seeks counseling to resolve a disappointing birth experience, the counselor, with respectful, nonjudgmental, empathic listening, encourages the survivor to tell her birth story. Open-ended, tentative statements or questions such as, "Tell me about...," "What happened next?" "I wondered about..., aid the mother in reconstructing her experience.

Various other methods assist with processing the birth experience. These include: 1) writing the birth story; 2) writing "letters" to the caregiver in which the woman expresses her feelings and asks questions (Because these are not sent to the caregiver, the woman can write whatever she feels.); 3) creating imaginary role plays such as imagining talking to the people involved, saying what she would like to say, hearing what she would have liked or needed to hear; 4) dream work using the Dream Interview Technique; 5) artwork, drawing her feelings or symbolically representing her actual experience and then redrawing it as she wished it to be; 6) body work, dance, movement to release the emotional trauma held in the body; 7) designing a ceremony to affirm her experience; and 8) reviewing the birth as if she were an observer watching it on a television screen, in order to clarify what happened, note any distressing triggers, identify what she wishes she said or did, and also acknowledge the challenges and some of the good things she did. In addition, recreating the birth as she wishes it had been can reaffirm the potential for such possibility. Many of these techniques are described in detail in this chapter and Chapters 9 and 11.

Sharing the story, letters, role play conversations, drawings, and visualizations with the counselor or other trusted person may help the woman recognize associations between some of her feelings about the birth and feelings evoked by past childhood traumas. Her new perspective helps not only in healing the recent birth, but also her past abuse. It will also be helpful if and when she has another child.

One good way for the woman to achieve a sense of closure to her traumatic birth experience is to write a thoughtful and constructive letter to her caregiver, with copies to all relevant staff members, for example, the hospital administration, the anesthesia department, the newborn nursery, and/or the obstetrical nursing coordinator. She may tell her story, praising the positive aspects of her experience, and expressing her anger, disappointment, or sense of violation over the negative aspects. By using "I messages" and avoiding extreme or highly emotional language, the letter is likely to be taken seriously, which is validating in itself. The woman's readiness to write such a letter usually does not come until she has had the opportunity to process the experience and vent her anger, hurt, and shame.

Throughout the process, the counselor should observe the woman's emotional state and, if needed, suggest such stress management techniques as relaxing breathing, release of physical tension, calming visualizations, and containment (See Chapter 9).

The counselor might suggest that if the woman becomes pregnant again and begins to worry about the upcoming birth, she meet with the counselor to examine her current fears and come up with strategies and a birth plan.

If these counseling methods do not alleviate the woman's distress, referral to a therapist who specializes in trauma therapy such as Eye Movement Densitization and Reprocessing (EMDR) may be the next step. (See Chapter 11.)

Counseling the Pregnant Woman Whose Previous Birth Was Traumatic

It is not unusual for women who have a traumatic birth experience to repress manifestations of PTSD. The joys of having a healthy baby, along with the demands of newborn care and feeding, employment, and other time-consuming burdens may push personal needs and feelings into the background.

Then, when these women become pregnant again, the repressed feelings and worries may resurface in the form of delayed PTSD, causing dread of the upcoming birth. The woman with delayed PTSD after childbirth may feel overwhelmed by her fears. Unless she addresses deeper issues, she may make questionable, impulsive, or poorly informed decisions. For example, she may decide to avoid a vaginal birth completely by planning a cesarean, or she may change to a different doctor, midwife, or place for birth, in hopes of avoiding a repeat experience. Certainly such options should be considered carefully, along with exploration of traumatic aspects of the previous birth.

Counseling for this woman is intended to help her recall her previous childbirth, understand why it left her with unresolved symptoms; develop self-help and partner-assisted techniques to reduce anxiety and pain; and work with her caregiver to develop a care plan that includes some limits in order to minimize the likelihood of another traumatic birth.

As the woman relates the story of her labor and birth, the counselor takes notes, highlighting aspects that were upsetting. Then they review and explore these aspects, which represent her triggers. They explore what was particularly disturbing. This work serves as the basis for the care plan for the upcoming birth.

Though it is unlikely that the woman will have a repeat of the first labor, it is desirable to plan as if she might, since the possibility of recurrence forms the basis of her fear. Then they plan strategies, putting limits on what she will have to tolerate. For example, a woman whose first labor stalled at 7 centimeters for 6 exhausting and depressing hours decided that if it were to stall again, they would not wait nearly so long before intervening. For the woman who was induced at 39 weeks for a "big baby," and gave birth to an average size baby after days of induced labor, the plan for next time was to avoid induction until 41-42 weeks, to give her a chance of going into spontaneous labor.

The woman's confidence grows from knowing ways to avoid a repeat of the previous birth trauma, and how to handle a difficult labor differently. The couple may, for example, practice self-help measures more than they did before; become more assertive in working with hospital staff; and hire a doula to be a guide and a continuous, comforting presence. If they feel their caregiver was a part of the problem with the previous birth, they may also seek a different caregiver who seems open to her needs.

Thus, counseling for childbirth after a previous traumatic birth is very similar to the trigger work described earlier, except that many of the triggers actually happened, and the emphasis is on ensuring that they do not happen again.

Conclusion

In this chapter, we have presented numerous techniques to aid abuse survivors and other emotionally troubled women resolve issues from their past that might interfere with their emotional well-being during labor or afterwards. The techniques require that the counselor have good communication skills and knowledge of pregnancy, birth, newborn care, and usual maternity care practices. Such counseling may enhance the women's satisfaction and self-esteem, and promote long-term healing from the debilitating after-effects of childhood sexual abuse.

11
Psychotherapy

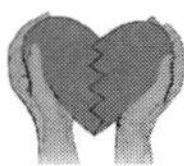

- I was afraid that when I'd get upset, the baby would feel it, too. During therapy I learned I could keep the baby safe from my abuse memories.
- I couldn't stop the flashbacks and anxiety that came up each time I went to the doctor's office. That is why I decided to talk to a therapist.
- I was so relieved to finally connect my early abuse with the awful feelings I've been having during this pregnancy. I know it will be a lot of work, but I'm really getting somewhere now.

Psychotherapy utilizes intensive in-depth methods and techniques for healing trauma. It requires more expertise and professional training of the therapist than either self-help or short-term counseling.

During the perinatal period, sexual abuse survivors seek psychotherapy for many reasons:

- They are already in psychotherapy for abuse when they become pregnant.
- Having been in psychotherapy in the past, they thought their abuse issues were resolved. Now that

they are pregnant, they become concerned about the effects of abuse on the unborn baby, as well as how to handle the birth or demands of parenting.

- They have begun for the first time to have troubling flashbacks, nightmares or frightening bodily sensations.
- They have no memories of abuse, and have come to therapy during pregnancy or the postpartum period for other reasons (unusual fear, anxiety, depression, physical symptoms, or relationship difficulties). During therapy they may recover memories of abuse.
- They have struggled for years with many of the symptoms described throughout this book—overwhelming feelings of inadequacy, shame, numbness, anger, low self-esteem, and self-injury, and have heard that therapy might help before taking on the responsibility of parenting.
- They want to approach the next birth with more than their present level of confidence, self-knowledge, and competence to handle the people, events, and their own body responses differently.

Although psychotherapy for survivors recovering from childhood sexual abuse usually involves extensive time and commitment, much healing can be accomplished during the limited period of childbearing.

Goals of psychotherapy for the survivor during this time include: staying grounded and centered to accomplish the birth; safely recognizing the association between past abuse and present distress; recognizing how present reactions when under stress resemble her reactions during past abuse; separating the past from the present and learning new, more appropriate ways to respond to present stressful situations; and accomplishing a significant amount of healing.

Choosing the Right Therapist

Finding the right therapist is the first and biggest decision. It is not unusual for a woman to change therapists if she discovers, after one or more sessions, that a particular therapist is not right for her. The questions below may help with the choice, but a sense of trust and safety with the therapist is a more reliable guide.

Questions to Ask

When considering therapy, survivors may wonder what is involved and whether they can trust a particular therapist. The following questions to the therapist may help.

- What training, certification, and credentials do you have?
- What experience do you have in working with childhood sexual abuse survivors, especially on issues relating to childbearing?
- Can you describe generally what happens in a therapy session?
- I'm concerned that I might become quite distressed sometimes during therapy. How might you help me with that?
- Are you ever available for phone contact between sessions?
- What are your fees? Are they covered by my health insurance?

The way a therapist responds to these questions is almost as important as what she or he actually says. Does the therapist seem thoughtful, respectful and considerate? Does the therapist evoke feelings of "safety" for the client as she anticipates working on potentially distressing issues? All these considerations will guide the survivor in choosing the right therapist for herself.

The Therapeutic Setting and Role of the Therapist

For many women, the first time they ever tell their story is in a therapy session. They are extremely vulnerable, filled with shame, anxiety, and fear of not being believed. They may have tried to tell someone in the past and were discredited, or ridiculed, or even punished. The therapeutic setting must provide an environment where the survivor feels a sense of trust, safety and clear boundaries. The therapeutic experience represents a microcosm of the safe world that the client will eventually create for herself when she is no longer in therapy.

The therapist's goal is to create a sense of trust and rapport with the woman through consistently supportive words and actions. The survivor comes to recognize the following:

- She can talk about her feelings and experiences without being judged;
- She will be listened to;
- She will not feel pressured to reveal what she is not ready to say or cannot remember;
- She will be heard and her feelings will be validated;
- She will not worry that her therapist cannot handle her strong feelings or the information she shares.

The therapist helps the woman learn how to release strong feelings safely within the therapeutic session, and how to contain these feelings later when they are intrusive, inappropriate or injurious. The client can employ these strategies as needed during the therapy session, as she leaves the session, and/or between sessions.

As part of recovery, survivors need to address memories of childhood. They will need safe ways to connect with or communicate with their hurt, inner child self. Survivors need a therapist who knows how to work with dissociation and other ways of shutting out traumatic memories and repression. These are emotional defenses from the past, in which the mind closed off the traumatic events and protected the child from being overwhelmed by painful feelings and memories. (See Chapter 2 for more on effects of sexual abuse on the child and adult.)

Many survivors fear dissociating or becoming "lost" during labor and birth or when caring for their baby, and want to avoid this reaction. Therefore, recalling forgotten traumatic events and understanding how she dealt with them as a child are essential steps in treatment. She can then begin to recognize that, although these defenses allowed her to survive during childhood, they are now obstacles to her happiness and ability to function comfortably in an adult world. She may see that her old ways of reacting to her abuse have spread to current situations that are reminiscent of the abuse. Now, as is true of many adult survivors, as an adult, she has the maturity and capability of "rewriting the script," to safely examine and replace these old defenses with adult understanding and less self-destructive responses.

The survivor may feel stuck in the childlike defenses she uses to deal with distressing events or thoughts. She needs help to access or develop inner nurturing or empowering resources to help free, protect, and have compassion for herself as a child as she works on her memories and deals with triggering events. In time, these self-nurturing methods are internalized by the survivor. They provide her with both a self-care model and a model for parenting her own real baby.

This process requires hard work and patience from the client, and there may be times when other demands in her life (such as looking after a new baby) make it necessary to take a break. The therapist can equip her with some useful strategies and self-help measures to use in periods of stress. (See Chapter 9 for descriptions of self help measures.)

The survivor needs a therapist who uses careful, safe, sensitive methods to uncover, explore, and work through traumatic memories or current triggers. Essential to this process is an assessment of the woman's life situation and whether she is emotionally and physically stable enough to handle trauma work. It is not the purview of this book to delineate the steps in this process, but only to call attention to the importance of this knowledge when doing therapy work.

Survivors benefit when the therapist has had specialized training in childhood sexual abuse, dissociation and trauma. The therapist must be able to recognize and reinforce the survivor's own comfort level, ego-strength, and emotional readiness to confront these past traumas. The survivor needs to feel in charge when working on abuse memories. She should be able to explore them at her own pace, and not be pushed into memories or feelings. This could be re-traumatizing.

Structure of Therapy Sessions

Therapy sessions usually have a predictable structure, based in part on their earlier discussion of the woman's hopes and goals. This provides a sense of security for the woman to know there is a beginning, a middle and an end, and to expect that she will leave the session feeling centered and present. For example, the sessions may begin with assessing a present concern. The middle section includes identification of a memory or distressing event, release of related feelings, and healing work. Before ending the sessions, new skills are learned for handling some of her strong feelings, and eventually facing new stresses with more confidence.

Along with creating a safe relationship with the therapist, such a structure provides the comfort of clear boundaries, and enhances a sense of containment or safety in the therapeutic environment and experience. However, therapy sessions are not so highly structured that they cannot be adjusted to a safe or appropriate pace for each woman.

Components of Therapy

Components of therapy include history-taking; assessing and establishing safety; ego-strengthening (finding inner resources and strengths) and emotional stabilization (to avoid being overwhelmed); goal-setting; telling the story; protecting the baby from the mother's distress; working with memories; healing associated traumas; and creating a positive outlook for the future.

In the early sessions the survivor should expect the therapist to ask about her current life situation and her present concerns and symptoms. The therapist will need to know if the survivor's life or emotional situation is truly stable. Is she in danger at home, or is there potential for self-harm? Along with her presenting concerns, it is important for the therapist to know the survivor's feelings and thoughts about her pregnancy, the upcoming birth, her relationship with her partner, her family of origin, her support system, and, if the baby has already been born, her feelings about the birth and motherhood. The therapist will also want to know how the survivor thinks those factors are affecting her and how she would like things to be different.

The therapist elicits the survivor's own hopes and goals for therapy, discusses some approaches they might use, and, if appropriate, describes different "homework" assignments to help with immediate goals. In these initial visits the survivor learns methods that will help her feel emotionally safe, grounded, and present; contain strong emotions; and to recognize her own sense of control.

Such methods include ego-strengthening (finding and developing inner resources and strengths); guided imagery to access inner places of comfort and safety; communication with inner advisors or observers, and communicating with her inner mind through ideomotor signals. In addition, the survivor is helped to imagine a protection around her unborn or newborn baby, in order to prevent unpleasant feelings that come up in therapy from carrying over to her baby.

Telling the Story

The next step is for the survivor to tell her story. The survivor and therapist choose specific memories or experiences to target for more exploration and deeper psychological work.

The survivor may be helped to communicate with her inner child self, that is, to access long-held emotions or beliefs that are related to her earlier abuse. This may be facilitated with guided imagery, family photos, artwork, speaking to feelings and body sensations, or addressing (when she is ready) different aspects of her self, which may be holding various aspects of trauma. For example, when Pamela and her therapist examined and discussed three photos of her family, taken over a span of six years (the last without her father), Pamela recognized the changing family dynamics and her changing feelings about her father and older brothers who had abused her during that time. This provided a valuable basis for further therapeutic work.

Along with acknowledging the survivor's story of her past, the therapist helps her recognize present fears or negative beliefs about herself or fears that block her from processing these events. Together, they will explore the needs of her child self, unspoken strong feelings that need to be expressed, and her lack of understanding of what was really occurring when the adults were abusing her. She comes to see that she blamed herself for the abuse, rather than blaming the perpetrator(s).

As is safe and appropriate, the survivor is helped to fully acknowledge the events and work through her legitimate feelings of anger, shame, fear, pain, sadness and grief over the losses suffered from these painful experiences. In time, she is ready to recognize more positive and realistic truths about herself and is able to go back in time with new resources to re-parent, heal, or nurture her younger self.

She is then ready to re-integrate her child self with her adult self and separate the past from the present.

Therapy often continues in circular layers. As one layer of experience is revealed and peeled away, the next layer appears. As each is worked through, there may be more distress for a while, followed by renewed energy as more and more pain is released. Merely learning about and uncovering early trauma is not healing in itself; in fact, it can be re-traumatizing. Trauma therapy, therefore, is based not only on recalling traumatic events, but also in working through feelings of grief and betrayal surrounding the abuse, and transforming them so that the survivor can activate her potential for healing. The survivor needs help to make new meaning of the trauma, by discovering inner strengths and resources that were not available at the time to help her resolve hurtful experiences in a new way.

One of the common fears of survivors about therapy is that their feelings of anxiety, anger, or grief will be overwhelming, and they will not be able to cope. Therapists teach their clients ways to calm and ground themselves, and contain their strong emotions until it is safe and appropriate to address them.

Closure

Each session should include closure to help the woman in the following ways:

- To recognize what she has accomplished in the session, for example, a new awareness about herself or her situation, such as, "I am moving through this now," or, "I am safe now;"
- To place her distress in a separate place, to keep it from interfering with her ability to function;
- To feel centered before she leaves the session;
- To remind her how to handle distress between sessions.

Subsequent Sessions

In subsequent sessions they discuss what has occurred in the survivor's life since the last session related to the concerns at hand. In addition, they include, as needed:

- Re-establishment of feelings of safety and groundedness;
- Re-evaluation and a mental internal review of the therapeutic work done in the previous session to see if anything needs further exploration;
- Completion of unfinished aspects of the earlier work;
- Recognition of any new aspect, memory, distress, or concern, and appropriate psychological work.

Deirdre

Following is a detailed description of Deirdre's psychotherapy, describing several psychotherapeutic techniques. As mentioned in Chapter 10, Deirdre had sought counseling to prepare for birth, and revealed to the counselor her discomfort and confusion at each meeting with the midwife. She also shared that she had been "involved" with her female high school teacher. It was not appropriate to deal with her unresolved abuse issues while she was preparing for birth, but a few months after the birth she returned to therapy to work further on the trauma she had suffered at the hands of this teacher.

Ego-Strengthening and Grounding

Before addressing Deirdre's traumatic memories, her therapist helped Deirdre learn relaxation and self-comforting techniques as well as methods to help her remain in the present, rather than in the past, where her painful memories lay. These processes created a measure of emotional safety for Deirdre.

(Chapter 9 describes these self-help measures.) To help herself relax, Deirdre chose to imagine being in a safe place—a special quiet and private cove at a favorite beach, which felt like a safe sanctuary.

She also used passive progressive relaxation, breathing slowly and timing the release of tension from one group of muscles after another with each out-breath. Such activities helped her remain in the present and to feel grounded in her body. She had employed this method to stay relaxed during labor.

Deirdre stated that she felt great shame over her past relationship with the teacher. One of the goals of therapy was to help Deirdre recognize that such feelings kept her captive to the past, and really belonged not to her, but to the abuser. Before addressing these feelings, however, the therapist felt it would be useful to enhance different positive resources within Deirdre.

During the preliminary sessions, the therapist explained methods to strengthen Deirdre's internal resources. She reminded Deirdre that she could use these any time during the session to re-ground herself, or between sessions whenever she felt unstable. Deirdre was also given other methods, such as journal-writing, expressing herself through art, and relying on supportive people to help her outside of the sessions.

The therapist asked Deirdre what qualities she would need to confront her memories. Deirdre replied, "Courage and my own truth." The therapist suggested that Deirdre remember a time when she felt particularly courageous and a situation in which she remembered feeling true in her convictions. Taking each situation separately, the therapist engaged Deirdre in guided imagery to enhance these memories with their attendant emotions and physical feelings of courage and truth. She helped Deirdre think of a symbol or cue that could elicit these feelings within herself whenever she needed them.

Telling the Story

The beginning phase of Deirdre's therapy included describing the abuse. Although it was difficult, giving voice to her experiences made the abuse more real and helped her begin to understand more fully its impact on her. The therapist's empathic listening and appropriate reflecting helped Deirdre to explore her feelings and recall more of the experience, while recognizing that she had been in an unequal relationship and was taken advantage of by her teacher, who was much more powerful.

Recalling Memories Safely

For Deirdre to process her memories of abuse, she had to recall her sensory and bodily feelings, thoughts, and emotions at the time of the abuse. There are many methods to create a sense of control and internalized emotional safety for a client while she does such memory work. In one exercise, for example, Deirdre imagined watching her younger self on a television screen, regulating the channel with a remote control to modulate the effect she was experiencing. Describing her feelings and thoughts at the time of the abuse, Deirdre could move back and forth in time, mentally holding onto the safety of being connected to the current environment, and then, as she felt ready, simultaneously re-experiencing the abuse events.

In this therapeutic process, Deirdre remained aware of being the observing "adult self," while at the same time being the "child self" experiencing the abuse. This helped her recognize the reality of what had occurred and her powerlessness in the relationship. For the first time, she could feel her sadness and be appalled by how she was used and trapped. She began to recognize the many ways she had felt inadequate, unsure of herself, and needy of nurturing while growing up. She also recognized the inability of her "child self" to see both her need and the entrapment. Now she could weep for her younger self and feel her adult anger.

Working through Feelings

Deirdre also used other methods to process her abuse-related feelings: role-playing (imagining speaking to the teacher/abuser, telling the teacher how she felt, how awful and confusing it was); writing an imaginary letter to the teacher (expressing her anger and all her feelings, as well as how this abuse hurt her and how it affected her whole life); ripping up and burning a picture of the teacher. By allowing her anger to come up in therapy sessions, Deirdre was permitted to safely release her fears and negative beliefs about herself, to feel legitimate righteous anger, and to place the responsibility and blame where it belonged. She could now begin to exonerate herself from the guilt, shame, and the burden of responsibility she had been carrying. She became able to reevaluate the meaning of her abuse experience and finally to integrate it into her adult life.

Resolving the Experience

After the major step of reevaluating the meaning of her abuse, the next step was to release the hold the abuse had on her life. The therapist also used Eye Movement Desensitization and Reprocessing

(EMDR) to facilitate a release and resolution of the abuse. Below is a simplified explanation of EMDR. In this process Deirdre was able to fully see the power differential in the relationship and how the teacher used a young girl's infatuation with her, an older woman, for her own gain; that the abuse was not her fault; that she could reclaim her own true sexuality, and could nurture herself now. She gained a strong inner connection to the maternal part of herself that she could now draw on for her own baby.

Eye Movement Desensitization and Reprocessing (EMDR)

EMDR is a comprehensive therapeutic method that is especially helpful to resolve trauma. It is based on the concept that during traumatic or other distressing events, the brain's ability to process information can get stuck, forcing the person to continue reliving the negative experience. EMDR follows a specific, well-developed and research-based protocol developed by Francine Shapiro, which includes specific phases of treatment and involves bilateral brain stimulation through rhythmic alternating eye movements, tones, or taps. EMDR accesses and releases the many layers of trauma-related symptoms that come up when the trauma is re-triggered, including such debilitating effects as negative beliefs about oneself, and related emotional, sensory and visceral responses. Before processing disturbing elements, the therapist helps the survivor discover potentially positive and more realistic beliefs about herself. Then by repeating the processing as needed and as she is ready, the survivor becomes freer and freer from the disturbing material and evolves to a clearer, stronger and healthier belief about herself. Therefore, EMDR initiates a fundamental psychological restructuring of experiences so that the survivor is able to re-think and re-feel them from a place of strength and a positive belief framework.

Working Through Birth Trauma and Its Association to Past Trauma

Carrie's story illustrates a different manifestation of early trauma from Deirdre's, and other therapeutic interventions.

Carrie

As Carrie, another pregnant survivor, looked toward her second birth, she began to feel extreme fear of the pain of labor, and of pushing the baby out. She also worried that the birth would cause her to recall traumatic body memories. In her first labor, when her doctor checked her vaginally during a contraction, Carrie relived with terror the feeling of "a white hot steel poker going up inside me."

Healing the Inner Child

Within several therapy sessions, Carrie was able to recognize that the feeling of the "white hot steel poker" was in truth a body memory that symbolized the rape by her father. She uncovered completely the real memory of rape and became able to separate that "pain" from the birth of her first son. In therapy she could feel her anger, and speak to her father in her imagination. She then imagined her "little girl self" being helped, going "to a soothing magic pond to heal with cleansing water and medicine," and being safely held while allowing her tears and hurts to be expressed and validated. She was then helped to review her first birth and recreate it the way she wished it had been, using her imagination to reinterpret the pain caused by the baby coming down her birth canal to the baby "taking the pain away." As she rehearsed a visualization for the upcoming birth, she developed with the therapist similar positive imagery for the birth itself, and was able to visualize herself again floating in beautiful and soothing waters.

Keeping the Baby Safe

The pregnant survivor in therapy is likely to express concern over possible effects of her abuse-related or pregnancy-related distress on her unborn baby. One of the essential elements of therapy is to help the pregnant woman create a context of safety for her unborn baby and for her pregnancy. Will her baby somehow get a message of being unwanted, or the cause of her distress? If she is not calm and peaceful, but tense and upset part of the time, will her baby be harmed? Is it better for her baby if she tries to ignore or suppress unpleasant thoughts? In addition, the woman's inner child self needs to be acknowledged and feel safe.

To validate the emotional or psychic connection between woman and infant, the therapist or counselor can help the mother-to-be visualize her baby in a safe place, comfortably separated from the issues to be dealt with. One method is to ask the woman to close her eyes, to tune in to her own inner knowledge for information and guidance to find a way to provide safety for the baby. Carrie, for example, found that she could keep the baby safe from "my old stuff" by saying out loud to her baby: "Baby, my fears and distress have nothing to do with you. They are about things that happened to me long ago. You are safe and I want to love and care for you." Somehow, by verbalizing this message to her baby, she was able to reassure herself that her baby could be safely separated from her own pain. She also pictured her baby basking in warmth and surrounded with light.

Somatization: Discovering the Meaning of Physical Symptoms

Some exaggerated symptoms during pregnancy may be unconsciously related to childhood trauma and can cause extra discomfort. "Irritable uterus" is one such symptom. For example, although preterm labor must always be considered in pregnant women with an "irritable uterus" (uterine contractions without cervical change), many of these pregnancies will go to term and beyond. The women are usually closely monitored, and may be put on bed rest or even hospitalized and given medications to stop the contractions.

Naomi

Naomi's story illustrates how unresolved emotional trauma and resulting anxiety were instrumental in causing painful preterm contractions. Naomi's therapist helped her search for emotional distress that may have exacerbated her symptoms of premature contractions. She asked Naomi to close her eyes and let herself imagine "talking" to a part of herself that may have knowledge of the symptom. "Is there a part of you that knows about the premature contractions?" After a short period of silence, Naomi nodded her head. The therapist continued: "Would it be all right to learn the purpose of this symptom for you?" "Yes," Naomi continued, "this 'part' said: 'Don't forget about us.' " The therapist asked, "Who is 'us?' " Naomi searched further and said that "us" referred to her self at younger ages still holding the abuse trauma, who feared Naomi would stop paying attention to them (and to the abuse memories). The therapist suggested that Naomi thank these inner hurt parts of herself for reminding her that they were there; she should also reassure them that she would not forget them and would learn more about them when she could. However, because the pregnancy required so much attention at this time from the adult Naomi, the therapist suggested asking them if it would be all right during this time not to use the symptom of premature contractions as a way to get attention. They "agreed."

The contractions abated, but did not go away completely. In the next session the therapist asked Naomi to ask her inner mind if there was any other concern that might contribute to her premature contractions. Naomi remembered that the contractions started soon after she felt the baby move at 20 weeks, making her suddenly aware of the full import of having a child. The thought that came to Naomi was a fear of not being able to protect her infant just as she herself had not been protected. The therapist reframed this fear with the question, "Would it be helpful to recognize that Naomi's adult self, knowing how important it is to protect little children, would now know how to use her adult resources to do this for her child?" Naomi received a response of "Maybe." The therapist suggested that Naomi picture herself in her current life (her home and her stable relationship with her partner), and notice how she is safe; for example, the skills she has to protect herself and her own boundaries; her ability to say "No," and to ask for what she wants; and the provisions she has made for the new baby. The therapist then asked, "Does the inner part of Naomi that has been holding this fear now recognize grown-up Naomi's ability to protect a baby?" The inner part responded affirmatively and within a day the premature contractions quieted down and soon stopped completely. This type of psychological transference onto the fetus or the pregnancy is not uncommon when unresolved traumas become stirred up.

In another session, the therapist helped Naomi plan real life strategies for the coming birth. She also created a guided visualization to help Naomi envision a positive birth experience and a secure postpartum experience, feeling confident that she now knows how to protect herself and her baby.

Dream Work

Therapy before birth often involves dealing with the woman's significant dreams. Understanding and resolving the meaning of the dreams for the survivor can be helpful and healing. Dream work at a self-exploratory level (see Chapter 10), or in a therapeutic setting may give both client and therapist some symbolic key to unlock the survivor's fears, or to learn more about them. This is an opportunity to bring fears into the open, address them, and plan around them. At a deep therapeutic level, dreams have much emotional and psychological "material" to explore. By relating the dream and the meaning she gives to the symbols, the survivor is helped to discover important associations between her current fears about birth and her abuse experiences.

Barbara

After childhood sexual abuse was brought up in her childbirth class, Barbara began feeling anxious and distressed. She did not know what her fears were about, but she worried that they were related to being sexually abused when she was a little girl. She mentioned them to her midwife, who told her that some women who were sexually abused in childhood have trouble pushing the baby out. After that, Barbara started having frightening dreams and became alarmed. Since her birth was imminent, Barbara's midwife referred her to a therapist.

Barbara had had some upsetting and confusing sex-related experiences with her father but had not considered them to be sexual abuse. She had vivid memories from age 7 of being deliberately exposed several times to her father's erect penis. Her mother would bring her into their bedroom and tell her, "Look at your father." Barbara felt sick and very scared. She did not understand why they did this. For years, Barbara sometimes wondered about it and continued to feel distressed, but chose not to address it in therapy. Now she found herself thinking about it often and worrying that it might somehow cause difficulties during labor.

Because Barbara's baby was due in two weeks, the therapist realized this was not the time for "trauma" work. Instead, she focused the therapy on the following: exploring feelings, exploring significant dreams using ideomotor signaling techniques to quickly elicit the symbolic meaning (see the box on the next page); reframing the meaning; creating "containment" and "safe place" imagery; self-hypnosis, with suggestions for birth visualizations that would create feelings of empowerment and safety.

This process required two sessions.

Ideomotor Signaling

Ideomotor signaling, developed by David Cheek M.D., helps one recognize the subconscious meaning of disturbing feelings or reactions, especially for emotional or physical symptoms with a psychological or traumatic origin that would be exacerbated by distress. It is based on the premise that recurring thoughts and mental images have corresponding responses in the body. The first unconscious responses are usually physiological, such as increased heart rate, sweating, blushing, or rapid breathing. The next level of unconscious responses to distressing situations are physical in nature (bodily movements, jaw clenching, hand wringing, and others). The third level is conscious, expressed as thoughts or words. The therapist teaches the survivor to use simple finger movements to help bring the meaning of the bodily responses to her consciousness, while maintaining control and emotional safety. For example, the therapist asks the woman to close her eyes, move into a relaxed reverie or light trance, and to think the word "yes" repeatedly, allowing the movement of a finger, the "yes" finger, to indicate a response. She does the same for "no" and "I'm not ready to answer yet." The responses let the woman control whether, what, and how much she is ready to know. This is also a way for the therapist to ask the survivor's inner mind to reveal information about the source of her thoughts, dreams, fears, or body responses. The survivor can then understand and process traumatic experiences for her eventual healing.

Communicating with One's Inner Mind

In the first session, Barbara described recurring dreams of being confronted by snakes, and recently had a dream of a child being pursued by a brown bear.

Before exploring the dream, Barbara learned

imagery for staying relaxed and feeling safe. Then, the therapist and Barbara explored the dream together, and Barbara recognized that the symbolic meaning was about herself as a small child being pursued by a "dark figure." She expressed fears that she "did not feel safe" and could not "keep my child safe." The therapist asked if there were some place where she had felt safe as a little girl and if the little child could go there. Barbara remembered feeling safe at her aunt's house, especially in the cozy family room where she, her aunt, and Daisy, the family dog, would often sit together. The family room, including the big friendly dog, became Barbara's "safe place."

Communicating with One's Inner Baby

In the next session another dream was explored, this time with ideomotor signaling. The symbolic meaning for Barbara was "a death of a child." When asked if another thought might come to her to make the meaning clearer, Barbara's finger indicated "yes," and she said, "A part of me died." The therapist helped reframe that belief by addressing the "little part" of Barbara:, "Will the little part recognize that at that time she had to go away and hide from hurt, but now as a strong adult, she can remain safe?" Barbara replied, "It's difficult to trust the world, or to trust that the baby can be safe." The therapist suggested, "Go inside your uterus, communicate with your baby, and think about what he needs from you." The response was, "I need to shelter him and let him go (be born)." The therapist asked, "Any other concerns?" Barbara indicated "Yes." Her concern was from another dream of "being punished and cut up" after she died. She realized she held a fear of being "cut up" with a cesarean section or episiotomy at the birth. "Does your inner mind realize this is just a dream?" "Yes." Are there any old fears and hurts connected to this dream?" "Yes." "Can they rest until a safer time after the birth?" Barbara said, "I don't want to answer yet." "What is the fear?" "I can't keep him safe. My mother didn't keep me safe."

Reframing a Negative Interpretation into a New Perspective

The therapist explored "mothering" with Barbara, and reframed her fears into an indication of her power to love.

"Is there a part of you that knows how to love a baby?" the therapist asked. "I don't know," replied Barbara. "Is it okay to recognize that your concern for your baby and your desire to protect him are a strong indication of your love? And that the first step in being a good mother is love?" "Yes." This is how the therapist helped Barbara reframe the meaning. Only after addressing this deeper fear of identification with her mother could Barbara accept the reframing. "Is it okay now to recognize that you are not your mother?" "Yes."

"Knowing now that your mother did not protect your younger self as you needed her to, could we let little Barbara know we hear her and she can be safe now, while grown-up Barbara can help her own baby differently?" "Yes."

Adult Self Comforting Child Self

The therapist then suggested, "Hold little Barbara, help her feel secure, safe, and confident enough to allow her own independent self to grow. Let me know when you feel more peaceful, and when you recognize that you can keep her safe now—with her own new resources." "I can keep her safe. Yes."

Re-Integration and Transformation

Barbara was asked to rest for a while, then share her feelings and thoughts. She said the experience was quite profound. She now realized how upset and confused she felt, and how these thoughts tapped into a deep sadness that she had covered up with anger throughout her life. She now felt more confident that old memories would not surface in labor and that her own little girl self was safe. She understood that her fear of letting her baby out (opening the vagina) had meant to "become a mother," and that becoming a mother meant becoming like her mother. She could now perceive herself as separate from her own mother. She had needed help to perceive that she had separated from her mother, freed herself, and would not re-enact the mother-child relationship that she had experienced with her own mother. With help, she was now able to visualize her upcoming birth, picture many positive examples of the strength and wisdom of her body in knowing how to give birth, and imagine healthy productive contractions bringing a vigorous baby boy into her arms. She imagined the date, time, and number of hours she would be in labor, and a normal vaginal birth.

As the survivor works out fears or issues about the upcoming birth, she feels freer to imagine it. The therapist reminded Barbara that the gender, birth date, and number of hours of labor that she visualized might or might not turn out to be true. Being able to picture herself in a healthy labor, however, was a good sign, and would plant healthy suggestions in her own mind. In the therapist's experience, the birth usually occurs within a few days of the imagined date. In fact, Barbara had an 8 lb. boy within 1 day of her imagined date and within 2 hours of her imagined duration of labor.

If Barbara had not been able to visualize as she did, then it would be important to check whether she still had any other concerns that might impede her progress in labor.

Imaginal Recreation of Distressing Events

Tara

During her first pregnancy, Tara developed a severe and painful contortion of her mouth and neck, a condition called wry neck, which seemed to worsen under stress. She was referred for counseling in hopes that stress management or imagery and self-hypnosis for pain control might alleviate the symptoms. The therapist who taught her relaxation techniques recognized that Tara's wry neck might be a reaction to unexpressed inner conflict.

In the first session, as the therapist helped Tara explore the origin and meaning of the symptom, Tara remembered an upsetting experience. Walking home from school one day when she was eight years old, she was accosted by a bigger boy who pushed her onto the ground, held her down, and molested her in her vagina. He held her mouth and head with one hand while he molested her with the other. When he finally released her, she ran home, shaking and trembling, and told her parents what had happened.

As Tara recalled the experience, she remembered

that her parents acted in a passive and confused manner, and when they finally called the police, appeared to minimize the situation. She heard her father say to her, "Well, at least you won't get pregnant." She then remembered, as she internally reviewed the experience, that her father did not console her. He made her go to the police station and describe the exact details to the policeman, and the policeman made her repeat the events over and over again. She didn't know then what re-traumatization was, but that experience of repeating the story to the policeman made her feel sick, scared, humiliated, and ashamed. Tara felt the policeman didn't believe her and that he was too interested in her—almost intrusively so. Subsequently, she began to doubt herself and developed anxiety and fear about talking.

The therapist then asked Tara to visualize the situation again, but this time as she would have wanted it to be. This technique is called "imaginal recreation of distressing events." By recreating the situation differently, she realized she needed to express her fears and anger to the boy, her hurt at her parents' behavior and disbelief, and her distress and anger at the policeman.

Rather than continue to relive and recall the childhood experience, Tara could bring her adult self forward to visualize her younger self with a voice that was heard and believed. Also, in this first session, Tara recognized that becoming pregnant might have reactivated memories of the abuse event. She could understand that her unexpressed hurt and anger after the incident was associated with the tension and contortion of her wry neck.

In her next therapy session, Tara reported that

she had less tension in her neck and jaw and actually had moments of relief from the pain. She also revealed that in her relationship with her husband she also had difficulty speaking up and expressing anger. She was able to look at this silence with new awareness and a growing confidence and could now process it with the therapist.

In expressing her feelings in therapy about the abusive incident, Tara began to see that if the important adults in her life had validated her experience at the time, held and nurtured her, let her cry and be angry, and reassured her that she was good and normal and that the abuse was not her fault, she could have healed from this event when it occurred.

In the same session, Tara recognized that her negative beliefs helped to keep the trauma embedded in her unconscious, only to resurface as a debilitating reaction during pregnancy. Using EMDR, she was able to address these negative beliefs. They included:

- I have no voice
- I am powerless
- It isn't safe to tell anyone
- There is something wrong with me
- I am bad for being sexual

She gradually released the different levels of long held emotional distress, the tensions in her neck and body, and the old entrenched negative beliefs. She then reframed the negative beliefs into positive experienced beliefs such as:

- I have a voice
- I can be true to myself

- I am perfectly normal
- I have a right to be heard
- My feelings are valid
- I have equal power and value
- I have a right to be angry
- I can be real with my feelings without fear of abandonment or anger.

In two more sessions she released a great deal of trapped anxiety and felt herself as an adult in the present, competent and unafraid of expressing her feelings and needs. Her neck and jaw relaxed, she began to feel stronger in her relationship with her husband, and she began to plan appropriately for the upcoming birth.

Inner Review: a Method for Processing a Traumatic Birth

Ashley

At different times between the ages of four and sixteen, Ashley was raped by her father, a brother, and her stepfather. Although she had many conscious memories of the abuse, she had repressed significant portions. She began long-term therapy, which focused on safely uncovering and working through those memories.

During her long-term therapy, Ashley married a kind but rather passive man and became pregnant with her first child. She planned well for the birth, which was clinically "normal." She continued making progress in her therapy. Two years later, she became pregnant with her second baby and began to dread the upcoming labor. As is often the case, only when reviewing her first birth in preparation for the second did Ashley recall some of the events that caused her distress. Because the birth had been "normal," she felt that her distress was not valid, and succeeded in ignoring the troubling events until the prospect arose of a repeat of the first childbirth. Here is a summary of Ashley's first childbirth and its connections to earlier negative events of her childhood.

The therapist introduced the "inner review" to Ashley, a process of repeatedly imagining her previous labor and her feelings at the time. With each review, she was asked to take a slightly different perspective. The reviews would bring up negative feelings and memories, and were intended to help Ashley discover, explore and resolve distressing aspects of her first labor. Used in conjunction with EMDR and many of the other techniques described in this chapter, Ashley was able in a few sessions to resolve much of the trauma of her first birth and of her early sexual abuse.

The therapy sessions devoted to processing her previous birth typically followed this structure: 1) establishing a "safe place" for Ashley; 2) describing the events of labor as she recalled them; 3) in a light trance state, mentally re-experiencing any disturbing aspects; 4) sharing what she was noticing, feeling, sensing, and what these perceptions had led her to believe about herself.

Sometimes the review of labor would bring up an earlier memory relating to her abuse; it would need to be processed with EMDR before continuing. The therapist would then ask Ashley to think about what she would rather believe about herself. Being able to express a new preferred belief was an important step in becoming "unstuck." Through EMDR, the therapist helped Ashley to release disturbing elements of the memories as well as the negative beliefs, and replace them with a more positive reality. As the session continued, Ashley internalized new truths about herself. EMDR processing is usually repeated until it strengthens this internalization and the negative beliefs and reactions are replaced.

Over the course of several inner reviews, the story of Ashley's first childbirth gradually came out. This is how she recalled the events and the associations and beliefs they elicited.

Contractions began and continued for seven hours, then stopped for several hours. Ashley was frustrated, felt clueless, and worried whether she was doing things the right way. She slept and dreamed of her grandfather saying, "It's okay. I'll take care of you." The dream was very upsetting, and Ashley woke up trembling and crying, picturing herself back with her grandfather, who did not take care of her. As she recalled the dream during the therapy session, she blurted out, "Screw that! You never took care of me then. You're not here now! I'm scared and I'm all alone in this! You say it's okay–like all the others said it [the abuse] was, but it wasn't." She recalled that it was nighttime, the labor room was quiet, she was alone, and the nurses hardly came into her room. The room was small, like her childhood bedroom. "I was trapped in that room; I thought I had to stay in there. I was trapped in my bedroom when I was a child. I was afraid. It was night. I was fighting it, just like during the abuse. I have always had anxiety attacks when the sun went down." Her memories shifted back and forth between childhood and labor. The doctor came in the morning to break her bag of waters "with that hook, and I was still in the hallucination of my bedroom. That's why it felt so horrible."

Labor contractions resumed when morning came, it was daylight, and there were more people around. "I felt safer and I could proceed."

After the inner reviews, Ashley said, "I see I got hooked into past stuff–because in reality people were there. I was safe. I was not alone. I didn't know how to let people help me then. I couldn't trust them. Only when I became thoroughly exhausted did I let people help. All the overwhelming feelings colored my perspective. No blame, it just triggered a difficult time. It's simple to realize it all now–parallels between the hospital and the abuse. I feel better already, to recognize it, to express it. I feel lighter, freer, more confident."

The repeated inner reviews of her first labor, combined with EMDR processing, allowed Ashley to understand how specific labor events triggered memories of past abuse. She also began to see how her abuse triggered many negative responses to her labor. As she revisited her first labor, she discovered further negative beliefs, identified how she would rather believe, and replaced the negative with more positive and realistic beliefs.

Here are examples of Ashley's lingering worries: fears for the safety of her two children; fear about the pain of contractions (which cycled over and over, but to a lesser extent each time); losing control if she relaxed (she had always protected herself by stiffening); a need to remain vigilant and have a "radar system" to detect strangers coming into the room (related to abuse from behind in the dark); a terrible tension in her head coupled with a feeling that she was going to die ("My head was the only part of me free to move. It was trying to do so much to protect me. It must have been a terrible burden."); a fear of the amnihook used to break the bag of waters ("I see the needle, it's like a penis! I feel the gush down my legs. I hate it.").

Each new distress was addressed by the therapist, who helped Ashley remain with the feelings, express them, and release them, "What do you want to say to your younger self who had to bear this fear and pain? How would you like to re-create the event differently?" She helped Ashley separate the old hurts of her childhood from the present circumstances, helping Ashley discover ways to ensure that her inner child parts could remain safe, while her mature adult self would remain in the forefront throughout the upcoming labor.

They then addressed the protective purpose of her tension ("Clenching up is the only way I know to protect myself"), and the costs of this type of protection (pain and exhaustion). They looked for other more adult ways she could protect herself, using her new knowledge of the purpose of contractions and the pain-reducing value of relaxation.

With her therapist's help, Ashley went on to mentally recreate the first birth as she wished it had gone, free from the need to resist her contractions, and from the fear of being alone in her room at night. She was able to picture her adult self successfully handling labor.

Ashley was able to internalize positive self-nurturing

and ego-strengthening statements that reflected her new-found understanding of her own needs and new self-confidence, such as: I'm relaxed; The more I relax, the more powerful and productive are my contractions and the better I feel; I am in a safe, nurturing, loving environment; I have people around me who are knowledgeable and who want to help and support me.

Preparation for the next birth, then, consisted of developing tools and techniques to keep her inner child safe and to empower her adult self to remain in the present throughout labor. She learned relaxation, self-hypnosis, and other self-help techniques for labor. She and her partner discussed his role and had more specific ideas for how he could help. They found a kind, experienced doula to reassure and guide them throughout the labor and birth. They prepared a birth plan, in which she disclosed some concerns and needs. This was well-received by her doctor and nurses.

Ashley's labor went exceedingly well. She had a 9-pound baby, a normal delivery, and felt quite positive about the outcome. She said she was calm, could feel herself relaxing her pelvic floor and always felt in control. Ashley had told her doula about her abuse history and asked the doula to check often with her if she drifted off, to be sure she was not dissociating to a scary place. Ashley had used the imagery of a pond and self-anesthesia techniques she had learned in the self hypnosis sessions, and birth visualizations done in therapy. However, she realized that she had so turned off pain sensations by her own ability to self hypnotize that she didn't know how her contractions were progressing. She needed feedback and reassurance that good progress was being made and that the contractions were powerful.

She recognized how much more present she was during this baby's birth, and said, "With my first baby, I felt that the force moving through me came, not from within me, but from the outside. This time I was present, I was there, it was up to me to push—it was not done for me."

She remembered the work on triggers and the positive beliefs during therapy and kept them in her mind. She could talk freely about what she wanted and needed. When the doctor suggested rupturing the membranes, she decided to do it, and she asked her husband and the doula to remain on each side of her so she could feel in control and safe. She needed words of comfort, reassurance, and confidence, such as, "Breathe through it, you're doing great." It helped when the doctor said, "Keep letting those muscles relax." The doula also reminded her during pushing that she would soon be holding her baby. She had planned such words of encouragement with the doula beforehand. She remembered a big effort in pushing the baby out. She needed to rest after the birth but felt supported, safe, and good.

Although both of Ashley's labors were successful and normal obstetrically, her inner experience was quite different in the second. She felt truly present and in control. She did not have the nameless fear or anxiety, and she was not triggered to any past abuse memories. Her satisfaction with the birth, her partner, the caregivers, and with herself as well as her free joyful welcoming of her baby continued to sustain Ashley in her present day life as she continued processing the remaining effects of past abuse.

Conclusion

Psychotherapy in the perinatal period has the potential to help survivors avoid re-traumatization and to empower and strengthen their self-image as mothers and as women. The techniques described in this chapter are not intended to instruct the reader in their use, but rather to illustrate how they are used and the kinds of results they many bring. The techniques require specialized training and experience of the therapist, and are especially useful to people who are confronting deeply ingrained trauma. They facilitate non-threatening access to these traumas to allow their release, and finally, healing.

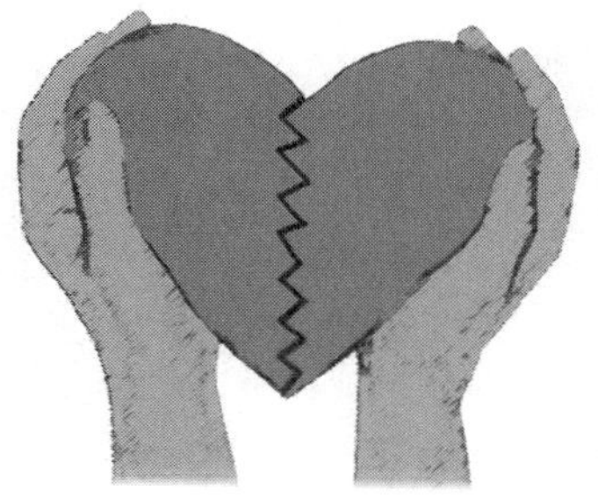

Part III: Clinical Challenges and Solutions

12
Doing a Pelvic Exam with a Woman Who Has Experienced Sexual Abuse

by Yeshi Sherover Neumann, MA, CNM, MPH

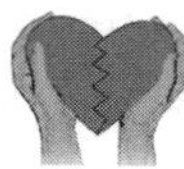

[*Authors' note:* We have invited Yeshi Sherover Neumann, CNM, to write this chapter. She has extensive experience working with abuse survivors. She presents detailed instructions for performing a sensitive, non-traumatizing pelvic exam.]

A pelvic exam is an opportunity for growing, learning and healing. When we do a pelvic exam with the intention of healing, we encourage a woman's positive future relationship with her body, her sexuality, her self-image, and the care she takes of herself. In addition, we take a stand in the struggle of women against the worldwide epidemic of sexual exploitation.

Preparing Ourselves as Practitioners

Because many women have occluded their experience of sexual abuse (that is, they have blocked it from their consciousness), or are unwilling to reveal it, we must assume that every woman with whom we do a pelvic exam may have experienced sexual abuse—perhaps a long time ago, perhaps yesterday. If we do not treat the woman with respect, tenderness, and patience, we are adding another layer of mistreatment. There is no neutral ground.

It is crucial to understand the difference between the restimulation or reactivation of the memory of abuse and a further act of abuse, re-injury. Elements in the pelvic exam can bring up emotions, sensations, images or memories of prior sexual abuse. This does not make the exam inherently abusive. Sexual abuse is always an abuse of power. It is done at the expense of a person's well-being for the purpose of satisfying someone else's need. A woman who experiences painful emotions during a pelvic exam is not being re-injured provided she has fully consented to the exam and the exam is being done for her benefit by a caring practitioner. In that context the reminder of previous sexual abuse creates an opportunity for healing.

As practitioners we have a responsibility to educate ourselves fully on abuse and its impact, to work on our own issues, and to get the help we need in order to do so. The more we examine our own authentic response to sexual abuse—as survivors, perpetrators, or bystanders—the more effective we will be as agents of healing for our clients. If we have not worked through our own issues and lack of understanding, we may act out of emotions that undermine our intention to be helpful. Following are examples of unhelpful attitudes:

- We are afraid that by addressing a woman's experience of sexual abuse we are involved in creating a new hurt. Instead we can learn to trust that a woman will only go as far into this territory as she is ready to go. Our job is not to define her safety but to provide a safe container within which she can do her own healing work.
- We ourselves are in a kind of panic mode when faced with the issue of sexual abuse and rush to rescue our client from feeling bad. "Getting the exam over with" is not necessarily the kindest path. A woman may need

us to slow down so she can actually notice that this time, when she is being touched, she is safe.

- We feel impatient, irritated or embarrassed about the emotion a client shows. In such case, we may be passing on the mistreatment that women often experience as they seek help and are told to "get over it" or "stop making a mountain out of a molehill."
- We feel overwhelmed, helpless or powerless. If so, we will not be able to empower our client and guide her as she navigates the tumultuous waters of her own experience.

A sensitive and empowering pelvic exam requires forethought and preparation, a willingness to accommodate the special needs of each woman, unrushed and considerate care during the exam, and thoughtful follow-up afterwards.

Before the Exam

1. Have materials in your waiting room describing the purpose and procedure of the pelvic exam, the prevalence and nature of sexual abuse, and the difference between restimulation and re-injury (as discussed above).

2. In taking a woman's history, include both direct and indirect questions about possible history of sexual abuse. Have your eyes, ears and senses open for possible symptoms of prior sexual abuse: distrust of you, marked body tension, disassociation, fear or crying at the possibility of a pelvic exam.

3. Following is a list of helpful things to communicate to your client.

Prepare the client for the exam while she still has her own clothes on. For some women the vulnerability of being undressed and barely covered by a flimsy gown that is not their own can make it impossible to take in any information. What you say and when you say it (in advance, immediately before, during or after the exam) depends on the woman's state of readiness to address the experience of sexual abuse, whether or not her experience is occluded. Communication during a pelvic exam cannot proceed by formula. You need to be present, listen carefully, and think flexibly about each woman. What does this particular woman need to hear from you now?

Recognize that your client might have a different view from yours regarding what it means to be treated with respect. This might be rooted in differences between you and your client regarding ethnicity, country of origin, class, background, religion, age, sexual orientation, or presence of a disability. Tell her your intention is to treat her with respect and kindness and ask her what that would entail for her. Then listen.

If your client has disclosed a history of abuse, you may acknowledge the possibility of linking the two, by reminding her that there are elements in a pelvic exam that could bring back memories of sexual abuse; for example, lying down, being touched in the genital area or in a particular way, having something inserted in her vagina, having parts of her body exposed, and spreading her legs apart. Naming specific elements that the pelvic exam and sexual abuse have in common can help her assess what aspects of her experience of abuse might be triggered by the exam. Encourage her to notice what is the same in this situation and what is different from her prior abuse. Listen carefully. Remind her that one of the differences is that you intend to take care of her.

Describe the purpose of the pelvic exam. Be specific about the benefits to her of doing the exam as well as the risks of not doing it. Many women were (and are) mistreated with the justification that "it is for your own good. " Listen to whether it makes sense to her to have the exam. What questions does she have? Do not proceed unless you are clear that her consent is informed. Remind her that your priority is her overall well-being, not whether you have accomplished the procedure. Be aware of any bias or urgency you have that she must have this exam at all costs. Be willing not to do the exam. Balance not doing the exam with the knowledge that, besides the diagnostic benefits, she can emerge from the pelvic exam with some degree of healing, including a sense of accomplishment, a sense of her own courage, greater trust in and knowledge about her body, and trust of another person in a vulnerable situation. Let her know about these potential benefits of the exam.

There are some women whose experience of sexual abuse involved so much fear and force that they literally cannot say "no" to an authority proposing a medical procedure. Such a woman is not capable of informed consent because she is not capable of choosing freely. When this is the case, it is important to have her actually practice withholding and giving consent. For example: You say (after describing the pelvic exam),"Is it all right to go ahead now?" "She says, "No, I don't want you to," then, "Maybe, I'm not sure," and then, "Yes, you can go ahead." Have her say no several times if necessary. Be prepared for her to feel a huge amount of fear as she says, "No."

Remind her that in addition to choosing whether to have the exam, she has choices about specific aspects of the exam (see "Immediately Before the Exam").

Honor her behaviors (for example, having difficulty opening her legs, not wanting the exam at all, "making a fuss"), whether or not they appear to you to be dysfunctional. Let her know that you see them as survival strategies—brilliant, valiant attempts to fight back and get through adverse or unbearable situations. Review with her the ways this present situation is different from the abusive one and that she has the option of choosing different behaviors.

Ask her about her experience with previous pelvic exams. Listen to her sense of both the positive and negative aspects, and respond appropriately. If, for example, she was treated roughly, tell her there is never a reason during a pelvic exam (or ever) that justifies rough treatment of her and that you are going to treat her as gently as possible.

Immediately Before the Exam

Again, use your judgment about what the woman needs to hear and when she needs to hear it.

1. Remind her you are working together with her. Your job is to take care of her. Her job is to take care of herself and let you know if you can do a better job taking care of her. Listen. Acknowledge her authority; she's the expert on her own experience.

2. Let her know that her expression of emotion is not only OK, it is an important part of her healing. Acknowledge that in abusive situations children and women are often threatened with worse abuse if they cry or make noise. This exam, on the other hand, is an opportunity to safely express emotions.

3. Explain that the more she can relax her body, the less uncomfortable the exam will be, and the more useful the exam will be for her to know the status of her own health. Talk about the relationship between fear, tension and pain. Explore with her ways to relax that she already knows. If she doesn't know any ways to relax, show her slow rhythmic abdominal breathing. Show her how to breathe in through her nose and out through her mouth. Discuss visualization. It is important not to impose your images but have her draw strength from her own. Ask her what images evoke for her both empowerment and relaxation rather than those that evoke passivity and being used: for example "a redwood tree swaying in the wind" rather than "a "limp rag doll." See Chapter 9 for suggestions on ways to relax and use visualization to enhance her comfort.

4. Let her know the things over which she can have choice. Too many choices can be overwhelming, rather than making the exam more manageable. Assess which ones to

present and when. Too many choices can be overwhelming rather than making the exam more manageable, for example:

- Timing of exam: at the beginning or end of the visit (this visit or next visit).
- Pacing of the exam: get it done as quickly as possible or take it slowly.
- Her position: how much she wants to recline, does she want a pillow behind her head?.
- Presence of another person: either someone she brings with her, or a "chaperone" type person. Even if you present yourself as a person with whom she can be safe she may not feel safe unless there is someone else there.
- The use of a mirror to see inside her own vagina.
- The chance to explore the workings of the speculum.
- Being told about normal findings as you go along, or waiting until the end.
- Control over whether or when you will STOP the exam. Assure her that you will stop either altogether or until she is ready to continue. This is critical. Her informed consent is progressive, not a blanket permission for you to go ahead no matter what happens as the exam proceeds.

5. Explain the overall process of the exam and tell your client you will keep her informed every step of the way about what you will be doing. Tell her you will let her know if something you are about to do could be uncomfortable, painful, or messy.

6. Ask her to empty her bladder so that the exam will be more comfortable and it will be easier to palpate her pelvic organs.

Doing the Exam Itself

[NOTE: For purposes of this article, I will focus on only one aspect of the pelvic exam: the speculum exam. All the principles hold true for all other parts of the exam: inspection of external genitalia, examination of the urethra, Skene's and Bartholin's glands, the bimanual and the recto-vaginal exam. For technical step-by-step manipulation of the speculum and details of other aspects of the pelvic exam see the textbook, *Varney's Midwifery*, by Helen Varney (See Resources: Books). The context of this article is a regular office visit. Doing a pelvic exam in the context of the criminal justice system on a woman who has been raped has other specific parameters, which are beyond the scope of this article.]

1. Assist her to position herself on the table, as reclined as she would like to be, using a pillow or something rolled up behind her head. Adjust the stirrups (covered with potholders or something soft) to her comfort. Explain that her buttocks need to be at the edge of the table so that the table will not be in the way of the handle of the speculum. Help her to know how far down the table to go by telling her to move until she touches your hand, which you have placed just beyond the edge. Have her place her arms either beside her or rest them on her abdomen rather than behind her head so that her abdominal muscles can relax, making palpation of her organs easier.

2. Drape the woman so that she is as unexposed as possible.

3. Make sure that she can see your face. Make sure you can see her face when you are doing the exam so you can notice her moment-to-moment reactions and assess how to proceed.

4. Wash your hands and put on gloves.

5. Ask the woman to let her legs open. Never try to open

a woman's legs no matter how gently you think you are doing it. One way to help her is to have her own hands or your hands gently touching the outside of her thighs and ask her to move the hands by pushing them with her thighs. This allows her to be the active one in the interaction between you. Continue having her do this until her legs are wide open.

6. Do not tell her to relax without reminding her how to relax either with breathing techniques or visualizations. Do not proceed unless she can relax her legs. You cannot do a useful exam if the woman has her legs clenched around the speculum or your hand. You must have her "embodied consent" as well as her verbal consent. Otherwise you are re-injuring her. If she tightens her legs at any point, STOP: do not move your fingers, hand or speculum. Ask her what the problem is. Do not proceed until you have addressed the problem and she gives you permission to proceed.

7. Select the speculum that will provide the woman with the least discomfort and still enable you to adequately visualize her cervix and vagina. Use the Pederson, which has narrower blades than the Graves, if possible.

8. Make sure the speculum is warm. Warm it beforehand in a warming drawer or with a heating pad, or now with warm water, your hands, or a light.

9. Lubricate the speculum with warm water only. Jelly or cream might invalidate cytological or other tests.

10. Ask the woman if the temperature of the speculum is OK by placing it on her inner thigh near her external genitalia. This action reminds her that you care about her comfort.

11. Encourage the woman to relax by taking some slow deep breaths and tell her that she will first feel your fingers touching her on the outside and then she will feel the speculum going inside her vagina. Remind her that you will be gentle and that feeling the speculum going in might be an

unusual sensation but does not in itself need to cause pain. Be aware that many women have been told "this won't hurt" by their abuser, so remain alert to her response. Insertion of the speculum is often the most feared part of the exam so check in with her afterwards.

12. Before you open the speculum tell the woman that she will feel pressure. Show her approximately how much pressure by pressing your fingers on her inner thigh. Ask her if she feels pain when you press her thigh. Ask her to notice the pressure inside her vagina as you gradually open the speculum. One of the most important lessons a woman can learn at this moment is the difference between pressure and pain, and between fear of pain and actual pain. Ask her to see if she can tell the difference. Keep checking in with her about what she is feeling.

13. Keep letting her know where you are in the progress of the exam. Are you half way done, almost done? Keep noting your client's nonverbal responses. Are her eyes tearing up? Are they opening wide in fear? Does she have the blank look of someone dissociating from her body? Is she grimacing in pain? Let her know that you care about her responses. You can give her feedback either in the moment or later, depending on your assessment of what would be useful. (See After the Exam: Immediate Closure.)

14. During the exam keep telling the woman that she is doing well in some specific way, for example, relaxing her legs, letting you know how she is feeling, etc.

Ending the Exam

1. Wipe off any secretions or discharge or lubricating jelly from the woman's external genitalia. Keep letting her know what you are doing.

2. Help her return to a sitting position. If the procedure has been emotional, encourage her to sit for a few minutes before she gets dressed. Help her recognize that she is safe in

the present moment by asking her to place her attention on something that is benign. For example, have her look around the room and notice the colors or the pictures on the wall.

3. Let your client know to expect some bleeding, and tell her why so she won't be surprised and scared. Give her a sanitary pad.

After the Exam: Immediate Closure

It is very important for a woman's growth and healing that she has a chance to say how the exam was for her. What did she learn about herself and her body? What did she do well? What was hard? What challenges remain? Validate her statements and give her specific positive feedback.

What you discuss will depend on how much she connects the exam with her history of abuse, where she is on her path of healing, and what you are willing to take on as her practitioner.

Example 1: If the woman has said that she does not have a history of sexual abuse, yet during the exam you noticed tears running down her cheeks. This might be an appropriate time to say something like: "When I was taking your history I noticed you said that you had not been sexually abused. Yet when I was doing your exam I noticed that you were crying. I wonder if this exam reminded you of any experience you have had with your body in which you were hurt." Clearly, if you are going to open up this topic you need to have time to listen to her response and have closure before she leaves your office.

Example 2: The pelvic exam has triggered the woman's memory of her experience of sexual abuse. She sobs and shakes. Be with her like a protective safe harbor. Offer to hold her, being aware that she may have trouble saying "no": "Part of me would like to hold you but I am not sure what you would want." Reassure her that the fact that her abuse came up means she is ready to face it; that facing it is part of her journey of healing. Validate the pain of her emotions, and reassure her that it is now safe to feel and express the terror, grief or rage that wasn't safe to express or even feel when the abuse was actually happening. Acknowledge her courage and tell her that this time she does not have to deal with the experience alone. Before she leaves your office, help her figure out whom she can call (right away, if necessary) for further support.

Example 3: She is pregnant and has learned to tolerate a vaginal exam without suffering. You might reinforce the value of using what she has learned about the difference between pressure and pain, between fear of pain and actual pain to assist her through labor.

For many women undergoing a pelvic exam, being treated with respect and kindness is a huge triumph. Congratulate her and celebrate her triumph with her.

After the Exam: Follow Up

It is ideal to see the woman again at a subsequent visit to follow up. What happened to her when she left your office? How has her story unfolded? A pelvic exam done with the intention of healing can have enormous repercussions. For example, if the pelvic exam brought up previously occluded sexual abuse memories, the woman may be just at the beginning of a long healing process. Check in with her about what help and support she has and what she needs. Refer her to other resources (books, support groups, therapists, body workers), even if you are willing to continue to support her in her process. The pelvic exam may have been a significant positive turning point in her trust of and comfort with her own body. Encourage her to notice what has been useful and good for her. How can you support her continuing journey toward health?

13
The Use of Nursing Care Plans to Ensure Client Satisfaction and Appropriate Care

By Carla Reinke, BSN, MN, CNM,
and Ann Keppler, BSN, MN

Authors' note: We have invited Carla Reinke, RN, MN, CNM and Ann Keppler, RN, MN, to describe the approaches they devised as perinatal clinical nurse specialists when employed at Virginia Mason Medical Center in Seattle, Washington and Evergreen Hospital in Kirkland, Washington, respectively.

Carla illustrates her approach with a number of case reports, which detail the careful exploration of issues with each woman, their goals for care, and individual care plans she and the women designed to achieve the goals. The outcomes of each case are also presented.

Ann presents the abuse history and has shared the relevant records (the nursing care plan and birth plan) of a client whom we were also able to interview about her perceptions of her birth experience and the care she received.

Obstetrical Care Planning for Women with a History of Sexual Abuse

by Carla Reinke, RN, MN, CNM

Virginia Mason Medical Center's Birth Center (which is now closed) based its philosophy of care on a respect for both the individual and the birth experience. For years we encouraged communication with patients throughout their childbearing experiences. One of the most useful tools for understanding our clients was the use of the birth plan, where the client expressed her desires and preferences, as well as concerns and fears. It was the philosophy of our care providers to try to meet the needs and preferences of our clients. This article was written when the Birth Center was still open.

The Nursing Care Plan: Step by Step

During the course of prenatal care the primary provider sometimes becomes aware of excess anxiety or fear in a particular woman. This may become evident because of the woman's birth plan that conveys a strong message, "Don't touch me," or a major theme indicating an inability to trust the staff. Or the woman may have related a history of sexual abuse and linked that history to anxiety about her forthcoming birth. The provider then refers the woman to the perinatal clinical nurse specialist. Our goal is to help the woman become comfortable enough to nest in our birth center. We hope to reduce her fear of the "institution" by actively listening to her concerns and demonstrating flexibility and a willingness to individualize her care. Every attempt is made to listen carefully to the woman and treat all her concerns as reasonable, even if unusual. After the initial interview, a nursing care plan is written. The patient is given a copy and has an opportunity to revise it. Team meetings with nurses, midwives and/or physicians may occur to trouble shoot some ways of dealing with specific fears and concerns.

The first interview between the clinical nurse specialist and the woman is by telephone. It focuses on the woman's concerns and fears. Those clients who have been in therapy are usually able to identify and communicate their fears and concerns specifically. Others are less able to identify their desires or to specifically address their fears. If they have given birth before, we ask about the birth and what they found troublesome or what they would like to be different this time. We identify their support people and how they can help. We explore their coping abilities and strategies. Then their homework is to identify their fears more specifically. What does that fear do to them, and what does it mean? This allows us to bring their fears into more specific and manageable concerns that we can troubleshoot.

For instance, one woman with a strong needle phobia reported that she was worried because she needed almost a day to rest and recuperate after a blood draw. She feared she wouldn't be able to cope with labor after an event that so depleted her. Upon further exploring her fear, we found out that having to anticipate the stick wore her out, and also a good, quick puncture was a lot better than a long drawn out procedure, possibly including multiple sticks. Our mutually developed care plan was to do the blood draw soon after admission, and to be all set up to draw the blood before even telling her of the need to do it, so that she would have less time to anticipate the blood draw. We also planned to pull in our most highly skilled nurse for the draw.

During the face-to-face meeting between the client and the clinical nurse specialist, we explore her concerns and fears more in depth and try to create a realistic care plan. Some items such as preservation of modesty are easy to meet. Others cannot be promised, such as no needle punctures, (described above) or no male providers, but can be approached with the goal of creating a workable compromise. For example, if the woman wants no males providing care, we can honestly tell her we'll try, but on certain call days it is not possible. Since it is not possible to promise that the men won't be involved in her care, we work on the issues that can make it better. This may involve protecting her modesty, keeping her covered during vaginal exams and during most of second stage, continuing to wear a hospital gown or being covered by a towel while in the bath or minimizing the number of vaginal exams. It may mean that female nurses do all the vaginal exams and the coaching during second stage, with a proviso that if a slow labor needs a more thorough evaluation, a male provider may need to do that exam. It most likely means that she doesn't want any communication from any providers, be they male or female, who dismiss her or diminish her.

If the care plan presents difficult logistical problems, consultations with the nurses, midwives and physicians are done to solve the problem. With some very challenging issues, a special care team may be formed to act as primary nurses for the woman. For example, one patient was easily angered, and verbally lashed out at anyone when angry. A team was formed whom we thought could give compassionate care in spite of potential anger and obscenity. Another team was formed for a mother who was opting not to breastfeed. On one level she felt bad, but on another she felt emotionally unable to have so much physical contact with her breasts. We formed a postpartum team of nurses who would deliver non-judgmental care and not attempt to promote breastfeeding.

Sometimes we have a meeting between the nursing care team and the primary provider. If the patient expresses distrust in the hospital and resistance to interventions in labor, the usual care plan is for the nurses to be totally positive about the progress of labor and leave it completely and solely up to the provider to discuss any deviations from normal and the possible use of medical interventions. This allows the nurses to provide consistent care which focuses on a positive, low risk childbirth and to let the patient know we are doing our best to follow her wishes and make sure that no inconsistent information is given about interventions, should they be necessary.

In summary, our recipe for satisfying care for childhood sexual abuse survivors consists of the following steps:

- Identification of clients' concerns
- Troubleshooting
- Reduction to manageable concerns
- Problem Solving

Translation to a Nursing Care Plan and Action

Basic Principles

It helps if the clinical nurse specialist comes into an interview with no preconceived ideas and no general assumptions about the problems and solutions faced by abuse survivors. For example, not all women who were abused will have difficulty with labor. Not all survivors of sexual abuse will have difficulty with male providers. The keys to meeting the needs of survivors of sexual abuse are the same for all patients: listening very well to the patient, acknowledging her feelings, and responding by individualizing care tailored to meet her needs.

During the interviews, we elicit dissatisfaction with a previous birth experience and explicit and general fears. We find that the easiest women to work with are the ones who are able to communicate their fears. The more difficult are those who have fewer communication skills and less ability to specifically identify their fears. These women were also more likely to have extremely difficult times with vaginal exams, and to have more somatic complaints, pregnancy pain, preterm labor, or prolonged labor. They may or may not have acknowledged a history of sexual abuse. It helps to encourage expression of specific fears.

In the interview it helps to give control and choice to the woman. It helps to acknowledge her fears and to reflect to her that her feelings and fears are normal. It helps to take the fears and break them down into smaller pieces. If she hates vaginal exams, discuss every aspect of the exam that she hates. For example, the cold metal, a fast exam, just anything in the vagina, "having someone do it to her," or the opening of the speculum, within her vagina.

Building a Team Approach

Most of the time the care team in our hospital has been very willing to help create and to follow nursing care plans and birth plans. The person writing the care plan needs to know when the plan is pushing the boundaries of standard care, or asking for a lot of compromise from the providers. In those situations, a team meeting is called, because consensus needs to be reached. Exclusion of male providers is one example of the long term consequences of sexual abuse of women by men. Sensitive, caring male providers can feel punished and excluded despite trying to do their best for women. Less sensitive men may react to requests for their exclusion with hostility and disregard for the woman's wishes and well-being, which reenact her degradation. In team building, it helps to acknowledge the male providers' feelings, while explaining why meeting the woman's emotional needs is important.

Keys to Success

The key measure of success is not the type of birth outcome (i.e., vaginal or cesarean birth), but that the woman will describe being treated with respect and no hint of feeling revictimized. In a hospital birth center, this success is dependent on communication and teamwork. Our communication methods include the referral to the perinatal clinical nurse specialist, and talking with childbirth educators, therapists, doulas, nurses, midwives, and physicians as needed. The tool for communication is the nursing care plan. This care plan is always shared with the client, and placed in the prenatal record. It is sometimes circulated among a special nursing care team ahead of time. Sometimes those members meet the woman ahead of time. Communication is vital to getting "stretch" to the system, so that all providers will attempt to deliver care in a flexible, personalized manner.

Our failures occurred when a team member let the patient down by not treating her with respect and dignity. This is the key element to feeling victimized again. Body language or words, which in any way degrade the patient, are likely to be noticed and be painfully felt by the patient. A survivor of sexual abuse is likely to have a tenuous hold on feelings of self-worth. Any behavior that denigrates her personhood is worse than non-therapeutic; it is a reenactment of abuse—therefore the careless provider risks becoming a perpetrator.

Case Reports: Application of the "Recipe"

Here are some cases to illustrate our approach to providing appropriate care for abuse survivors. The form that we use for our nursing care plans is a 3 column form that lists the client's identified concern, the desired outcome after it is all over, and the strategies planned to achieve those outcomes.

The First Case: Patient A

Patient A is a 24-year-old, primigravid woman referred because she did not believe she could possibly deliver vaginally and was very afraid of being ripped apart. In discussing this with her, she revealed that she believed that her vagina was too mutilated to deliver a baby. She described a history of frequent constipation and an inability to strain when needing to have a bowel movement or to urinate.

Patient A's Nursing Care Plan

Identified Concern	Desired Outcome	Strategies
Anxiety regarding the pain of labor.	Patient expresses satisfaction with support with coping strategies utilized.	Patient A will have support people present for her: her boyfriend, and family or friends. Even though she is worried about the pain of labor, she prefers a narcotic analgesic and coping strategies rather than an epidural. Help patient A stay in the present: to focus on each contraction as it occurs, rather then worrying about the pushing phase or what her future labor will be like. Praise her efforts and reassure her about labor progress and her own and her baby's condition.
Concerns about maintaining modesty.	Patient will express satisfaction that modesty has been preserved.	Patient A does not want family and friends (and a "bunch of people") present during times of exposure such as vaginal exams or when breasts are exposed. Please ask visitors to step out. Keep covers in place during vaginal exams. Allow her to wear a hospital gown during tub use. During delivery, she would like all family and friends at the head of the bed (not staring at her perineum), or outside of the room, except her boyfriend, who may watch the birth. As much as possible, and for as long as possible, keep her covered during pushing.
Fear concerning birthing events that might be reminders of childhood abuse. Patient A gets tense and emotional during vaginal exams. She feels like she "has been invaded" when a vaginal exam is done.	Patient describes satisfaction that providers sensitively met her needs.	Patient A prefers to avoid rupture of membranes. The insertion of the amnihook is frightening to her. As a coping strategy, she is planning on rubbing her belly. This will probably be more effective than having someone hold her hand. She finds exams easier if done by the same person than by different people. Try to limit their number. She understands that in some situations this is not possible.

Identified Concern	Desired Outcome	Strategies
Fear of ripping or tearing during delivery. Patient A is very concerned about having too big a baby. Her baby's weight is average.	Patient either has no tears or is satisfied with the care done to prevent tearing.	Patient A anticipated that pushing will be hard for her and she "can't see myself pushing hard." If possible, allow her to ease into second stage. See how effective pushing is with time and a good urge to push. She is willing to use positions such as squatting to more effectively push. She understands that in certain situations she may be asked to push hard and long, especially to respond to fetal distress to get the baby low enough for forceps or vacuum extraction. Try to coach Patient A to stay present with the birth of this baby. Help her stay focused on the birth.
Fear related to the possibility of a cesarean.	Patient either doesn't have a cesarean or is satisfied with the care provided before and during the cesarean.	If an emergency cesarean is done, try to keep things as smooth and calming as possible. Keep her current on her baby's condition both before and after delivery. Would prefer either intrathecal or epidural morphine. At this point, she is not at any risk for a cesarean. Reassure her that she is healthy and normal and as it is happening, that labor is progressing normally and well. Because of her history of keloid scar formation, she has added desire to avoid a cesarean. Be sure surgeon knows her history of keloids. She has found that when tapes were left in place longer, there was less keloid formation. If a cesarean is necessary, apply more tape over scar and leave for longer period than average.
Concerns about breastfeeding	Patient satisfied that modesty was preserved during breastfeeding, and that the best start with breastfeeding was made.	Patient has had breast reduction surgery and has had significant keloids develop around the scars. When her breasts are exposed, she is comfortable only with her boyfriend present, so make sure family and friends are asked to step out during breastfeeding attempts. Sensitively deliver breastfeeding support. Always ask before touching the breasts. Make sure Patient A knows her resources for breastfeeding support prior to leaving the hostpital. Pediatric exam should probably be made within one week of delivery rather than two. Please try to get a private room for her postpartum care.

Patient A's Outcome

Patient A had spontaneous rupture of membranes at 39 weeks and subsequently needed an induction because labor did not start spontaneously. Pitocin was started, the first stage of labor was short (latent 7 hours and active labor 2 hours). She utilized an epidural for pain relief and had 5 hours of second stage. Patient A said the hardest part of the labor was dealing with the pain. She said it took too much energy to cope with the pain. She cried, and moaned and groaned a lot during labor, enough to frighten her boyfriend. She found trying to push without any feeling very bewildering and her fear of ripping apart stayed with her. A key to the progress in second stage was doing a bladder catheterization, which she found terrifying and painful. When forceps were brought up as a possibility and described as two "blades" she envisioned two knives and was very frightened. A vacuum was attempted and popped off, so there was discussion of a cesarean. At this point she rallied and "pulled energy from between my toes to behind my ears" and spontaneously pushed out a 7 lb., 1oz. healthy boy. She was getting milk and successfully breastfeeding her son, who had regained his birth weight at two weeks of age.

Case 2: Patient B

Patient B is a 34-year-old, first-time mother, who has been in therapy for "quite a while." She describes herself as "phobic" about punctures anywhere on her body. With blood draws, she nearly always faints, and needs a half to a whole day of bed rest after the event. When intravenous lines have been started to give her medications, she has required 2 days of rest for recovery. Her major concern is a specific fear about what she perceives as a debilitating procedure with no opportunity to recover because of the ongoing need to continue to cope with a stressful labor. For Patient B, episiotomy and a cesarean are not as frightening as venipunctures because they come at the end, and are not followed by the need to cope with labor.

For Patient B, visiting the hospital on the tour was a source of increased anxiety, associated with dying. She has a vague memory of hospitalization when she was 5 for facial surgery. When she was told, at age 23, that she has urethral scarring, and urethral stretching was suggested for therapy, she opted not to do it. After our first meeting, her "homework" was to explore her fears in more depth and to come back with any ways she thought of to cope. She came back with both her husband and her doula. The plan was to discuss her specific fears related to blood draws, IV starts, epidurals, labor, episiotomy and cesarean birth.

Patient B's Nursing Care Plan

Identified Concern	Desired Outcome	Strategies
Anxiety relating to possible punctures such as blood draws, IV starts and epidurals. Patient B has a history of fainting and being bedridden after blood draws and IV usage, related to a previous history of abuse.	Patient states any needle use was tolerable and she was able to maintain labor coping strategies.	Patient B has a history of fainting and being bedridden after blood draws and IV usage, related to a previous hx of abuse. She will use coping strategies—focusing away, holding partner's hand and he will talk to her. Despite this she will need 12-24 hours of bedrest after the puncture. Things to try: Do her hematocrit prenatally at 39 weeks. Draw blood when IV started to avoid a puncture. Cover work area and arm to prevent seeing the site. Use ethyl chloride for numbing. Hold needles and catheters out of sight. If an IV is used—cover the site of puncture with opaque material so the puncture site is not visible to her. Try to start IV in forearm, not hand. She finds it easier to cope if there is not a prolonged period to fret about something. Don't say, "If this labor doesn't pick up in 1 hour, we will need to start the Pit." Go from decision to quicker action, for example, "We'll need to start the Pit, and so we'll start the IV in just a few minutes." Technique does matter. When it is quick and slick she copes better. Use your best resources for blood draws and IV starts.
Potential for anxiety related to necessary medical intervention to enhance labor progress. Constipation is a continuing problem. Patient B fears it may slow labor progress.	Patient B either has normal labor progress or is satisfied that an augmentation was necessary and managed in an acceptable way that is, she maintains her ability to cope with labor.	Patient B would like to avoid Pitocin if possible. I have encouraged her to use labor enhancing strategies from the beginning such as: doula, ambulating, frequent position changes, and enema, if her usual pattern of constipation persists. Assess need on admission. Currently she plans to self-administer an enema at home in early labor. Patient B would prefer alternatives including extra time before the use of Pitocin, although she is open to its use if other strategies fail.

Identified Concern	Desired Outcome	Strategies
History of anxiety attacks related to epinephrine use. Fear that epinephrine will be used with anesthesia. Anxiety over anesthesia administration, because of the punctures involved.	No anxiety attacks associated with anesthesia use.	Patient B has a history of anxiety attacks when exposed to epinephrine. I have advised her to go to pre-op clinic and discuss this with anesthesia ahead of time. Patient B prefers not to have anesthesia because of all the punctures associated with its use, but because this may become necessary, it may become less frightening if she talks with the anesthesiologists ahead of time.

Patient B's Outcome

Patient B went into spontaneous labor just a few days after her due date. Both her active labor (9 hours) and her second stage (4 hours) were long. The blood draw was done quickly and expertly shortly after admission. She felt it was done well and according to the plan, and she recovered easily. With each contraction for the last 6 hours of her labor from 8 cm on, she expressed fear she wouldn't be able to cope with each contraction. However, with nursing, doula and family support, she found the strength to cope and push with each contraction. Her nurse said she was easy to take care of because she expressed her concerns and fears and could ask for what she needed. Patient B said that during the last two hours of birth she was very frightened that she or her baby would die. Her partner described all the providers as a perfectly fitting mosaic; each personality provided a positive component to the birth experience. Patient B said everyone treated her as important. She liked the obstetrician and her cheer leading during second stage, and the family practitioner's attempt to stretch her perineum. She did not have any pain medications, no IV, no epidural, no episiotomy, no tearing and no stitching—the only puncture was the one blood draw. When after delivery her lochia flow was heavy, the nurse suggested and she used nipple stimulation and fundal massage effectively enough that neither intramuscular Pitocin or an IV start was necessary. The professionals in the room found this an awe-inspiring birth, because she was able to overcome her fears and found so much strength to cope. Her doula said it was a privilege to be there.

Case 3: Patient C

Patient C is a 39-year-old primigravida who was referred by her childbirth educator because she was easily angered and clearly had a profound distrust of hospitals. She met with the nurse to create a care plan, with a secondary goal of preparing the staff for any difficulties that might arise with this patient. She revealed that she was in therapy, but did not want to tell her midwife the name of the therapist or the purpose of her therapy.

Patient C's Nursing Care Plan

Identified Concern	Desired Outcome	Strategies
Concerns related to maintaining control over medical decisions about her care.	Patient will feel satisfied if she fully participated in decisions about her care.	Because of possible misunderstandings, try to have only the midwife on call and/or RB (the midwife who is "specialing" her) to provide Patient C with information on her condition (especially if it deviates from normal), and to provide choices and options. Give Patient C time to assimilate any need for intervention, and obtain her verbal consent before any procedures. Try to use the same nurses as much as possible (12-hour people are a good choice).
Desire for unmedicated NSVD (normal spontaneous vaginal delivery) and a distrust of medical interventions and personnel.	Patient will either have an unmedicated NSVD or feel satisfied that the best efforts were made to achieve it.	Patient knows strategies to aid labor progress; encourage her to use them (i.e.,. ambulating, or sitting upright, frequent position changes if in bed, good support). Be encouraging if labor is slow, let her midwife introduce the possibility of medical interventions, if necessary. Be positive and encouraging in your support. Let her know you want her goals to be met. Aid her in her coping strategies.
Need for privacy and modesty	Patient feels modesty was protected	Limited providers involved in her care No students. Protect her privacy/modesty during times of vulnerability (i.e., vaginal exams, pushing). If possible she prefers female providers.
Anxiety related to separation from baby and someone taking her baby from her.	Patient will state she was satisfied with the amount of time with her baby.	Try to provide total rooming-in. Notify nursery ahead of time, so they can plan to do the baby admission in her room, if possible. Request a private room. Involve her in baby's care as much as possible; for example, do Apgar while baby is on mother's abdomen and explain results; do newborn procedures in her presence; explain them ahead of time. Anticipate some resistance to infant procedures and if she resists, use the midwife and/or pediatrician chosen to deal with this resistance. (Also if baby is ill and needs interventions, call in the midwife and pediatrician.) Patient wants to bathe the baby herself. Please note: Patient is emotionally labile, she may cry and anger easily. Allow her time to vent and let it roll off.

Patient C's Outcome

Patient C had written a specific birth plan expressing a strong desire to have an unmedicated, vaginal birth without medical interventions. Also, she expressed strong concerns for no separation from her baby. She knew going into labor that her midwife was very concerned about the adequacy of her pelvis and that she was potentially a candidate for cesarean. Most of her birth plan did not happen. She had an epidural and an augmented labor, and while she progressed to complete dilation, after failed vacuum and forceps attempts, she had a cesarean birth. She also was unable to breastfeed. She had had breast reduction surgery, and after a week her baby wasn't getting enough milk and she had to formula feed.

She was a difficult and challenging patient to care for in labor. She would make a choice about care and then lash out at providers for the consequences of those decisions. For example, she insisted on staying in the hospital after rupture of membranes with no labor, but then was angry when she did not get good sleep. She asked her midwife to go away and leave her alone, and then was angry at her for being gone. Providers and her support person would endure her anger and need to quietly leave the room for a while. She seemed unaware of the effort it took to remain civil with her. There was not a healthcare provider, nurse, midwife or doctor who did not find her extremely challenging. Yet she was only aware of one negative response by any of her healthcare providers. One physician rolled her eyes at a request to give her some time and space before applying the forceps. For the woman, that was the low point of her entire birth experience, a moment of being perceived as less than human. She could not describe this without crying. She felt overall that a good attempt had been made for a vaginal birth and that except for this one incident, she had been respected and treated very well. The staff, on the other hand, felt like they needed time off. Thus the enormous efforts by the staff to accommodate Patient C's needs for individualized care were successful, but they needed reassurance that, although they experienced the brunt of her anger and distrust, they were not the cause, nor were their actions the real reasons for her negative reactions.

Case 4: Patient D

Patient D was referred to us by her therapist. We were told she was a survivor of "terrible" abuse and trauma. She was going to a practice that had 75 percent male providers, and her primary doctor was a male whom she had been unable to approach about her concerns. She found the prospect of a cesarean terrifying. The key points of her care plan were: to treat her with respect and dignity and to provide medication for both the pain and fear. The nurse spent a lot of time discussing medications with her, and the best ways to meet her needs. They also went over the details of the cesarean operation and sensations she might experience. For each step they discussed her fears and possible coping strategies.

Patient D's Nursing Care Plan

Identified Concern	Desired Outcome	Strategies
Pain and/or anxiety regarding pain.	Pain will remain tolerable, needs related to fear of pain will be met.	Help with coping strategies, as needed. Utilize analgesia, as ordered and indicated (Patient D finds medications that help decrease anxiety appealing.) Epidural, as ordered. Plan to have anesthesiologist see her in early labor for assessment and consent. Plan care (IV, labor assessment for early identification of active labor) to maximize accessibility of the epidural. Dr. B has okayed the use of nitrous oxide if necessary.
Fear and anxiety about modesty issues.	Patient D will be comfortable and secure with all providers and during procedures.	Patient D has a strong and important preference for female providers. Primary nurse to manage labor and 2nd stage, do vaginal exams, etc. Ask male providers to sensitively deliver care (i.e., respect her needs for modesty). Take extra care to protect her modesty: keep her covered as much as possible. Keep door closed, curtains drawn, etc. In potentially stressful procedures (vaginal exams, forceps, vacuum, internal monitors) explain procedures, allow Patient D time to figure out how she needs to cope. Patient D has used dissociation to cope with stressful events. Ask her in early labor and during stresses if that is how she wants to cope or if she would like directive support for coping. Patient D would prefer her partner to be at the head of the bed for pushing and delivery. Patient seems to be very accommodating and I am concerned that she will give up what she cares about. Try not to ask her to relinquish any key concepts about care. Patient D understands that procedures may be medically necessary (such as vacuum, episiotomies) and is okay with that, but she asks that: a) she be treated with dignity and respect; b) procedures are explained prior to doing them. Help her plan coping strategies as needed.
Learning needs	Patient expresses satisfaction that learning needs were met.	Patient has read a lot and has a high level of understanding, but she has not finished the childbirth series. Assess individual learning needs at appropriate times.

Identified Concern	Desired Outcome	Strategies
Infant Nutrition	Infant nutritional needs are met.	Patient D plans to bottle feed—please don't ask her preference. Make no attempts to try to talk her into breastfeeding. Respect her decision.
Anxiety related to possible cesarean	Patient expresses satisfaction with the way surgery was handled, if it occurs.	The possibility of a cesarean is very frightening and potentially a reminder of past abuse. In the hurry to do procedures, stay in touch with Patient D. Keep her apprised of what is happening; forewarn her about anything she might feel or experience. Does not want arms restrained (this is a reminder of ritualized abuse). Is scared of the possibility of feeling "tugging and pulling." Would rather have a higher block. Warn her about possible sensations during delivery. Antiemetics/sedatives during surgery after delivery are okay. Versed, not OK; does not want any memory loss. PCA (Patient controlled analgesia) for post-op pain is preferred. In general, keep her in touch with the situation and reality.
Discomfort, embarrassment about past history of abuse.	Patient expresses satisfaction with how she was treated.	She prefers not to discuss her past. If she does, it is to explain her needs. Don't probe for details. She feels it is okay for providers to have a general idea about her background, so they will understand her needs better. She would prefer not to explain herself. Patient D feels there are 3 possible ways she may cope: Normally, Dissociating, Panic. While the first two are okay, she is most concerned about panicking. Strategies to help decrease the likelihood may include: Always treat her with dignity and respect. Being treated as an object or not present may be the most difficult for her. Offer lots of reassurance about her baby's well being, her well being and how she is coping, and how her labor is proceeding. Teach coping strategies as appropriate. Have person designated to offer continual intense support. (Liz and her doula are all available to give additional support.)

Patient D's Outcome

We had expected that her birth would go well, because her demands or expectations were not out of the ordinary and she is well a well educated woman with excellent communication skills and coping skills. We had not, however, anticipated reluctance on the part of the physician to come in a timely manner to proceed with the epidural, nor his dismissal of her dignity in caring for her. Patient D is a highly perceptive woman who did not miss the verbal cues or body language of others. She saw her nurse's frustration, and the doula's efforts in trying to get him to be responsive to her needs for an epidural, and she saw the dismissive and degrading attitude he had toward her. The physician did not arrive until late active labor and, as a result, she did not get her epidural until 7 centimeters. Also, as was his standard practice, he turned off the epidural when she was completely dilated, failing to appreciate that the pain of second stage was terrible for her and eventually inhibited her pushing efforts. After 1 hour and 50 minutes, she asked for a vacuum birth and received it. She needed both a local and pudendal for the episiotomy and vacuum-assisted birth. The birth was extremely traumatic, and it would have required very little to make it a satisfying birth.

This birth represents some key points. Dignity and respect are key to humane care for all women in labor and birth, and are especially important for survivors of sexual abuse, who were robbed of these essential human responses during their trauma.

Case 5: Patient E

Patient E was 22 years old, having her first birth. She was supported by the father of the baby. She was referred because of anxiety and fear about labor and a past history of rape and abuse. Her main issues were fear of the pain and concerns about modesty. She had a total of 11 prelabor admissions for a variety of complaints, including flu, decreased fetal movements, questionable rupture of membranes and multiple admissions for labor evaluation of "cramping." Patient E found the "cramping" very distressing and a source of lost sleep during the last two weeks of her pregnancy.

Patient E's Nursing Care Plan

Identified Concerns	Desired Outcome	Strategies
Anxiety related to modesty issues.	Patient will express satisfaction that her sense of modesty was preserved	Protect modesty: cover her during vaginal exams and pushing. Offer a gown to wear while using the tub. She prefers female providers and minimal vaginal exams.
Anxiety related to the pain of labor.	Patient will express satisfaction with pain management during labor.	Tub use in early labor and early active labor. Epidural for pain relief when available. Don't turn the epidural off in second stage.

Patient E's Outcome

The nurse found that Patient E tolerated vaginal exams well if they were done very slowly, allowing her time to adjust and cope and giving her some control. She felt very well supported by the staff and her female physician. She said she was treated well and that everyone followed her care plan, with the exception of one nurse who she said was "cruel" but she couldn't elaborate further. She was glad she had finally been induced, following 14 days of prodromal labor.

The nurses reported some initial anxiety in Patient E immediately after birth. When she looked at her baby who had head molding and skin tags on each hand, she was initially very frightened about her baby's well being. The nurse was concerned because she wouldn't interact or breastfeed her baby during recovery. This seemed totally resolved by the next day.

Conclusion

We feel that we have succeeded in providing good care if the woman and her baby have a healthy outcome with no further trauma. But some births feel like triumphs. When a woman overcomes her fears, the pain and vulnerability of labor, and she finds inner resources and strengths, she may heal some broken pieces of herself. Childbirth provides an opportunity for such growth but only if the providers and the institution in which she is giving birth can provide care in a respectful and adaptive manner.

Collaboration between Woman and Nursing Staff: a Nursing Care Plan, a Birth Plan, and a Follow-up Interview

By Ann Keppler, BSN, MN

[*Authors' Note:* Here is a sample Nursing Care Plan for the nursing staff, prepared by Ann Keppler in collaboration with the woman, an abuse survivor, and her husband. It is more of a narrative than the ones provided by Carla Reinke, but is similar in that it maintains a respectful tone throughout and was most useful in helping the nurses understand and accept the woman's birth plan, which might otherwise have seemed somewhat demanding or inflexible.]

Patient Care Plan for "Toni and Don Jones"

By Ann Keppler, BSN, MN

Toni is a 31-year-old, second-time mother and a patient of Dr. U. Toni and her husband Don have a 14-month-old daughter, who was born here. Toni's first birth was very traumatic for her. She is also a rape survivor, and because of these past experiences, her labor and birth need to be handled with great sensitivity. She asks for your acceptance and patience. You will see in her enclosed birth plan that she needs to know everyone who is in the room. She needs you to help her with any procedures that become necessary, to be gentle, and to "persuade with logic and patience." If events become too scary, she will dissociate, and while her body cannot leave, she will leave in her mind. Toni is very articulate about her feelings when she feels safe. A safe and satisfying birth experience this time could be very healing for her.

Following are some guidelines for care:

(Please see her description of her "ideal nurse", in her birth plan, which follows.) She had "Nurse A" last time and really enjoyed her gentle style. She has also been cared for by "Nurse B" and liked her very much. She also knows and likes "Nurse C". If any of these nurses is on when she comes in, she would like to have them assigned to her care.

Toni had great difficulty with breastfeeding last time. She received the support of the Breastfeeding Center and tried many techniques and much equipment for an extended time. She has chosen to formula feed this time and would really appreciate not having to explain to everyone or be forced to justify it.

Toni, like many rape or sexual abuse survivors, really needs to feel a sense of control. Underneath some of the strong requests in her birth plan is a very tender and vulnerable woman.

Here is her written birth plan:

Birth Plan for Toni and Don Jones

OB Physician: Dr. U

Primary Care Physician (whole family): Dr. L.C.

Important Note: Dr. U has written a note in my chart that if he is not available, call any doctor besides Dr. N, whom I will not accept.

Philosophies and Expectations:

I expect all medical personnel to introduce themselves when they enter the room and explain what they're doing before they touch me.

I expect to be well informed about what's going on, both with the baby and myself.

I want to stay as mobile as possible and with the fewest interventions possible.

I expect to be informed about any scheduled tests or procedures for the baby and me (e.g., blood pressure/temperature checks, etc.).

I expect all medical personnel to give care and support in a non-confrontational/non-demanding manner—to explain things and request my cooperation, both before and after the birth.

Labor Support/Privacy: Don should be the only person in the room other than medical personnel. Please exclude all other people from our labor and birth, and honor our "do not disturb" sign whenever your presence in the room is not medically necessary or as scheduled.

Pain Relief: I will try Stadol relatively early in labor, beginning with a half dose to see how I respond. If I am in significant pain even with the Stadol, I may decide to have an epidural later in labor. I would appreciate being asked if I've decided I want an epidural some time during active labor. If I have not had an epidural, I'll need a local anesthetic before the baby is born.

Interventions and Emergencies: I expect someone to explain each procedure to Don and me, including what could happen if the procedure is not done, and what my options are.

In an emergency, if I am not able to make decisions, Don is the person who should be consulted on my behalf.

Miscellaneous Items:

Internal exams: Ever since my first daughter's birth, internal exams cause me great pain. I expect all medical personnel to be sensitive to this, give me fair warning to try to relax first, and to perform the minimum number of internal exams, and only when medically necessary.

Positions: I want the remote telemetry external monitor—I'll want to be in whatever position feels most comfortable, and to be as mobile as possible—to walk around, etc. as long as I can.

Food/Liquids: I want to know what I can eat or drink (popsicles, juice, etc.) and expect to be informed when drinking or eating is or is not be allowed.

Cutting the cord: In general Don does not expect to be actively involved in delivering the baby, cutting the cord, etc.

Contact with baby: I want to hold the baby as soon as she is born, but we understand she will be examined and put into a warmer shortly after birth.

Hospital Discharge: My insurance will pay for me to stay in the hospital as long as it is medically necessary (call the company if a longer than normal stay is necessary). I expect to have all the doses, schedules, etc. given to me in written form prior to discharge, for myself and for the baby if any medicine is necessary for her.

Baby Stuff:

Names: We'll make the final decision once we see our new daughter, but we are thinking of calling her "Becca."

Feeding: Bottle-feeding

Circumcision: If this baby is actually a boy, we would like to have him circumcised.

Rooming In: We will be rooming in with the baby unless the nursery is medically necessary.

Education Needs:

We have taken the Labor and Birth series and Cesarean class approximately 1 year ago at Evergreen. Since we already have a child, we don't need direction in baby care; however, timely support when requested in diapering, swaddling, feeding, etc. will be much appreciated.

Ideal Nurse:

Helpful when asked, but not bossy or directive

Explains procedures and options clearly

Caring, considerate

Gentle in doing internal exams

Relaxed, calm manner

Communicates progress, any schedule and what comes next clearly

Don's "To Do" List:

Help get explanations for procedures and interventions if not explained:

Why?

What will happen if you don't do it?

Are there any alternatives?

Keep the music going, even if it is just the radio.

Ask me only yes/no questions

If the nurse is bossy or isn't explaining things or it is obvious I don't like her, request a change.

Remind me to take a deep breath after each contraction

Help me remember my options/ask me now and then if I'd like to:

Get an epidural after all

Get more Stadol (if possible)

Have a massage (shoulder, back, whatever)

Have an icepack/hot pack or both

Wet washcloth

Ice chips

Juice/water/popsicle

Get in the bathtub

Walk

Sit in the chair

Put the bed up or down

Hang from the squatting bar

Change the room temperature

Change the lighting to darker/lighter

Outcome

Toni's second birth experience was "great." Her favorite doctor was on call and her nurse was most helpful, as was Don, who had his own "To Do" list of helpful things he could do. Toni knew "more about what to expect, and felt stronger, more in control, and more confident." Her birth plan was followed. She found the Stadol unhelpful in easing her pain and only made her feel drunk, so she switched to the epidural, which worked very well. Toni felt that "everyone went out of their way to make this a good experience."

Her baby had trouble breathing at first, and had to go to the nursery for observation and oxygen for several hours. Toni said if that had happened the first time, "it would have freaked me out, because I couldn't trust anyone and they were so mean." As it turned out, she was able to handle the worrisome situation calmly.

Long-term Impact

In an interview 18 months after her second child's birth, Toni stated she felt much better after her second child's birth, partly because it was her second, but also because it was so much better managed. After the first birth, Toni felt great guilt over putting her baby through so much trauma. She also felt that they had "gone through a war together," and she had an "us versus them" feeling of protection for her baby and lack of trust toward authority figures. She feels that from the beginning she had a much more normal relationship with her second baby, which she attributes to insights gained in psychotherapy and the empowering second birth experience.

Toni has noticed that in the 18 months since her second baby was born, she feels more competent and confident, as a mother and in her work. She can now speak up and voice her needs and concerns in all aspects of health care and at work. She was recently promoted, and generally feels more successful and powerful.

Conclusion

Many aspects of contemporary maternity care are impersonal and routinized, presenting challenges to abuse survivors who may feel overwhelmed not only by childbirth itself, but also by the adjustments they must make to the procedures that comprise obstetrical care.

The contributors to this chapter have shown how to tailor care to the needs of the individual, and by doing so, to improve psychosocial outcomes.

14

Opening the Door: Informed Decision-Making and Advocacy

by Kristine M. Zelenkov, M.D., F.A.C.O.G.

[Authors' note: We invited Kristine Zelenkov, an obstetrician in private practice who also provides backup consultation for midwives, to explore important issues regarding informed decision-making by maternity patients, including abuse survivors.]

Labor is a time of great vulnerability for women, in some cases because of biologic issues, but in all cases because the laboring mother is often not able to advocate for herself given the physical demands of the process. Furthermore, in many developed countries today, labor is no longer a spontaneous process but is much more of a medically managed event, where multiple decisions are made that directly impact the outcome. The woman with a history of sexual/physical abuse has heightened feelings of vulnerability and may refuse to accept decisions that are made for her by providers she does not know or trust.

A recent review of over 2,000 studies by the Center for Health and Gender Equity (CHANGE) found that one in three women has been physically and/or sexually abused. Of these women, 20-70% have not told anyone of their history. It is therefore critical for providers to approach all women as possible survivors of early abuse who deserve respect and who should be empowered as individuals to make their own medical decisions on the basis of education and support. By helping a previously victimized woman work through the physical and mental challenges of pregnancy and labor, we are empowering her to trust in her own body and to trust the people around her.

Problems in Client-Caregiver Communication

Medicine has long been thought to be synthesis of art and science, but in these days of technology and information expansion, the understanding of the art of medicine is less valued. Communication of information is often not face-to-face, but disseminated through means such as the written word and the Internet. Many methods of communication, such as the telephone, are limited because participants are unable to read each other's body language or facial nuances. When face-to-face dialogue finally occurs, there is often a burden of time and efficiency, which does not allow real discussion of the complexities of decision-making in modern maternity care.

Many care providers attempt to compensate for these problems by simplifying the options they present to the client, if they present them at all. They essentially decide for the client, rather than allow her to participate in the process, because, by its very nature, the latter takes more time. This ultimately leads to an authoritarian model of medicine, which may have had a place in the past when the primary provider was a country doctor and a long-time friend and confidante of the family, and options were minimal at best. It has no place, however, in today's medicine and does in fact carry the potential for harm. This is most clearly seen in women with a history of physical/sexual abuse but is also true for all clients. Many abuse survivors learned as children that they were not safe with people whom they perceived as persons in authority. This lesson may persist into adulthood, even with well-meaning authority figures. When sharing decisions with her caregiver and being a partner in the process, the survivor is less likely to be reminded of or to re-experience her former vulnerability.

Informed Consent versus Informed Decision-Making

"First Do No Harm" has been the ethical imperative that has governed the practice of medicine since Greek times. It is relatively easy to understand the potential for physical harm with medications and surgery, so the concept of informed consent evolved. To gain informed consent, the provider (authority figure) details the procedure or medicine (P), alternatives (A) and risks (R). PAR is then documented in the chart and the patient (defined as the person who will be treated passively) either gives verbal or written consent, theoretically acknowledging that she has been informed of her options and agrees to whatever treatment the provider recommends. This model has the potential to function well when there is an established trust relationship between the provider and client and the choices of treatment are few. If harm occurs, the patient knows in a very real way that the provider has tried his or her best and that the client made the decision for herself based on a complete understanding of the situation.

In today's world, there are many choices of therapy. Evidence-based medicine has shown that approximately 80% of commonly prescribed treatments or procedures have not been "proven" to work or may be no better than alternative treatments. Many providers offer treatment recommendations on the basis of their own training, past experience and continuing medical education that reflect so-called "expert" opinion. Consequently opinions will vary widely as to the "correct" treatment, from country to country, region to region and even within cities and hospitals. This is why it has become of paramount importance for consumers to search for providers who are open-minded and capable of educating them on the full spectrum of choices. Twenty percent of the time the choice will be clear-cut and have a proven benefit. Even then, the decision is and should always be in the hands of the client. An example that comes to mind is the proven benefit of a regular Pap smear to identify malignancies of the cervix. A sexual abuse survivor may avoid or refuse the procedure, even though she knows it has benefit for her. For her, the trauma and invasion of her vagina with instruments may override any potential benefit. She must of course make her decision understanding the benefits and risks.

What is the difference between informed consent and informed decision-making? As discussed above, informed consent is the minimum explanation that is found in PAR as discussed above. Informed decision-making is well defined in a study published by C.H. Braddock, et al., in the *Journal of the American Medical Association* in 1999 (see Recommended Resources: Papers). The author analyzed 1057 office encounters for the thoroughness of informed decision-making for simple, intermediate and complex medical decisions in primary care and general/orthopedic surgery. The following seven elements constitute informed decision-making and the office encounters were analyzed for their presence or absence:

Discussion of the patient's role in decision-making

Discussion of the clinical issue or nature of the decision

Discussion of the alternatives

Discussion of the potential benefits and risks of the alternatives

Discussion of the uncertainties associated with the decision

Assessment of the patient's understanding and

Exploration of patient preference.

The results were that only 9.0% percent of the decisions met all seven criteria for completeness, with specific values of (17.2% percent for simple decisions, 0% percent for intermediate decisions and 0.5% percent for complex decisions). Remarkably, element number 6, the assessment of patient understanding, occurred in only 1.5% percent of all the encounters. The mean time of each encounter was 16.5 minutes for family practice and 13.6 minutes for surgeons. This paper performs the valuable service of distinguishing informed consent, which is based upon an authoritarian or dominator model, from informed decision-making, which is predicated on a participatory/partner model. In addition, the above list thoroughly outlines the elements that should occur between provider and client prior to treatment.

Issues in Informed Decision-Making

Two specific issues regarding informed decision-making are addressed here: first, the inherent problems of communication for the consultant or on-call backup provider; and, the problem of "the difficult patient."

The role of consultant in the healthcare arena is that of a specialist who has expertise and advanced specialized skills in diagnosing and solving problems that are beyond the skills of the consulting provider. For example, an obstetrician will consult with a perinatologist (high-risk pregnancy physician) for a family with special genetic questions. A midwife will refer her client to a radiologist to obtain an ultrasound for a baby that seems to be showing a lag in growth on the basis of uterine measurements. In most cases, the consultant will not have the same degree of rapport or trust with the woman as the original provider. The consulting provider can expedite the development of trust by communicating clearly to the client why the consultation is needed and providing a sense of what will occur during the exam.

In the strictest sense, a provider who is "covering" for another provider for a delivery or visit is in a similar situation in that he or she is essentially a new individual to whom the client must relate. The difference is that he or she brings no additional expertise to the care, as does a consultant.

The consultant relies entirely on the primary provider and the client to supply all the pertinent historical and biologic information to make the best decision, sometimes in a very short period of time, as in the case of an emergency or a rapid delivery. Unfortunately, in labor, the client herself is, many times, completely preoccupied with the requirements of labor and depends on the advocacy of the partner, family, doula and primary provider to help her make decisions in her best interest. This is the chief reason for the prior education of the mother. She can become aware of the risks, benefits and alternatives when she is unencumbered by the stresses of labor, and develop a plan that expresses her preferences and expectations. The birth plan provides an important vehicle to assess the adequacy of comprehension of the issues between provider and client/family.

Unfortunately, in these days of efficiency, the provider may not spend the time to go over the birth plan in detail or may delegate the responsibility to an individual who does not know the intricacies of decision-making in labor. It is very important for the client to request the level of discussion that she personally wants or needs, and in the company of those who will be helping her make decisions during labor.

The consultant should present an assessment of the problem, the causes (as well as they are understood), and the options for treatment. Then the consultant works with the woman and her support group to make the best decision. The primary provider should relay to the consultant any important information, such as sexual abuse history, as well as a summary of the labor and anticipated dilemmas, prior to meeting the client, so the consultant can be prepared to individualize a response. Every request by the family should be anticipated, respected and resolved to their satisfaction.

The ethical responsibility of the consultant and all healthcare providers is to advocate for the patient.

There are three distinct problems that may arise during a consult.

First, there may be a difference between what the primary provider is recommending or anticipating and what the consultant sees as the best plan for the client's care. Although this may be an uncomfortable situation between colleagues, in the long run, the client's well being must be the determinant of the consultant's decisions and the underlying reason for the request for the consult.

Second, the best solution for the problem may not be within the normal scope of the consultant's practice or comfort level. One hopes that the consultant is using his or her most ethical standards and will facilitate the transfer of care to another consultant who can provide the service that best meets the client's needs and expectations, if possible, within the timeframe needed.

The "Difficult Patient"

Lastly, the patient may not be willing to accept the consultant's recommendation. This is the most difficult situation for a healthcare team, as it may constitute a very dangerous situation for the laboring woman and child. It goes to the very heart of the decision-making process and represents the failure of communication between the various parties. To the client, refusing the consultant's recommendations represents her attempt to control her medical care or body image, but to the healthcare team, her decision represents a denial of their authority and ability to provide appropriate medical care. Often, this type of patient is categorized as "a difficult patient" even if she has not yet refused care but is seriously questioning the choices she is being given. For a consultant or other member of the healthcare team, it is very important not to allow this type of characterization of an individual to occur, even in one's own mind. It will undermine the respect of the client that is critical, if trust is to be established and a mutually satisfactory solution found.

It is in these challenging situations that care providers must remain flexible and listen carefully to the client in order to understand exactly what she needs in order for her to give consent. She must be respected as the person who is ultimately in charge of her decisions, although care must be taken to ensure that her fears from the past do not blind her to the correct or safest solution for the current problem. Legally, consent must be obtained from her if she is of legal age and sound mind, even if the child's life and health are in jeopardy. Without her consent, any physical contact will constitute "battery" and, as such, exposes the healthcare providers to personal liability, which is not covered by malpractice insurance. The following steps may be helpful in reducing the likelihood of a complete breakdown of communication.

Prior to meeting a client, as either an unfamiliar primary provider or a consultant, inform yourself as much as possible as to the background of the patient and her expectations and support systems. This is, of course, possible only in non-emergent situations.

Allow the client to express in her own words, her understanding of her medical and emotional status and the medical choices available to her, as well as her preferences.

Using her own level of understanding as a benchmark, clarify your recommendations for her care, and discuss any alternatives that are available and safe, even if they are not ones that you would necessarily choose. By detailing risks and benefits of all the choices, you will enable the client to understand your particular recommendation.

Always maintain an open mind and recognize when you are not doing so. Inflexibility and/or a judgmental approach represent a lack of objectivity and sensitivity on your part and may lead to miscommunication or, in a worst-case scenario, a breakdown of trust and dialogue.

Utilize and respect all the support systems, both to understand the complexity of decision-making for the woman, as well as to optimize the final outcome.

Lastly, if one feels that communication and trust are not present, care of the patient should be transferred to a third party, and legal consultation should be obtained in order to ensure that the provider does not, in the legal sense of the term, either abandon care of the patient (that is, the provider refuses to follow the plan the client wants or to provide medical care) or commit assault and battery (that is, the provider forces the client to submit to the provider's plan).

Summary

As experts in our respective fields, it is our professional duty to guide our clients to make the best possible decisions regarding their health and well-being. To do so, we must first understand for ourselves the complex medical dimensions of the decision (benefits, risks and alternatives). Then, we need to translate that complexity to each client in an understandable manner, so that she may ultimately make the decision. To do that, we need to comprehend the personal and emotional history of each client and adjust our communication to her circumstances. Care of the woman with a history of sexual abuse provides the medical professional with a perfect example of the complex and often hidden dimensions that one may encounter in the daily administration of that duty. In seeking to understand the client as completely as possible, we will spontaneously assess the accuracy of their perceptions and provide the partnership role that is the basis for outstanding medical care.

15
Afterword

We have explored the possible effects of sexual abuse on a young girl as she grows into adulthood, becomes pregnant, enters maternity care, labors, gives birth, and parents a newborn baby. As an adult, and specifically, during the childbearing years, she may revert to old thought patterns and reactions, learned during childhood, when confronting stressors that resemble the original abuse. Such reactions are often more harmful than helpful to the woman, causing tension, helplessness, panic, resistance, confusion, anger, distrust, hopelessness, or dissociation, and robbing her of the ability to bring calmness, self-confidence, and trust to this demanding period.

Much can be done by the woman herself, using self-help measures to calm and comfort herself, and good communication skills to recruit the help and support of loved ones, friends, and maternity professionals. Beyond these, short-term, focused counseling and psychotherapy assist her to identify and explore distressing birth-related feelings and reactions and to develop individualized strategies to minimize their negative impact.

At the very least, the goal of self-help and communication techniques, as well as counseling and psychotherapy, is to prevent re-traumatization. Beyond that minimal goal, however, lies potential for a significant degree of healing.

In parting, we ask you, our readers, to ponder the immense emotional and physical costs borne by abuse survivors, and the struggles they encounter to find happiness and security. Each time you read or hear a report of a child who is kidnapped or sexually exploited, of child pornography, of a priest or minister or athletic coach or teacher or scout leader who has victimized numerous children, a parent or step-parent who is arrested for molesting a child, remind yourself that putting a stop to the abuse is only the first of many steps in controlling the damage. The effects of abuse do not end when the abusive acts end. Think about the extra challenges these victims will face for years to come. Think about their future challenges in childbearing. Think about their children.

Our primary task with this book was to provide practical information and guidance to survivors, their healthcare providers and psychotherapists to minimize or eliminate the negative impact of early sexual abuse on childbearing and parenting. On a larger scale, we hope this book is instrumental in awakening interest and hope for more effective health care for all those who have suffered trauma during childhood.

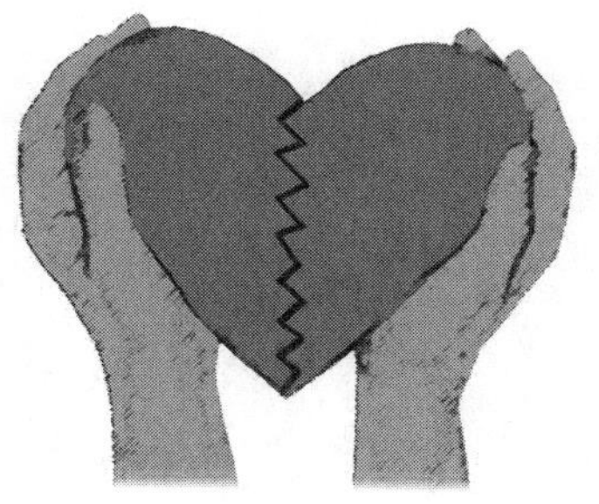

Part IV: Appendices and Resources

Appendix 1
Unhappiness After Childbirth: A Self-Assessment Tool

Please circle the answer that comes closest to how you have felt in the past seven days, not just how you feel today.

1. I have been able to laugh and see the funny side of things...

   a) as much as I always could.

   b) not quite as much as I used to.

   c) definitely not as much as I used to.

   d) not at all.

2. I have looked forward with enjoyment to things...

   a) as much as I always have.

   b) not quite as much as I used to.

   c) definitely not as much as I used to.

   d) not at all.

3. I have blamed myself unnecessarily when things went wrong...

   a) not at all. b) very little.

   c) some of the time. d) most of the time.

4. I have been anxious or worried for no good reason...

   a) not at all. b) very little.

   c) some of the time. d) most of the time.

5. I have felt scared or panicked for no good reason...

   a) not at all. b) very little.

   c) some of the time. d) most of the time.

6. Things have been getting on top of me...

   a) not at all; I've been coping very well.

   b) very little; I've been coping pretty well.

   c) some of the time; I haven't been coping as well as usual.

   d) quite a lot; I haven't been able to cope at all.

7. I have been so unhappy that I've had difficulty sleeping...

   a) not at all. b) very little.

   c) some of the time. d) most of the time.

8. I have felt sad or miserable...

   a) not at all. b) very little.

   c) some of the time. d) most of the time.

9. I have been so unhappy that I've been crying...

   a) not at all. b) very little.

   c) some of the time. d) most of the time.

10. The thought of harming myself or my baby has occurred to me...

    a) not at all. b) very little.

    c) some of the time. d) most of the time.

If you have a "feeling" after completing this form that something "isn't right" or if you have any questions, please contact your childbirth educator, doula, or care provider, or a mental health therapist.

Adapted from: Cox JL, Holden JM. "Detection of postnatal depression: development of the 10-item Edinburgh Postnatal Depression Scale," *Br J Psychiatry*. 150:782-786, 1987.

Appendix 2
Postpartum Mood Disorders: Risk Factors, Symptoms, and Recovery

Possible Risk Factors for Postpartum Mood Disorders

While it is not possible to identify all women who are likely to develop a postpartum mood disorder, there are a number of predisposing factors. Many predisposing factors may be present in one individual. For example, a sexual abuse survivor may have been raised by alcoholic or mentally ill parents, and have suffered from mental illness in the past, and may have reproductive losses and an abusive or non-supportive partner. A combination of risk factors increases the risk of postpartum mood disorder. In fact, women who have been sexually abused in childhood tend to have several predisposing factors and are more likely to develop a postpartum mood disorder. They are also more likely to perceive the birth as traumatic.

An awareness of predisposing factors may help some women, their families, and their caregivers to anticipate a more difficult adjustment in the postpartum period and be ready to seek help sooner than later. On the other hand, it may cause preoccupation with and overreaction to the normal ups and downs. Furthermore, the list of predisposing factors is surely not complete, and a certain percentage of women without them or with no evidence of previous mood instability sometimes develop postpartum mood disorders. It is also important to note that a significant number of women grow up under serious adverse conditions and still manage to adjust in a healthy manner to life with their newborn without experiencing a mood disorder.

Possible Risk Factors for Postpartum Mood Disorders

Family History and Physical Health.

1. A personal or family history of mental illness, especially depression, anxiety, panic, or previous postpartum mood disorders.

2. A history of severe PMS, eating disorders, or thyroid disease. (It is important to check the postpartum woman's thyroid function after childbirth if she has symptoms of depression or anxiety as mentioned above. An over- or under-functioning thyroid can wreak havoc with the new mother's physical and emotional health and mood.)

3. A physical complication during the birth or afterward, such as an infection or postpartum hemorrhage. The fear that remains can be instrumental in panic or depression later.

4. History of alcohol or substance abuse.

Problems Related to Pregnancy, Birth, or the Baby

1. Depression during pregnancy, distressing symptoms, previous losses such as miscarriages, abortions, stillbirth, fertility problems, or unwanted pregnancy.

2. History of unresolved traumatic or negative childbirth, or traumatic events with the current birth.

3. Significant problems with the infant, such as a high-risk or high-need baby, illness, developmental delays, separation from baby.

Psychosocial Family History

1. Being raised by alcoholic, abusive, or neglectful parents or parent figures.

2. Childhood sexual abuse.

3. Family dysfunction.

4. Serious childhood illness.

5. Unresolved parent or family loss.

Interpersonal Relationships

1. Marital dysfunction, divorce or separation during pregnancy.

2. Lack of support from partner and or family of origin.

3. Social isolation, lack of support systems.

4. Spouse abuse.

Life Stresses

1. Recent major moves or other major life changes or stresses, including illnesses, recent loss of a loved one, number of children, divorce, financial problems.

Personal Variables

1. Perfectionist personality tendency.

2. Negative or very high expectations for birth or parenting.

3. Low self-esteem, anxious need to please, need to always be in control.

4. Rigid thinking.

Postpartum Mood Disorders

Baby Blues

The baby blues, which affect approximately 80% of all new mothers, occur in early post partum, and usually last a short period. The blues are not a mood disorder. Some typical symptoms include emotional lability, over-sensitivity, low self-confidence, diminished eating and sleeping, lack of energy, exhaustion, irritability and confusion, fear, physical pain, and anxiety. In general, what women need is rest and good physical care, continuous and strong emotional support and information about this normal condition after giving birth. If the baby blues continue for more than 2 weeks, or if they worsen, postpartum depression must be considered.

Postpartum Depression

The symptoms of postpartum depression are quite varied and range from mild to severe. The onset may begin within two weeks after birth or any time within the first year. Postpartum depression affects approximately 20% of new mothers. Fathers and adoptive parents can also suffer from this disorder. Following is a description of symptoms of postpartum depression; one needs to experience four or more of these to be diagnosed as depressed.

Many of the "Baby Blues" symptoms continue or worsen. Women often feel hopeless, helpless, despairing. They are filled with self-doubt and worry about their ability to be a good mother. They may be either over- or under-concerned about the infant. Their depressed mood makes it difficult for them to get up in the morning. Typically, there is a loss of interest in their usual activities. They have difficulty thinking or concentrating. They may have an unrealistic perception of themselves or others. They may feel they are going crazy and experience shame, guilt, and feelings of inadequacy, which often prevent them from seeking help and support. In this depressed state they do not want to go out or be seen, and they become socially isolated, which is very damaging to new mothers. They may feel angry, irritable, hollow, and empty. Women speak of many physical complaints—headaches, stomach-aches, and slowed mental and physical functioning. Sometimes they are haunted by a desire to harm themselves or the baby. They have much guilt about not living up to their own high standards. Depressed mothers have an emotional pain that is confusing and doesn't let up.

Early diagnosis and treatment are most important. Most women can remain at home for treatment which includes a great deal of emotional support and practical help, therapeutic counseling, and, if necessary, appropriate medication. Women with suicidal thoughts or who have stopped functioning need immediate medical care, continuous supervision, and possible hospitalization along with medication and psychotherapy.

With treatment, the prognosis is very good, and the majority of women will recover within 3 to 6 months. If there are underlying unresolved issues from the past, therapy may take longer.

Postpartum Anxiety and Panic Disorder

Symptoms of postpartum anxiety and panic disorder have a gradual onset and can be difficult to recognize. Symptoms appear after the first three months, just when most new mothers are pretty well adjusted. Tearfulness, emotional ups and downs, unhappiness, and anxiety predominate, but there is no confusion or impairment in the woman's perception of reality.

Symptoms of postpartum anxiety resemble those of generalized anxiety disorder. Anxiety is often associated with depression, and both postpartum anxiety and depression need to be treated. Symptoms include feeling shaky, nervous, and fearful, difficulty falling asleep (even when the baby is asleep), and appetite disturbance. Other physical symptoms are heart palpitations, churning in the stomach, headaches, muscle tension, gastrointestinal distress, dizziness, hyperventilating. Women often feel trapped and anxious about the baby's health. They usually feel better when they are with people than when alone.

Postpartum panic attacks include symptoms of extreme anxiety such as shortness of breath, chest pains, choking or smothering feelings, tingling in hands and feet, trembling, sweating, faintness, hot or cold flashes, fear of going crazy, losing control, extreme irritability, and fear of dying.

These symptoms seem to have no precipitating event and make women feel even more out of control and helpless. A panic attack is agonizing and contributes to a cycle of anxiety and worry about a future recurrence.

Treatments today include social and psychological interventions with medications prescribed as appropriate.

Most women with mild to moderate symptoms do well and recover with appropriate therapy, social and emotional support, and practical help. They also must learn stress management techniques and practice self-care. Women benefit by understanding that vulnerability and fatigue, along with unrealistic expectations or lack of support contribute to the high level of stress. (Chapter 9 gives suggestions for what to do in panic attacks.)

Many women with more severe symptoms will benefit from medications, a number of which are now considered to be safe for breastfeeding. Without help, a significant number of symptoms will persist into the child's second year and can affect the child's development and behavior, the mother-baby relationship as well as the marital relationship.

Obsessive-Compulsive Disorder

Obsessive-compulsive disorder is characterized by obsessive thoughts and compulsive ritual-type behaviors. The symptoms include repetitive, persistent thoughts and images of a disturbing and alarming nature. Thoughts appear unexpectedly with no way to control them, often about harming one's baby or other loved ones. Other intrusive thoughts are about not being a good mother. With this disorder, women have a clear awareness that it would be absolutely wrong to act on these thoughts. Women develop compulsive behaviors to try to stop these thoughts, such as putting knives away, closing windows, and not bathing the baby for fear of hurting it.

Women feel very upset and angry at themselves for having such thoughts and cannot understand why they are replaying them over and over in their minds. Sometimes the distressing and persistent thoughts are symbolic of other negative feelings that have not been expressed or understood. For example, a survivor may feel angry and frustrated with her partner or her role as a mother. She may feel just plain overwhelmed. There may be no opportunity to talk about these feelings and she may have no help to organize this new experience. Furthermore, women believe they have no right to complain or have these negative thoughts, which only compounds their anxiety. It's almost like saying, "Don't think of a pink elephant!" and of course, that's impossible. Women feel much shame and fear about this. If women recognize that acting on their negative thoughts, such as hurting the baby, is wrong, then they can be reassured that they will not act out these thoughts.

Priscilla

Priscilla had repeated mental images of knives, which frightened her, because she knew she did not want to hurt anyone. She was afraid to use a knife and hid them. After talking to her therapist, she realized the knives symbolized unexpressed anger toward her unsupportive husband, and in a deeper sense, toward her cousin, who abused her for years. Once she understood this, she could talk about her real feelings and current needs with her husband, and work on her past trauma issues in therapy. The knife images disappeared.

Survivors will benefit from talking to an empathic mental health professional, in the hope of gaining understanding into underlying causes of their distress. Counselors should always ask women if they have had any unusual thoughts lately, and acknowledge that some women have such thoughts. They may be related to unrecognized stress, or other factors. Short-term counseling or psychotherapy and on-going support can be instrumental in alleviating the symptoms. If this type of intrusive, obsessive thinking does not go away, more psychological treatment and medication are needed.

Postpartum Psychosis

A very rare but more serious disorder is postpartum psychosis, affecting only one or two women per thousand. It occurs within a short time after the birth, sometime within the first two weeks. It may be preceded by several days of insomnia or unusually hyperactive behavior.

Symptoms include being speeded up, obsessive frantic activity, often refusal to eat or sleep, extreme agitation and confusion, and racing thoughts. Women will have bizarre hallucinations, such as a sense that the walls might be talking or the baby is speaking. They will be unable to differentiate reality from hallucinations. Their thinking is irrational and delusional with poor judgment, impulsivity, inability to make decisions, and loss of memory. They may appear disoriented, suspicious, unable to recognize familiar people or places, and preoccupied with trivia.

This condition must be treated as a medical emergency. The symptoms are potentially dangerous and present a risk to both mother and baby. However, psychiatric treatment is very successful. Women can be helped and within a few months of on-going therapy, physical and emotional health can be restored.

Posttraumatic Stress Disorder (PTSD)

This condition includes symptoms similar to panic attacks described earlier, but the PTSD response is more likely associated with a specific trauma, either the recent birth, or memories from the past that were triggered during birth. Postpartum PTSD deserves special mention since it is frequently linked with a history of sexual abuse and can be confused with depression or panic disorder, or other mood disorders. (Chapter 2 describes PTSD in detail, and it is further explored in Chapter 5.)

Conclusion

The most important factor in recovery from a postpartum mood disorder is that it be recognized. Women, their families, and healthcare professionals need to realize that the woman is unhappy or exhibiting unusual behavior and thoughts, and to get needed help. The use of the "Unhappiness After Childbirth: A Self-assessment Tool" (Appendix 1) is an aid to recognition, and may help with the decision to seek appropriate helpful resources.

Appendix 3: Strategies for Specific Triggers Form

1. List of things that make you feel safe.

2. Your usual way of coping with pain and fear.

3. List of possible triggers of anxiety, body memories or flashbacks that may occur during childbirth. Check those that evoke anxiety reactions. These are the "triggers," the items for which to plan specific personalized strategies. The woman describes what makes each trigger fearful and with the counselor strategizes ways to avoid it or cope with it. (Refer to Chapter 10.) Keep this sheet to discuss with your caregiver and to refer to in labor.

✓	Trigger	Personal Meaning	Strategy
	Changed appearance (make-up, hairstyle, clothing)		

✓	**Trigger**	**Personal Meaning**	**Strategy**
	Nakedness/exposure of sexual parts of the body		
	Secretions (show, blood, amniotic fluid)		
	Body positions (hands and knees, squatting, on back with legs spread)		
	Hospital environment (smell, machines, sounds, uniformed personnel)		
	Blood draws		
	Intravenous fluids		
	Vaginal exams/AROM		

✓	Trigger	Personal Meaning	Strategy
	Connection to lines from body to machines or containers (EFM cords, IV line, continuous BP cuff, bladder catheter, epidural catheter, oxygen mask)		
	Restriction to bed		
	Pain with labor contractions		
	Pain-related behavior, panic, loss of control		
	Expressions of pain (facial, vocal, bodily tension)		

✓	Trigger	Personal Meaning	Strategy
	Pain medication “trade-offs”: • Narcotics (groggy, sleepy, less pain, more relaxation) • Epidural (numb, less participation, inability to do as much, possible inadequate pain relief/less pain, more relaxation)		
	Relationship with your doctor or midwife (gender, familiarity, trust, expectations, confidence)		
	Strangers (nurses, unfamiliar caregivers)		
	Behavior of caregiving staff toward you (respect, control, individual treatment, asking before touching)		

✓	**Trigger**	**Personal Meaning**	**Strategy**
	Issues re partner, doula, family, friends (disapproval, abandonment, unreliability, inadequacy, disagreement, trust, dependency)		
	The actual birth, baby bulging the perineum, emerging from your body		
	Pushing effort, sounds and the pain Episiotomy/tearing		
	Forceps or vacuum extractor delivery		
	Cesarean section		
	Holding and suckling baby		
	Postpartum (inspecting vaginal canal, stitches, fundal massage)		

Appendix 4
Birth Plan

(to be prepared by the pregnant woman and shared with her care providers)

Birth Plan for____

My primary caregiver is______________________________

and my due date is __________________________________

These people will support me during labor and birth:

Introducing myself/ourselves:

Important issues, fears, concerns:

First stage of labor preferences:

- Controlling pain
- Medical interventions

Second stage preferences:

- Positioning
- Pushing efforts
- Medical interventions

Other important items regarding labor and birth:

Preferences if unexpected events occur during labor:

- Complicated or prolonged labor or fetal problems

- Cesarean delivery

Post partum for mother:

- Infant feeding: Breastmilk or Formula

- Concerns, questions, needs, visitors

- Controlling pain

- Follow-up after discharge

- Educational needs

Newborn Care Plan
for the baby of (parents' names)

____

____

Baby's doctor______________________________________

Newborn care issues, fears, or concerns:

Infant feeding: Breastmilk or Formula

Newborn exam and procedures:

Unexpected problems with the newborn:

Educational needs (baby care and feeding):

Appendix 5
Two Case Histories

Following Women Through the Counseling Process: Abuse History, Triggers, Birth Plans, and Outcomes

Case #1. Joanna, 34 year old primigravida

Joanna's sexual abuse history and birth story were presented in Chapter 4. Here we provide details of the trigger work that she did with her counselor, and relevant excerpts from her birth plan. By reading her whole story, one can recognize how the birth counseling helped her to a rewarding and empowering birth.

Joanna's triggers, their personal meanings, and planned strategies

In Joanna's sessions with her birth counselor, she listed some items and techniques that help her feel safe: being able to move around freely; her beloved teddy bear from childhood; reminders of her favorite place in Montana; and aromatherapy. Her triggers, summarized below, centered on her trust issues with authority figures in general, and males in particular, and on worry about relapsing into active drug use if she took narcotics for pain during labor. She worried about losing her temper with her caregivers or dissociating during the stress of labor.

✓	Trigger	Personal Meaning	Strategy
✓	Secretions (show, blood, amniotic fluid, stool)	Blood – scary. May gross husband out. Feels shame, no control.	Wear own underpants and pad.
✓	Body positions (hands & knees, squatting, on back with legs spread)	Squatting & naked; vagina exposed; people whom I can't see coming up behind me	Cover exposed parts when in squat or on hands & knees, and face door to room
✓✓	The actual birth, baby bulging perineum, emerging from your body	Embarrassment, repulsion & joy; terrifying; vulnerable with all those men around; may not want Paul to see	Think of baby as healer; Pushing out baby = pushing out pain. Expulsion is pathway to freedom
✓	Intravenous fluids	Fear of needles; not in control of what is going into my body; trust issues re entrances and exits to my body	Only use if medically necessary; needle in non-dominant hand above wrist (to allow most movement); tape a washcloth over wrist
✓	Vaginal exams	Having a vaginal exam with husband in room – terrifying	Explain to Paul that he must leave for exam
✓	Connection to lines (monitor cords, IV line, blood pressure cuff, bladder catheter, other)	Claustrophobic; I panicked when tied down with anesthesia for wisdom teeth removal; couldn't talk. I am chemically sensitive	Plan to move even if lines are in. Tell RN it is important that I be able to move
✓	Episiotomy/ tearing	May faint; fear of splitting in two; pain & more blood; gaping wounds	Do not watch; ask for reassurance about perineum from RN, Dr. Don't want Paul to see
✓	Cesarean section	Baby coming out through a slice in the skin; tremendous amount of trust required; scary	Express feelings; ask Dr. to tell me what she's doing, talk to me

✓	Trigger	Personal Meaning	Strategy
✓	Relationship with doctor	Some questions about technical competence of family Dr. in charge of birth	Talk to her about it; ask for a consult with an obstetrician
✓	RN/Dr handling your breast to help baby with latch-on	Someone grabbing; I'll rage at that.	Let me try by myself first; ask permission before grabbing my breast
✓✓	Pain with labor contractions	Picture myself as desperate for a way out. May go into a rage, want drugs; Fear of unknown reactions; want help not to be overcome	Get an empathic (not bossy) doula; doesn't want to feel victimized
✓	Pain-related behavior	May rage or be abusive toward Paul or doula. I don't want him to see me that way	Will need room to physically act out rage & fear (e.g., punch birth ball), wail and yell.
✓	Pain medication "trade-offs": • Narcotics • Epidural	Fear of narcotics; I'm chemically sensitive; Plan to have epidural	Meet anesthesiologist on call when in labor; avoid narcotics; use bath first

After exploring her triggers and developing strategies, Joanna and Paul prepared a birth plan that reflected her trigger work. Following are relevant excerpts from her plan:

Introduction: I have several very important requests, in order for me to feel as safe and supported as I need to be. Please read this – I have issues that need to be recognized!

If it is a difficult labor, I want to have an epidural available. I am chemically sensitive and if pain medications (narcotics) are used, strong reactions are possible. I would like to meet the anesthesiologist on duty upon arrival, if possible.

Most important issues.

I want control over who is in the room and why. I'd like privacy – the door closed.

I need warning and to be asked before being touched.

Please do not surprise me from behind.

Please include me in all decisions.

I can react to feeling claustrophobic–connection to lines. I need to always have the option to move and stand when possible.

I have a history of fainting at the sight of blood and wounds.

If I become very emotional (or should I say when), I want to be supported. It is important for me to deal with the experience fully.

I need gentleness.

Drugs—I am chemically sensitive and dependent – preferring not to use narcotics. I have had strong reactions to anesthetics.

Vaginal exams – please no males in the room for vaginal exams – unless necessary.

I prefer not to have an episiotomy.

Cesarean birth. If there is time, I might want to call my therapist.

I don't want to see the procedure.

I might need help with breastfeeding, but please ask before touching me.

Joanna's assessment of her birth experience

The actual story of Joanna's child's birth is told in Chapter 4. In comparing her triggers, strategies, and birth plan with her actual birth story, we note that she accurately predicted many of her needs. Even though she had stated 3 times in her birth plan that she is "chemically sensitive," and even though the doula had tried to remind her of her chemical sensitivity during labor, Joanna still agreed to take narcotics, and did indeed have a frightening reaction. Later,

Later, however, she said that her "bad trip" was only a "glitch on the screen" of her entire labor. Most of the things she requested in her birth plan were done. For example, she did experience a great deal of fear in early labor, and needed support and patient understanding as she dealt with it. As she had expected, she did need to have Paul leave when she felt she was losing control.

In the end, Joanna found the birth experience to be most rewarding, although stressful at times. She feels strong and capable, and that she accomplished significant healing through the long challenging labor because she was surrounded by caring, respectful people, and was able to make important decisions and to stay in the present throughout the entire labor.

Case 2: Sherry's Story

Sherry was referred for childbirth counseling by her social worker at the prenatal clinic, in hopes of reducing some of her anxiety. She was 17 years old and pregnant for the second time. She dropped out of school at age 16, was unemployed, and was living with Dan (the baby's father) and Dan's mother. He was employed at minimum wage by a fast-food chain. He was sometimes violent. He would hit Sherry and push her down when he was angry. She said, "He scares the crap out of me, then leaves."

Sherry is the oldest of six children. Her mother was alcoholic and addicted to drugs. Sherry has been told she was born with 4 teeth, green eyes, and lots of long dark hair—"a little hellion." Because her mother was unable to care for the children, they were dispersed among various relatives from the time Sherry was 2 years old, and she changed homes frequently. Sherry was severely abused, emotionally and physically. She was "always in trouble," and her aunt called her a "devil child."

Sherry was repeatedly abused, both sexually and physically, from age 10 to age 14 by at least one cousin and an uncle. Sherry blacked out during the abuse and only remembers forced oral sex and getting to the point of forced intercourse, then remembers nothing more. Her aunt would punish her for "messing with the boys again." She ran away from home when she was 14.

Sherry terminated her first pregnancy at age 16, two months prior to the current pregnancy. The abortion was emotionally traumatic: She saw the baby on ultrasound and has vivid memories of hearing the suctioning. She has had nightmares related to the abortion, and passed out when she accompanied her favorite younger sister to the doctor's for a vaginal exam.

In exploring her triggers, Sherry identified the following:

She feels fat and ugly and has a large birthmark (a "big black spot") on her abdomen that she perceives as a mark of shame. She has "a problem with not being clean," and takes three showers a day.

She was raped from behind and does not want to be on hands and knees where people can approach her from behind.

She cannot imagine the baby coming out and her body going back to normal. She pictures herself as having "a big black hole inside."

With vaginal exams, she suspects that male caregivers "are trying something else. I'm open to the world."

Invasive procedures are scary. She remembers a time when she had to have a bladder catheter, screaming and blacking out when they started inserting it.

Regarding episiotomy, she said, "I don't want to be cut down there." She worries about having stitches in the "big hole."

The vacuum extractor brought up memories of her abortion, when she "could hear the sucking and then it was gone." She worried that she might associate the vacuum delivery with the aborted baby.

If a cesarean were done, she worried about the disfigurement of a scar.

The thought of having a light shining into her vagina for a postpartum inspection felt very threatening. The caregiver would see what she imagined as a "deep, dark hole opening to my whole insides."

She did not want a nurse "grabbing my breast" to help her breastfeed.

She had many issues over pain. She worried that she would black out or dissociate with the pain, as she had so often in the past. She did not want to miss the birth by being "gone." She also knew that she would never tell people about or show them her pain or ask for pain medication. "I will grit my teeth, hold my breath, and bite my tongue off before I'll show that I'm in pain. I'll probably black out before letting people see me writhe in pain." Always during abuse, she had refused to let her abusers see how much they were hurting her. This was a point of pride for her. They couldn't make her break down.

Sherry's birth plan reflected her triggers, even though she chose not to reveal her abuse history. She decided to have a doula to help her with some of her requests. She also wanted Dan to be there. Her most important issues, she said, were 1) controlling pain; 2) avoiding the hands and knees position; 3) having no one behind her when she was kneeling or in a vulnerable position; 4) not dissociating; and 5) preserving her own modesty.

She decided she would like to receive pain medication as soon as the nurse would allow her to have it. This meant that she would not have to ask for it (which she felt incapable of doing).

She asked that they avoid the use of light on the perineum as much as possible (because it "focuses too much attention on my perineum"). Regarding labor interventions, she requested that midwives do the vaginal exams and "avoid a male touching me, if possible." "Wait for the epidural to take effect before putting a catheter in"; "Avoid episiotomy, if possible."

For the delivery, she asked that they "avoid the use of light shining on her perineum," and if a vacuum extraction is needed, "please discuss it with me first." All she asked in the case of a cesarean was that she not be left alone, that Dan remain with her.

As it turned out, Sherry's birth experience exceeded her expectations. She gave birth to a little girl, and described the birth as "...absolutely wonderful. I never zoned out. I started to, but I told myself to stay. And Dan and his mom would squeeze my hand. The nurse offered me an epidural, but I didn't feel like having it. I had no episiotomy and no tear. There was no blood, so I stayed pretty clean." Because she went into labor three weeks before her due date and had not yet met with the doula, she did not have a doula with her.

Sherry did not have the resources for psychotherapy, which could have provided her with the opportunity to heal from her life of horrendous abuse. At least, however, she did have this special memory of being cared for and listened to, and she can always carry the memory of the joy and empowerment that she achieved in her birth experience. Her social worker, who continued to see her for a few weeks post partum, encouraged her to keep the thoughts and images of her childbirth in her mind, to remind herself of the good and powerful woman she is, and to foster goodness, beauty and hope in her child.

Appendix 6
Self-Assessment of Maternal Distress After A Difficult Birth

By Penny Simkin and Phyllis Klaus

This form may be enlarged and photocopied for use in counseling situations.

Name ______________________________

Today's date______________________________

Date of baby's birth______________________________

Please look back at your labor and birth and complete the following statements.

These are the positive things that I recall about my child's birth.

These are the negative things that I recall about my child's birth.

During my labor and birth, I felt supported and cared for

All or most of the time by ______________________________

Some of the time by ______________________________

A little bit by ______________________________

Not at all by ______________________________

These were some times when I was (or thought I was) in danger of death or injury:

During these times I felt:

☐ worried ☐ frightened ☐ helpless ☐ out of control

☐ numb ☐ don't remember ☐ angry ☐ terrified ☐ disbelief

☐ near death ☐ detached ☐ other (what?)

These were times when the baby was or seemed to be in danger.

During the times the baby was in danger, I felt

☐ worried ☐ frightened ☐ helpless ☐ out of control

☐ numb ☐ don't remember ☐ angry ☐ terrified ☐ disbelief

☐ near death ☐ detached ☐ other (what?)

I reacted to the danger to myself or my baby by

☐ panicking ☐ dissociating ☐ feeling detached

☐ cooperating ☐ resisting ☐ tensing up ☐ giving up

☐ don't remember ☐ crying, trembling ☐ going blank

☐ falling apart ☐ other (what?)

Since about (how long after the birth?)____________________
I have had the following symptoms:

☐ sleep problems ☐ startle easily ☐ aloneness

☐ panic attacks ☐ nightmares ☐ poor concentration

☐ flashbacks ☐ preoccupation ☐ irritability

☐ poor appetite ☐ relive event ☐ avoid reminders

☐ distress if reminded of birth ☐ crying

☐ detachment from baby/loved ones ☐ other (what?)

I avoid things that remind me of the birth, for example:

☐ I did not return to my doctor or midwife for my postpartum checkup.

☐ If asked about the birth, I don't want to have to talk about it.

☐ I didn't attend parenting groups or my birth class reunion.

☐ I drive blocks out of my way to avoid going near the hospital.

☐ Other avoidance behaviors?

I feel flat or detached emotionally from my baby, partner, family, friends

☐ all the time ☐ some of the time ☐ never

I feel I was wronged or treated badly by the following people in the following ways:

I want and need these things:

Resources: Articles

1. Aalsma, M. C., G. D. Zimet, J. D. Fortenberry, M. Blythe, and D. P. Orr. "Reports of Childhood Sexual Abuse by Adolescents and Young Adults: Stability Over Time." *Journal of Sex Research* 39 (4) (Nov. 2002): 259-63.

2. "ACOG (American College of Obstetricians and Gynecologists) Educational Bulletin. Adult Manifestation of Childhood Sexual Abuse, Number 259, July 2000. Clinical Management Guidelines for Obstetrician-Gynecologists." *International Journal of Gynaecology and Obstetrics* 259 (July 2000): 1-10.

3. Alexander, P. C., L. Teti, and C. L. Anderson. "Childhood Sexual Abuse History and Role Reversal in Parenting." *Child Abuse & Neglect* 24 (6) (June 2000): 829-38.

4. Anda, R. F., D. P. Chapman, V. J. Felitti, V. Edwards, D. F. Williamson, J. B. Croft, and W. H. Giles. "Adverse Childhood Experiences and Risk of Paternity in Teen Pregnancy." *Obstetrics and Gynecology* 100 (1) (July 2002): 37-45.

5. Anderson, D. G., and M. A. Imle. "Families of Origin of Homeless and Never-Homeless Women." *Western Journal of Nursing Research* 23 (4) (June 2001): 394-413.

6. Arnold, R. P., D. Rogers, and D. A. G. Cook. "Medical Problems of Adults Who Were Sexually Abused in Childhood." *BMJ* 300 (Mar. 17, 1990): 705-08.

7. Bachmann, Gloria A., Tamerra P. Moeller, and Jodi Benett. "Childhood Sexual Abuse and the Consequences in Adult Women." *Obstetrics and Gynecology* 71 (4) (Apr. 1988): 631-41.

8. Ballard, C. G, A. K. Stanley, and I. F. Brockington. "Post-Traumatic Stress Disorder (PTSD) After Childbirth." *British Journal of Psychiatry* 166 (4) (1995): 525-28.

9. Beck, C.T. "Birth Trauma: In the Eye of the Beholder." *Nursing Research* 53 (1) (2004): 28-35.

10. Bloom, S. L. "Sexual Violence: the Victim." *New Directions For Mental Health Services* 86 (Summer 2000): 63-71.

11. Blume, E. S. "Post-Incest Syndrome in Women: the Incest Survivors' Aftereffects Checklist." *Treating Abuse Today* 9 (3) (2000): 41.

12. Bohn, D. K., and K. A. Holz. "Sequelae of Abuse: Health Effects of Childhood Sexual Abuse, Domestic Battering, and Rape." *Journal of Nurse-Midwifery* 41 (6) (Nov.-Dec. 1996): 442-56.

13. Braddock, C. H., 3rd, K. A. Edwards, N. M. Hasenberg, T. L. Laidley, and W. Levinson. "Informed Decision Making in Outpatient Practice: Time to Get Back to Basics." *JAMA* 282 (24) (Dec. 22-29, 1999): 2313-20.

14. Brems, C., and L. Namyniuk. "The Relationship of Childhood Abuse History and Substance Use in an Alaska Sample." *Substance Use & Misuse* 37 (4) (Mar. 2002): 473-94.

15. Briere, John. "Medical Symptoms, Health Risk, and History of Childhood Sexual Abuse." *Mayo Clinic Proceedings* 67 (1992): 603-04.

16. Briere, John, and Marsha Runtz. "Symptomatology Associated With Childhood Sexual Victimization in a Nonclinical Adult Sample. *Child Abuse & Neglect* 12 (1) (1988): 51-9.

17. Buist, A., and H. Janson. "Childhood Sexual Abuse, Parenting and Postpartum Depression — a 3-Year Follow-Up Study." *Child Abuse & Neglect* 25 (7) (July 2001): 909-21.

18. Burian, Jennifer. "Helping Survivors of Sexual Abuse Through Labor." *MCN. The American Journal of Maternal Child Nursing* 20 (5) (Sep.-Oct. 1995): 252-6.

19. Campling, Penelope. "Working With Adult Survivors of Child Sexual Abuse." *BMJ* 305 (6866) (Dec. 5, 1992): 1375-6.

20. Chu, James A., and Diana L. Dill. "Dissociative Symptoms in Relation to Childhood Physical and Sexual Abuse." *American Journal of Psychiatry* 147 (7) (July 1990): 887-92.

21. Chu, James A., L. M. Frey, B. L. Ganzel, and J. A. Matthews. "Memories of Childhood Abuse: Dissociation, Amnesia, and Corroboration." *American Journal of Psychiatry* 156 (5) (May 1999): 749-55.

22. Clarke, L. "Perinatal Care for Survivors of Sexual Abuse." *Nursing BC* 30 (2) (Mar.-Apr. 1998): 16-19.

23. Coll, L. "Homeopathy in Survivors of Childhood Sexual Abuse." *Homeopathy* 91 (1) (Jan. 2002): 3-9.

24. Courtois, C., and Riley C. Courtois. "Pregnancy and Childbirth as Triggers for Abuse Memories: Implications for Care." *Birth: Issues in Perinatal Care* 19 (4) (Dec. 1992): 222-23.

25. Cox, J. L., J. M. Holden, and R. Sagovsky. "Detection of Postnatal Depression. Development of the 10-Item Edinburgh Postnatal Depression Scale." *British Journal of Psychiatry* 150 (June 1987): 782-6.

26. Creedy, D. K., I. M. Shochet, and J. Horsfall. "Childbirth and the Development of Acute Trauma Symptoms: Incidence and Contributing Factors." *Birt:h Issues in Perinatal Care* 27 (2) (June 2000): 104-11.

27. Crompton, Judy. "Post-Traumatic Stress Disorder and Childbirth." *British Journal of Midwifery* 4 (6) (June 1996): 290-94.

28. Crompton, Judy. "Post-Traumatic Stress Disorder and Childbirth: 2." *British Journal of Midwifery* 4 (7) (July 1996): 354-56, 373.

29. Cunningham, Jean, Thomas Pearce, and Patti Pearce. "Childhood Sexual Abuse and Medical Complaints in Adult Women." *Journal of Interpersonal Violence* 3 (2) (June 1988): 131-44.

30. Czarnocka, Jo, and Pauline Slade. "Prevalence and Predictors of Post-Traumatic Stress Symptoms Following Childbirth." *British Journal of Clinical Psychology* 39 (Part 1) (Mar. 2000): 35-51.

31. DeMier, Richard L., Michael T. Hynan, Howard B. Harris, and Robert L. Manniello. "Perinatal Stressors as Predictors of Symptoms of Posttraumatic Stress in Mothers of Infants at High Risk. *Journal of Perinatology* 16 (4) (July-Aug. 1996): 276-80.

32. DiLillo, D. "Interpersonal Functioning Among Women Reporting a History of Childhood Sexual Abuse: Empirical Findings and Methodological Issues." *Clinical Psychology Review* 21 (4) (June 2001): 553-76.

33. Draucker, C. B., and D. Spradlin. "Women Sexually Abused as Children: Implications for Orthopaedic Nursing Care." *Orthopedic Nursing* 20 (6) (Nov.-Dec. 2001): 41-8.

34. Dubowitz, H., M. M. Black, M. A. Kerr, J. M. Hussey, T. M. Morrel, M. D. Everson, and R. H. Starr. "Type and Timing of Mothers' Victimization: Effects on Mothers and Children." *Pediatrics* 107 (4) (Apr. 2001): 728-35.

35. "Ending Violence Against Women." *Population Reports* 27 (4) (1999): 1-[40].

36. Everest, P. "The Multiple Self: Working with Dissociation and Trauma." *The Journal of Analytical Psychology* 44 (4) (Oct. 1999): 443-63.

37. Fahy, Thomas A., and John J. Morrison. "The Clinical Significance of Eating Disorders in Obstetrics." *British Journal of Obstetrics and Gynaecology* 100 (Aug. 1993): 708-10.

38. Farley, M., and B. M. Patsalides. "Physical Symptoms, Posttraumatic Stress Disorder, and Healthcare Utilization of Women With and Without Childhood Physical and Sexual Abuse." *Psychological Reports* 89 (3) (Dec. 2001): 595-606.

39. Fergusson, D. M., N. R. Swain-Campbell, and L. J. Horwood. "Does Sexual Violence Contribute to Elevated Rates of Anxiety and Depression in Females?" *Psychological Medicine* 32 (6) (Aug. 2002): 991-96.

40. Fisher, J. R., C. J. Feekery, L. H. Amir, and M. Sneddon. "Health and Social Circumstances of Women Admitted to a Private Mother Baby Unit: A Descriptive Cohort Study." *Australian Family Physician* 31 (10) (Oct. 2002): 996-70, 973.

41. Foa, E. B., and G. P. Street. "Women and Traumatic Events." *Journal of Clinical Psychiatry* 62 (Suppl. 17) (2002): 29-34.

42. Freud, Sigmund. "The Aetiology of Hysteria." *The Standard Edition of the Complete Psychological Works of Sigmund Freud. Tr. From the German Under the General Editorship of James Strachey, in Collaboration with Anna Freud; Assisted by Alix Strachey and Alan Tyson, Volume 3.* Ed. James Strachey. London: Hogarth Press, [1953-]. [203-].

43. Glasser, M., I. Kolvin, D. Campbell, A. Glasser, I. Leitch, and S. Farrelly. "Cycle of Child Sexual Abuse: Links Between Being a Victim and Becoming a Perpetrator." *British Journal of Psychiatry* 179 (Dec. 2001): 482-97.

44. Goldbeck-Wood, S. "Post-Traumatic Stress Disorder May Follow Childbirth." *BMJ* 313 (7060) (Sep. 28,1996): 774.

45. Goldberg, R. T., and R. Goldstein. "A Comparison of Chronic Pain Patients and Controls on Traumatic Events in Childhood." *Disability and Rehabilitation* 22 (17) (Nov. 2000): 756-63.

46. Golding, J. M., D. L. Taylor, L. Menard, and M. J. King. "Prevalence of Sexual Abuse History in a Sample of Women Seeking Treatment for Premenstrual Syndrome." *Journal of Psychosomatic Obstetrics and Gynaecology* 21 (2) (June 2000): 69-80.

47. Gorey, K. M., N. L. Richter, and E. Snider. "Guilt, Isolation and Hopelessness Among Female Survivors of Childhood Sexual Abuse: Effectiveness of Group Work Intervention." *Child Abuse & Neglect* 25 (3) (Mar. 2001): 347-55.

48. Grant, L. J. "Effects of Childhood Sexual Abuse: Issues for Obstetric Caregivers." *Birth: Issues in Perinatal Care* 19 (4) (Dec. 1992): 220-21.

49. Green, J. M., V. A. Coupland, and J. V. Kitzinger. "Expectations, Experiences, and Psychological Outcomes of Childbirth: a Prospective Study of 825 Women." *Birth: Issues in Perinatal Care* 17 (1) (Mar. 1990): 15-24.

50. Greenwood, Catherine L. "Prevalence of Sexual Abuse, Physical Abuse, and Concurrent Traumatic Life Events in a General Medical Population." *Mayo Clinic Proceedings* 65 (1990): 1067-71.

51. Harrop-Griffiths, Jane, Wayne Katon, Edward Walker, Louise Holm, Joan Russo, and Lee Hickok. "The Association Between Chronic Pelvic Pain, Psychiatric Diagnoses, and Childhood Sexual Abuse." *Obstetrics and Gynecology* 71 (1988): 589-94.

52. Hedin, L. W., and P.O. Janson. "Domestic Violence During Pregnancy. The Prevalence of Physical Injuries, Substance Use, Abortions and Miscarriages." *Acta Obstetricia et Gynecologica Scandinavica* 79 (8) (Aug. 2000): 625-30.

53. Holz, K. A. "A Practical Approach to Clients Who Are Survivors of Childhood Sexual Abuse." *Journal of Nurse-Midwifery* 39 (1) (Jan.-Feb. 1994): 13-18.

54. Howard, Fred M. "Abuse History and Chronic Pain in Women: I. Prevalences of Sexual Abuse and Physical Abuse." *Obstetrics and Gynecology* 85 (1) (Jan. 1995): 158-59.

55. Jacobs, James L. "Child Sexual Abuse Victimization and Later Sequelae During Pregnancy and Childbirth." *Journal of Child Sexual Abuse* 1 (1) (1992): 103-12.

56. Janson, P. O. "Domestic Violence –A Woman's Health Issue of Great Consequence." *Acta Obstetrica et Gynecologica Scandinavica* 79 (8) (2000): 623-24.

57. Johnson, C. F. "Child Maltreatment 2002: Recognition, Reporting and Risk." *Pediatrics International* 44 (5) (Oct. 2002): 554-60.

58. Johnson, D. M.; J. L. Pike, and K. M. Chard. "Factors Predicting PTSD, Depression, and Disassociative Severity in Female Treatment-Seeking Childhood Sexual Abuse Survivors." *Child Abuse & Neglect* 25 (1) (Jan. 2001): 179-98.

59. Kaplan, R., and V. Manicavasagar. "Is There a False Memory Syndrome? A Review of Three Cases." *Comprehensive Psychiatry* 42 (4) (July-Aug. 2001): 342-48.

60. Katon, W. J., and E. A. Walker. "Medically Unexplained Symptoms in Primary Care." *Journal of Clinical Psychiatry* 59 (Suppl. 20) (1998): 15-21.

61. Kearsey, K. "Listening for Silent Screams." *Registered Nurse Journal* (July-Aug. 2002): 12-17.

62. Kendall-Tackett, Kathleen. "Breastfeeding and the Sexual Abuse Survivor." *Journal of Human Lactation* 14 (2) (June 1998): 125-33.

63. Kenney, J. W., C. Reinholtz, and P. J. Angelini. "Ethnic Differences in Childhood and Adolescent Sexual Abuse and Teenage Pregnancy." *Journal of Adolescent Health* 21 (1) (July 1997): 3-10.

64. Kitzinger, J. V. "Counteracting, Not Reenacting, the Violation of Women's Bodies: the Challenge for Perinatal Caregivers." *Birt:h Issues in Perinatal Care* 19 (4) (Dec. 1992): 219-20.

65. Kitzinger, Jenny. "The Internal Examination." *The Practitioner* 234 (1492) (July 1990): 698-700.

66. Krantz, G., and P.O. Ostergren. "The Association Between Violence, Victimisation, and Common Symptoms in Swedish Women." *Journal of Epidemiology and Community Health* 54 (11) (Nov. 2000): 815-21.

67. LaFerla, John J. "Psychologic and Behavioral Factors in Hyperemesis Gravidarum." *American Journal of Obstetrics and Gynecology* 159 (2) (Aug. 1988): 532-33.

68. Leach, M. M., and C. Bethune. "Assisting Sexually Abused Adults. Practical Guide to Interviewing Patients." *Canadian Family Physician* 42 (Jan. 1996): 82-86.

69. Lechner, Michael E., Mark E. Vogel, Linda M. Garcia-Shelton, Jeffrey L. Leichter, and Kenneth R. Steibel. "Self-Reported Medical Problems of Adult Female Survivors of Childhood Sexual Abuse." *The Journal of Family Practice* 36 (6) (1993): 633-38.

70. Lent, Barbara, Patricia Morris, and Shelley Rechner. "Understanding the Effect of Domestic Violence on Pregnancy, Labour, and Delivery. *Canadian Family Physician* 46 (Mar. 2000): 505-7, 516-9.

71. Levitan, R. D., N. A. Rector, T. Sheldon, and P. Goering. "Childhood Adversities Associated with Major Depression and/or Anxiety Disorders in a Community Sample of Ontario: Issues of Co-Morbidity and Specificity." *Depression and Anxiety* 17 (1) (2003): 34-42.

72. Little, L., and S. L. Hamby. "Memory of Childhood Sexual Abuse Among Clinicians: Characteristics, Outcomes, and Current Therapy Attitudes." *Sexual Abuse* 13 (4) (Oct. 2001): 233-48.

73. Lodico, M. A., E. Gruber, and R. J. DiClemente. "Childhood Sexual Abuse and Coercive Sex Among School-Based Adolescents in a Midwestern State." *The Journal of Adolescent Health* 18 (3) (Mar. 1996): 211-17.

74. Lyon, Emily. "Hospital Staff Reactions to Accounts by Survivors of Childhood Abuse." *American Journal of Orthopsychiatry* 63 (3) (July 1993): 410-16.

75. McCann, Lisa, and Laurie Anne Pearlman. "Vicarious Traumatization: A Framework for Understanding the Psychological Effects of Working with Victims." *Journal of Traumatic Stress* 3 (1) 1990: 131-49.

76. McClelland L., L. Mynors-Wallis, T. Fahy, and J. Treasure. "Sexual Abuse, Disordered Personality and Eating Disorders." *British Journal of Psychiatry* 158 (Suppl. 10) (May 1991): 63-68.

77. Maeve, M. K. "Speaking Unavoidable Truths: Understanding Early Childhood Sexual and Physical Violence Among Women In Prison." *Issues in Mental Health Nursing* 21 (5) (July-Aug. 2000): 473-98.

78. Mazza, D., L. Dennerstein, C. V. Garamszegi, and E. C. Dudley. "The Physical, Sexual and Emotional Violence History of Middle-Aged Women: A Community-Based Prevalence Study. *The Medical Journal of Australia* 175 (4) (Aug. 2001): 199-201.

79. Menage, Janet. "Post-Traumatic Stress Disorder in Women Who Have Undergone Obstetric and/or Gynaecological Procedures." *Journal of Reproductive and Infant Psychology* 11 (1993): 221-28.

80. Moghal, Nadeem E., Inder K. Nota, and Christopher J. Hobbs. "A Study of Sexual Abuse in an Asian Community." *Archives of Disease in Childhood* 72 (1995): 346-47.

81. Nayak M. B., H. S. Resnick, and M. M. Holmes. "Treating Health Concerns Within the Context of Childhood Sexual Assault: A Case Study." *Journal of Traumatic Stress* 12 (1) (Jan. 1999): 101-9.

82. The NIMH Multisite HIV Prevention Trial Group. "A Test of Factors Mediating the Relationship Between Unwanted Sexual Activity During Childhood and Risky Sexual Practices Among Women Enrolled in the NIMH Multisite HIV Prevention Trial." *Women's Health* 33 (1-2) (2001): 163-80.

83. Oujevolk, America V., Claudia A. Christman, and J. Altrocchi. "Unusual Cause of Unresponsiveness During the Second Stage of Labor." *Journal of American Board of Family Practice* 8 (5) Sep.-Oct. 1995): 410-12.

84. Pope, Harrison G., Jr., and James I. Hudson. "Is Childhood Sexual Abuse a Risk Factor for Bulimia Nervosa?" *American Journal of Psychiatry* 149 (4) (Apr. 1992): 455-63.

85. Rapkin, Andrea J., Linda D. Kames, Laura L. Darke, Frederick M. Stampler, and Bruce D. Naliboff. "History of Physical and Sexual Abuse in Women With Chronic Pelvic Pain." *Obstetrics and Gynecology* 76 (1990): 92-96.

86. Richardson, J., G. Feder, S. Eldridge, W. S. Chung, J. Coid, and S. Moorey. "Women Who Experience Domestic Violence and Women Survivors of Childhood Sexual Abuse: A Survey of Health Professionals' Attitudes and Clinical Practice." *British Journal of General Practice* 51 (467) (June 2001): 468-70.

87. Rimsza, Mary Ellen, and Robert A. Berg. “Sexual Abuse: Somatic and Emotional Reactions.” *Child Abuse & Neglect* 12 (1988): 201-8.

88. Rodgers, C.S., A.J. Lang, E.W. Twamley, Stein, M.B. “Sexual Trauma and Pregnancy: A Conceptual Framework.” *Journal of Women’s Health* 12 (10) (2003): 961-70

89. Rorty, Marcia, Joel Yager, and Elizabeth Rossotto. “Childhood Sexual, Physical, and Psychological Abuse in Bulimia Nervosa.” *American Journal of Psychiatry* 151 (Aug. 8, 1994): 1122-26.

90. Rose, Anna. “Effects of Childhood Sexual Abuse on Childbirth: One Woman’s Story. *Birth: Issues in Perinatal Care* 19 (4) (Dec. 1992): 214-23.

91. Rouf, K. “Child Sexual Abuse and Pregnancy. A Personal Account.” *The Practising Midwife* 2 (6) (June 1999): 29-31.

92. Rubin, R. “Maternal Tasks in Pregnancy.” *Maternity Child Nursing Journal* 4 (3) (Fall 1975): 143-53.

93. Rubin, R. “Maternal Touch.” *Nursing News (Meriden)* 11 (Nov. 1963): 828-29.

94. Runtz, M. G. “Health Concerns of University Women with a History of Child Physical and Sexual Maltreatment.” *Child Maltreatment* 7 (3) (Aug. 2002): 241-53.

95. Ryding, Elsa Lena. “Investigation of 33 Women Who Demanded a Cesarean Section for Personal Reasons.” *Acta Obstetriia et Gynecologica Scandinavica* 72 (4) (1993): 280-85.

96. Ryding, Elsa Lena. “Psychosocial Indications for Cesarean Section: A Retrospective Study of 43 Cases.” *Acta Obstretriia et Gynecologica Scandinavica* 70 (1) (1991): 47-49.

97. Sahay, S., N. Piran, and S. Maddocks. “Sexual Victimization and Clinical Challenges in Women Receiving Hospital Treatment for Depression.” *Canadian Journal of Community Mental Health* 19 (1) (Spring 2000): 161-74.

98. Samson, A. Y., S. Bensen, A. Beck, D. Price, and C. Nimmer. "Posttraumatic Stress Disorder in Primary Care." *The Journal of Family Practice* 48 (3) (Mar. 1999): 222-27.

99. Saunders, E. A., and J. A. Edelson. "Attachment Style, Traumatic Bonding, and Developing Relational Capacities in a Long-Term Trauma Group for Women." *International Journal of Group Psychotherapy* 49 (4) (1999): 465-85.

100. Scaer, Robert C. "The Neurophysiology of Dissociation and Chronic Disease." *Applied Psychophysiology and Biofeedback* 26 (1) (2001): 73-91.

101. Seng, J. S., and J. A. Hassinger. "Relationship Strategies and Interdisciplinary Collaboration. Improving Maternity Care with Survivors of Childhood Sexual Abuse." *Journal of Nurse-Midwifery* 43 (4) (July-Aug. 1998): 287-95.

102. Seng, J. S., K. J. Sparbel, L. K. Low, and C. Killion. "Abuse-Related Posttraumatic Stress and Desired Maternity Care Practices: Women's Perspectives." *Journal of Midwifery & Women's Health* 47 (5) (Sep.-Oct. 2002): 360-70.

103. Sheldrick, Carol. "Adult Sequelae of Child Sexual Abuse." *British Journal of Psychiatry* 158 (Suppl. 10) (May 1991): 55-62.

104. Simkin, Penny. "Memories That Really Matter: Effect of Childhood Sexual Trauma on the Childbearing Woman." *Childbirth Instructor Magazine* (Winter 1994): 21-23, 39.

105. Simkin, Penny. "Overcoming the Legacy of Childhood Sexual Abuse: The Role of Caregivers and Childbirth Educators." *Birth: Issues in Perinatal Care* 19 (4) (Dec. 1992): 224-25.

106. Simpson, T. L. "Women's Treatment Utilization and Its Relationship to Childhood Sexual Abuse History and Lifetime PTSD." *Substance Abuse* 23 (1) (Mar. 2002): 17-30.

107. Smith, D. W., E. J. Letourneau, B. E. Saunders, D. G. Kilpatrick, H. S. Resnick, and C. L. Best. "Delay in Disclosure of Childhood Rape: Results from a National Survey." *Child Abuse & Neglect* 24 (2) (Feb. 2000): 273-87.

108. Stenson, K., G. Heimer, C. Lundh, M. L. Nordstrom, H. Saarinen, and A. Wenker. "Lifetime Prevalence of Sexual Abuse in a Swedish Pregnant Population. *Acta Obstetrica et Gynecologica Scandinavica* 82 (6) (June 2003): 529-36.

109. Tallman, Nora, and Cammie Hering. "Child Abuse and Its Effects on Birth. A Research." *Midwifery Today With International Midwife* (Spring 1998): 19-21, 67.

110. Taylor, R. R., and L. A. Jason. "Chronic Fatigue, Abuse-Related Traumatization, and Psychiatric Disorders in a Community-Based Sample." *Social Science & Medicine* 55 (2) (July 2002): 247-56.

111. Teicher, M. H. "Scars That Won't Heal: the Neurobiology of Child Abuse." *Scientific American* 286 (3) (Mar. 2002): 68-75.

112. Toomey, Timothy C., Jeanne T. Hernandez, David F. Gittelman, and Jaroslav F. Hulka. "Relationship of Sexual and Physical Abuse to Pain and Psychological Assessment Variables in Chronic Pelvic Pain Patients." *Pain* 53 (1993): 105-9.

113. van der Kolk, Bessel A. "The Body Keeps the Score: Memory and the Evolving Psychobiology of Posttraumatic Stress." *Harvard Review of Psychiatry* 5 (1) (Jan.-Feb. 1994): 253-65.

114. van der Kolk, Bessel A., and Rita Fisler. "Dissociation and the Fragmentary Nature of Traumatic Memories: Overview and Exploratory Study." *Journal of Traumatic Stress* 8 (4) 1995: 505-25.

115. Walker, Edward A. "Sexual Victimization and Physical Symptoms in Women." *Western Journal of Medicine* 160 (1) (Jan. 1994): 57.

116. Walker, Edward A., A. Gelfand, W. J. Katon, M. P. Koss, M. Von Korff, D. Bernstein, and J. Russo. "Adult Health Status of Women with Histories of Childhood Abuse and Neglect." *American Journal of Medicine* 107 (4) (Oct. 1999): 332-39.

117. Walker, Edward A., A. N. Gelfand, M. D. Gelfand, M. P. Koss, and W. J. Katon. "Medical and Psychiatric Symptoms in Female Gastroenterology Clinic Patients with Histories of Sexual Victimization." *General Hospital Psychiatry* 17 (2) (Mar. 1995): 85-92.

118. Walker, Edward A., W. J. Katon, J. Hansom, J. Harrop-Griffiths, L. Holm, M. L. Jones, L. R. Hickok, and J. Russo. "Psychiatric Diagnoses and Sexual Victimization in Women with Chronic Pelvic Pain." *Psychosomatics* 36 (6) (Nov.-Dec. 1997): 531-40.

119. Walker, Edward A., D. Keegan, G. Gardner, M. Sullivan, D. Bernstein, and W. J. Katon. "Psychosocial Factors of Fibromyalgia Compared with Rheumatoid Arthritis: II. Sexual, Physical, and Emotional Abuse and Neglect. *Psychosomatic Medicine* 59 (6) (Nov.-Dec. 1997): 572-77.

120. Walker, Edward A., D. Keegan, G. Gardner, M. Sullivan, W. J. Katon, and D. Bernstein. "Psychosocial Factors in Fibromyalgia Compared with Rheumatoid Arthritis: I. Psychiatric Diagnoses and Functional Disability." *Psychosomatic Medicine* 59 (6) (Nov.-Dec. 1997): 565-71.

121. Walker, Edward A., P. M. Milgrom, P. Weinstein, T. Getz, and R. Richardson. "Assessing Abuse and Neglect and Dental Fear in Women." *Journal of the American Dental Association* 127 (4) (Apr. 1996): 485-90.

122. Walker, Edward A., E. Newman, M. Koss, and D. Bernstein. "Does the Study of Victimization Revictimize the Victims?" *General Hospital Psychiatry* 19 (6) (Nov. 1997): 403-10.

123. Walker, Edward A., J. Unutzer, and W. J. Katon. "Understanding and Caring for the Distressed Patient with Multiple Medically Unexplained Symptoms." *Journal of the American Board of Family Practice* 11 (5) (Sep.-Oct. 1998): 347-56.

124. Walker, Edward A., J. Unutzer, C. Rutter, A. Gelfand, K. Saunders, M. VonKorff, M. P. Koss, and W. Katon. "Costs of Health Care Use by Women HMO Members with a History of Childhood Abuse and Neglect." *Archives of General Psychiatry* 56 (7) (July 1999): 609-13.

125. Walker, Edward A. "Medically Unexplained Physical Symptoms." *Clinical Obstetrics and Gynecology* 40 (3) (Sep. 1997): 589-600.

126. Walling, Mary K., Robert C. Reiter, Michael W. O'Hara, Alison K. Milburn, Gilbert Lilly, and Steven D. Vincent. "Abuse History and Chronic Pain in Women: I. Prevalences of Sexual Abuse and Physical Abuse." *Obstetrics and Gynecology* 84 (2) (Aug. 1994): 193-99.

127. Walling, Mary K., Michael W. O'Hara, Robert C. Reiter, Alison K. Milburn, Gilbert Lilly, and Steven D. Vincent. "Abuse History and Chronic Pain in Women: II. A Multivariate Analysis of Abuse and Psychological Morbidity." *Obstetrics and Gynecology* 84 (1994): 200-6.

128. Weaver, J. "Childbirth: Preventing Post-Traumatic Stress Disorder." *Professional Care of Mother and Child* 7 (1) (1997): 2-3.

129. Wolfsdorf, B. A., and C. Zlotnick. "Affect Management in Group Therapy for Women with Posttraumatic Stress Disorder and Histories of Childhood Sexual Abuse." *Journal of Clinical Psychology* 57 (2) (Feb. 2001): 169-81.

130. Yellowlees, Peter M., and Anil V. Kaushik. "A Case-Control Study of the Sequelae of Childhood Sexual Assault in Adult Psychiatric Patients." *The Medical Journal of Australia* 160 (Apr. 4, 1994): 408-11.

131. Zlot, S. I., M. Herrmann, T. Hofer-Mayer, M. Adler, and R. H. Adler. "Childhood Experiences and Adult Behavior in a Group of Women with Pain Accounted for by Psychological Factors and a Group Recovered from Major Depression." *International Journal of Psychiatry in Medicine* 30 (3) (2000): 261-75.

Resources: Books

1. Ainscough, Carolyn and Kay Toon. *Breaking Free: A Self-Help Guide for Adults Who Were Sexually Abused as Children.* Tucson, AZ: Fisher Books; 1993.

2. Baldwin, Martha. *Beyond Victim: You Can Overcome Childhood Abuse...Even Sexual Abuse.* Moore Haven, FL: Rainbow Books; 1998.

3. Bass, Ellen and Laura Davis. *Beginning to Heal: A First Book for Survivors of Child Sexual Abuse.* New York, NY: Harper Perennial; 1993.

4. *The Courage to Heal: A Guide for Women Survivors of Child Sexual Abuse: Featuring "Honoring the Truth, a Response to the Backlash."* New York: Harper Perennial; 1994.

5. Blume, E. Sue. *Secret Survivors: Uncovering Incest and Its Aftereffects in Women.* New York: Ballantine Books; 1990.

6. Briere, John N. *Child Abuse Trauma: Theory and Treatment of the Lasting Effects.* Newbury Park,CA: Sage Publications; 1992.

7. Capacchione, Lucia and Sandra Bardsley. *Creating a Joyful Birth Experience: Developing a Partnership with Your Unborn Child for Healthy Pregnancy, Labor, and Early Parenting.* New York: Fireside; 1994.

8. Chase, Truddi. *When Rabbit Howls.* New York: The Berkley Publishing Group; [1990].

9. Cheek, David B. *Hypnosis: The Application of Ideomotor Techniques.* Boston: Allyn and Bacon; 1994.

10. Cohen, Barry M., Mary-Michola Barnes, and Anita B. Rankin. *Managing Traumatic Stress Through Art: Drawing from the Center.* Lutherville, MD: The Sidran Press; 1995.

11. Copeland, Mary Ellen and Maxine Harris. *Healing the Trauma of Abuse: A Woman's Workbook.* Oakland, CA: New Harbinger; 2000.

12. Courtois, Christine A. *Healing the Incest Wound: Adult Survivors in Therapy.* New York: W.W. Norton & Co.; 1996.

13. Delaney, Gayle. *Living Your Dreams: Becoming Your Own Dream Expert.* San Francisco, CA: Harper; 1996.

14. Dolan, Yvonne M. *Resolving Sexual Abuse: Solution-Focused Therapy and Ericksonian Hypnosis for Adult Survivors.* New York: W.W. Norton; 1991.

15. Draucker, Claire Burke. *Counseling Survivors of Childhood Sexual Abuse.* Newbury Park, CA: Sage Publications; 1992.

16. Dunnewold, Anne and Diane G. Sanford. *Postpartum Survival Guide.* Oakland, CA: New Harbinger Publications; 1994.

17. Engel, Beverly. *The Right to Innocence: Healing the Trauma of Childhood Sexual Abuse.* New York: Ivy Books; 1989.

18. Farrell, Patricia. *How to Be Your Own Therapist: A Step-By-Step Guide to Building a Competent, Confident Life.* New York: McGraw-Hill; 2003.

19. Frank, Jan. *Door of Hope.* Nashville, TN: Thomas Nelson Publishers; 1995.

20. Gil, Eliana. *The Healing Power of Play: Working with Abused Children.* New York: Guilford Press; 1991.

21. Graber, Ken. *Ghosts in the Bedroom: A Guide for Partners of Incest Survivors.* Deerfield Beach, FL: Health Communications; 1991.

22. Hastings, Anne Stirling. *Reclaiming Healthy Sexual Energy.* Deerfield, FL: Health Communications, Inc.; 1991.

23. Herman, Judith Lewis. *Father-Daughter Incest.* Cambridge, MA: Harvard University Press; 2000.

24. Herman, Judith Lewis. *Trauma and Recovery.* New York: Basic Books; 1997.

25. Hopkins, Khristine. *Survivors: Experiences of Childhood Sexual Abuse & Healing.* Berkeley, CA: Celestial Arts; 1994.

26. Jehu, Derek. *Beyond Sexual Abuse: Therapy with Women Who Were Childhood Victims.* Chicester: John Wiley & Sons; 1988.

27. Johnson, Kendall. *Trauma in the Lives of Children: Crisis and Stress Management Techniques for Counselors, Teachers, and Other Professionals.* Alameda, CA: Hunter House; 1998.

28. Johnson, Janis Tyler. *Mothers of Incest Survivors: Another Side of the Story.* Bloomington, IN: Indiana University Press; 1992.

29. Karr-Moss, Robin, and Meredith S. Wiley. *Ghosts from the Nursery: Tracing the Roots of Violence.* New York: Atlantic Monthly Press; 1997.

30. Kluft, Richard P., ed. *Incest-related Syndromes of Adult Psychopathology.* Washington, DC: American Psychiatric Press, Inc.; 1990.

31. Kreisman, Jerold J., and Hal Straus. *I Hate You-Don't Leave Me: Understanding the Borderline Personality.* New York: Avon Books; 1989.

32. Kunzman, Kristin A. *The Healing Way: Adult Recovery from Childhood Sexual Abuse.* San Francisco, CA: Harper & Row; 1990.

33. Kirkengen, Anna Luise. *Inscribed Bodies: Health Impact of Childhood Sexual Abuse.* New York: Kluwer Academic Publishers; 2001.

34. Klaus, Marshall H., John H. Kennell, and Phyllis H. Klaus. *The Doula Book: How a Trained Labor Companion Can Help You Have a Shorter, Easier, and Healthier Birth.* Cambridge, MA: Perseus Publishing; 2002.

35. Levine, Peter A. *Waking the Tiger; Healing Trauma.* Berkeley, CA: North Atlantic Books; 1997.

36. Madsen, Lynn. *Rebounding from Childbirth: Toward Emotional Recovery.* Westport, CT: Bergin & Garvey; 1994.

37. Maltz, Wendy. *The Sexual Healing Journey: A Guide for Survivors of Sexual Abuse.* New York: Harper Perennial; 1991.

38. Mason, L. John. *Guide to Stress Reduction.* Culver City, CA: Peace Press; 1980.

39. Matsakis, Aphrodite. *I Can't Get Over It: A Handbook for Trauma Survivors.* Oakland, CA: New Harbinger Publications, Inc.; 1992.

40. Matsakis, Aphrodite. *Trust After Trauma: Theory and Treatment of the Lasting Effects.* Newbury Park, CA: Sage Publications; 1992.

41. Maybruck, Patricia. *Pregnancy and Dreams: How to Have a Peaceful Pregnancy by Understanding Your Dreams, Fantasies, Daydreams and Nightmares.* Los Angeles, CA: Jeremy P. Tarcher, Inc.; 1989.

42. Meichenbaum, Donald. *A Clinical Handbook/Practical Therapist Manual for Assessing and Treating Adults with Post-Traumatic Stress Disorder (PTSD).* Waterloo, Ontario: Institute Press; 1994.

43. Miller, Alice. *The Drama of the Gifted Child: The Search for the True Self.* Frankfurt, Germany: Basic Books; 1981.

44. Misri, Shaila. *Shouldn't I Be Happy?: Emotional Problems of Pregnant and Postpartum Women.* New York, NY: The Free Press; 1995.

45. Orleman, Jane. *Telling Secrets: An Artist's Journey Through Childhood Trauma.* Washington DC: CWLA Press; 1998.

46. Osborne-Sheets, Carole. *Pre and Perinatal Massage Therapy: A Comprehensive Practitioners' Guide to Pregnancy, Labor, Postpartum.* San Diego, CA: Body Therapy Associates; 1998.

47. Parnell, Laurel. *EMDR in the Treatment of Adults Abused as Children.* New York: W.W. Norton; 1999.

48. Peterson, Gayle. *An Easier Childbirth: A Mother's Workbook for Health and Emotional Well-Being During Pregnancy and Delivery.* Los Angeles, CA: Jeremy P. Tarcher, Inc.; 1991.

49. Resnick, Susan Kushner. *Sleepless Days: One Woman's Journey Through Postpartum Depression.* New York: St. Martin's Press; 2000.

50. Rogers, Wendy Stainton, Denise Hevey, and Elizabeth Ash, eds. *Child Abuse and Neglect: Facing the Challenge.* London: The Open University; 1989.

51. Rothschild, Babette. *The Body Remembers: The Psychophysiology of Trauma and Trauma Treatment.* New York: W.W. Norton & Company, Inc.; 2000.

52. Roy, Ranjan. *Childhood Abuse and Chronic Pain: A Curious Relationship?* Toronto, ON: University of Toronto Press, Inc.; 1998.

53. Rubin, R. *Maternal Identity and the Maternal Experience.* New York: Springer Publishing; 1984.

54. Salter, Anna C. *Transforming Trauma: A Guide to Understanding and Treating Adult Survivors of Child Sexual Abuse.* Thousand Oaks, CA: Sage Publications; 1995.

55. Scaer, Robert C. *The Body Bears the Burden: Trauma, Dissociation, and Disease.* Binghamton, NY: The Haworth Medical Press; 2001.

56. Scarf, Maggie. *Intimate Worlds: How Families Thrive and Why They Fail.* New York: Ballantine Books; 1995.

57. Schiraldi, Glenn R. *The Post-Traumatic Stress Disorder Sourcebook: A Guide to Healing, Recovery, and Growth.* Lincolnwood, IL: Lowell House; 1999.

58. Shapiro, Francine. *Eye Movement Desensitization and Reprocessing (EMDR): Basic Principles, Protocols, and Procedures, Second Edition.* New York: Guilford Press; 2001.

59. Sherman, Carl. *How to Go to Therapy: Making the Most of Professional Help.* New York: Random House, Inc.; 2001.

60. Sichel, Deborah and Jeanne Watson Driscoll. *Women's Moods: What Every Woman Must Know About Hormones, the Brain, and Emotional Health.* New York, NY: Quill; 1999.

61. Simkin, Penny. *The Birth Partner: Everything You Need to Know to Help a Woman Through Childbirth.* Second Edition. Boston, MA: The Harvard Common Press; 2001.

62. Simkin, Penny, Janet Whalley, and Ann Keppler. *Pregnancy, Childbirth and the Newborn: The Complete Guide.* Minnetonka, MN: Meadowbrook Press; 2001.

63. Strong, Susan. *Am I Cured?: A Guide for Healing from Physical Illness.* Berkeley, CA: Universe Press; 1990.

64. Stukane, Eileen. *The Dream Worlds of Pregnancy.* New York, NY: Quill; 1985.

65. Terr, Lenore. *Unchained Memories: True Stories of Traumatic Memories, Lost and Found.* New York, NY: Basic Books; 1994.

66. van der Kolk, Bessel A., Alexander C. McFarlane, and Lars Weisaeth, eds. *Traumatic Stress: The Effects of Overwhelming Experience on Mind, Body, and Society.* New York: Guilford Press; 1996.

67. Varney, Helen. *Varney's Midwifery.* Boston, MA: Jones & Bartlett; 1997.

68. Westerlund, Elaine. *Women's Sexuality After Childhood Incest.* New York: Norton & Co.; 1992.

69. Wijma, K., and B. von Schoultz, eds. *Reproductive Life: Advances in Research in Psychosomatic Obstetrics and Gynaecology.* Park Ridge, NJ: The Parthenon Publishing Group; 1992.

70. Williams, Mary Beth and Soili Poijula. *The PTSD Workbook: Simple, Effective Techniques for Overcoming Traumatic Stress Symptoms.* Oakland, CA: New Harbinger Publications, Inc.; 2002.

Resources: Websites

Adult Survivors of Child Abuse
http://www.ascasupport.org

ALACE: Association of Labor Assistants & Childbirth Educators
http://www.alace.org/

American Academy of Husband-Coached Childbirth (AAHCC)
http://www.bradleybirth.com/

American Massage Therapy Association
http://www.amtamassage.org

Birth Works
http://www.birthworks.org/

Body Therapy Associates
http://www.bodytherapyassociates.com

Breaking the Silence
http://breakingthesilence.com

CAPPA: Childbirth and Postpartum Professional Association
http://www.cappa.net/

Center for Health and Gender Equity
http://www.genderhealth.org

The Child Trauma Academy
http://www.ChildTrauma.org

Children of Alcoholics Foundation
http://www.coaf.org

Doulas of North America (DONA)
http://www.dona.org/

Education Wife Assault: Woman Abuse Links
http://www.womanabuseprevention.com/html/womanabuse_links.html

End Violence Against Women: Information and Resources
http://www.endvaw.org/

Healing Journey: Chat Rooms and Forums for Adult Survivors of Trauma and Abuse
http://www.healing-journey.net

International Childbirth Education Association, Inc.(ICEA)
http://www.icea.org/

Lamaze International
http://www.lamaze.org/

NAPCS: National Association of Postpartum Care Services
http://www.napcs.org/default.htm

National Association for Children of Alcoholics
http://www.nacoa.net

National Clearinghouse on Child Abuse and Neglect Information
http://www.calib.com/nccanch

National Organization for Victim Assistance
http://www.try-nova.org/

Penny Simkin: Author, Doula, Childbirth Educator, Birth Counselor
http://www.pennysimkin.com/

RAINN: Rape, Abuse & Incest National Network
http://www.rainn.org

Safe Horizon: Domestic Violence Shelter Information
http://www.dvsheltertour.org/index.html

Sheila Kitzinger's Birth Crisis Network
http://www.sheilakitzinger.com/Birth%20Crisis.htm

Trauma and Birth Stress
http://www.tabs.org.nz

About the Authors

Penny Simkin, P.T., is a physical therapist, childbirth educator, doula, counselor, and writer. Her books include *Pregnancy, Childbirth, and The Newborn: the Complete Guide; The Birth Partner: Everything You Need to Know to Help a Woman Through Childbirth; The Labor Progress Handbook: Early Interventions to Prevent and Treat Dystocia;* and *Episiotomy and the Second Stage of Labor.* She has produced two videos: *Comfort Measures for Childbirth,* and *Relaxation, Rhythm and Ritual: The 3 Rs of Childbirth.* She serves on the Editorial Board of *Birth: Issues in Perinatal Care,* and Boards of Consultants of the International Childbirth Education Association and Seattle Midwifery School. She travels extensively, presenting conferences and workshops for maternity professionals.

Penny is the mother of four grown children and grandmother of eight. Besides her professional work, she enjoys beach walks, crossword puzzles, family dinners, professional baseball (especially the Seattle Mariners), reading novels, classical, bluegrass, and folk music, family vacations, and her little pug, Hugo.

Phyllis H. Klaus, C.S.W., M.F.T., a psychotherapist, teaches and practices at the Erickson Institute in Santa Rosa and also in Berkeley, California. She specializes in the medical and psychological concerns of pregnancy, birth, and the postpartum period, as well as trauma, abuse, family of origin, and loss issues. She consults nationally and internationally, does research, and is coauthor of *Mothering the Mother: How a Doula Can Help You Have a Shorter, Easier, and Healthier Birth; Bonding: Building the Foundations of Secure Attachment and Independence*; *Your Amazing Newborn*; and *The Doula Book: How a Trained Labor Companion Can Help You have a Shorter, Easier, and Healthier Birth.*

Phyllis is the mother of three grown children and step-grandmother of five. Besides her professional work, she enjoys singing and listening to folk music, cooking and eating good food, reading novels, traveling abroad, speaking French, attending the opera and theatre, telling and hearing good stories (especially humor) and spending time with family and friends.

Index

(Note: names in **bold** indicate experiences of survivors)